————

NUMBER XI

GENETICS AND THE ORIGIN OF SPECIES

GENETICS AND
THE ORIGIN OF SPECIES

BY

THEODOSIUS DOBZHANSKY

PROFESSOR OF ZOÖLOGY IN
COLUMBIA UNIVERSITY

SECOND EDITION, REVISED

NEW YORK: MORNINGSIDE HEIGHTS

COLUMBIA UNIVERSITY PRESS

COPYRIGHT COLUMBIA UNIVERSITY PRESS, NEW YORK

Published in Great Britain and India by Geoffrey Cumberlege,
Oxford University Press, London and Bombay

FIRST EDITION 1937

First printing October, 1937

Second printing September, 1939

SECOND EDITION 1941

First printing September, 1941

Second printing January, 1947

Third printing August, 1947

TO THE MEMORY OF MY MOTHER

EDITOR'S PREFACE

IT IS fitting that the Columbia Biological Series should resume publication with a discussion of the same problem to which the first volume in this series was devoted. Forty years ago evolution was a problem in history, and in *From the Greeks to Darwin* H. F. Osborn traced the origins and development of the idea of gradual change as the means by which the world and its inhabitants had assumed their present forms. It was not only the ideas and theories which were studied as history; the facts of evolution itself were shown to be determined by changes in the past history of the earth. The essence of Darwin's theory was just this, and the efforts of biologists were concentrated on describing as completely as possible this record of the past.

But description and reconstruction fail to satisfy for long even the most ardent historians of nature and it was Darwin's second great service to have focused the attention of biologists upon the forces that caused the changes and particularly upon the problem of what agencies brought about and maintained the diversification of animals and plants into distinct species. His own theory of natural selection, by appealing to two occurrences of which the details were quite unknown—the origin of new variations in animals and plants and the perpetuation of these by heredity—served as a great stimulus and provided much of the motivation for biological research in the period which followed 1859. There were at that time, however, no reliable methods by which these two problems could be studied. The history of genetics since the rediscovery of Mendel's principles in 1900 is a history of the development of just such methods, and it is possible now to take stock of what these methods have done to improve our understanding of what has been, in spite of all research, so great a mystery—the origin of species.

This is what the present volume attempts to do. When one considers that this is 1937, a hundred years after the germ of the theory of natural selection first stirred in Darwin's mind, and nearly forty years after Mendel's theory and methods came to recognition, one might be tempted to suppose that such a reassessment of evolution was long overdue. But a glance at the sources of Professor Dobzhansky's material shows that this is not the case. The works cited in his bibliography are largely products of the twenties and especially the thirties of the present century. This expresses very well the recency of much of our knowledge of the actual factors involved in the differentiation of species.

The reasons for this are not far to seek. Variation and heredity had first to be studied for their own sakes and genetics grew up in answer to the interest in these problems and to the need for rigorous methods for testing by experiment all ideas we might hold about them. The requirements of this search drove genetics into the laboratory, along an apparently narrow alley hedged in by culture bottles of Drosophila and other insects, by the breeding cages of captive rodents, and by maize and snapdragons and other plants. Biologists not native to this alley thought sometimes that those who trod along it could not or would not look over the hedge; they admitted that the alley was paved with honest intentions but at its end they thought they could see a red light and a sign "The Gene: Dead End."

That condition, if it ever existed to any marked degree, is again changing, and Professor Dobzhansky's book signalizes very clearly something which can only be called the Back-to-Nature movement. The methods learned in the laboratory are good enough now to be put to the test in the open and applied in that ultimate laboratory of biology, free nature itself. Throughout this book we are reminded that the problems of evolution are given not by academic discussion and speculation, but by the existence of the great variety of living animals and plants. The facts and relationsships found in nature have to be examined from many points of view and by the aid of many different methods. Evolution, in the author's words, is a change in the genetic composition of populations, and populations follow laws which may be derived by mathematical reasoning as extrapolations of the known behavior of the fundamental units of reproduction—genes and chromosomes. It is a kind of tour de force that in this book the recent work in this field is fitted into its important place in a way which does not offend the sensibilities of those who are repelled by mathematical formulas. Cytology too has become an essential weapon of those who would attack the species problem, and full advantage has been taken of the newer methods of studying chromosomes in Chapter four. Here too one may read a cytological detective story from the author's own experience, which, while it may shock the older makers of phylogenies, will convince the modern man that the riddle of speciation is by no means hopeless. Still other methods are brought to bear on the questions of sterility in species hybrids and of the mechanisms which are effective in keeping species separate, a field which has been recently illuminated by Professor Dobzhansky's original contributions.

In all this, the author appears not only as geneticist and as student of natural history, but as one who received his training in both fields in Russia. English-speaking biologists have special cause to be grateful for this last fact, for it has enabled Professor Dobzhansky to make available to us many important contributions from workers in the Soviet Union, where researches in this field have been actively prosecuted.

There was need for such a summary and synthesis of the new experimental evidence, and for reassessment of the older theories. It is of less importance that of these latter natural selection has survived the ordeal than that both the theory and the underlying reality, the species, have taken on new, and as one may guess, more fruitful meanings.

L. C. Dunn

Columbia University
August, 1937

PREFACE

THE PROBLEM of evolution may be approached in two different ways. First, the sequence of the evolutionary events as
they have actually taken place in the past history of various organisms may be traced. Second, the mechanisms that bring about evolutionary changes may be studied. The first approach deals with historical problems, and the second with physiological. The importance
of genetics for a critical evaluation of theories concerning the
mechanics of evolution is fairly generally recognized. The present
book is devoted to a discussion of the mechanisms of species formation in terms of the known facts and theories of genetics. Some
writers have contended that evolution involves more than species
formation, that macro- and micro-evolutionary changes may be distinguished. This may or may not be true; such a duality of the
evolutionary process is by no means established. In any case, a geneticist has no choice but to confine himself to the micro-evolutionary
phenomena that lie within reach of his method, and to see how much
of evolution in general can be adequately understood on this basis.

Considerations of space have forced us to refrain from a detailed
discussion of some of the objections that have been advanced against
the genetic treatment of evolutionary problems. Thus, Lamarckian
doctrines find but a brief mention. The treatment had to be made
assertive rather than polemic, dogmatic rather than apologetic.

This book is based on a series of lectures delivered at Columbia
University, New York City, in October, 1936. Each lecture was
followed by a discussion in which representatives of various biological disciplines took part. To these colleagues, as well as to Drs.
Edgar Anderson, A. F. Blakeslee, M. Demerec, L. C. Dunn, T. H.
Morgan, A. H. Sturtevant, and Sewall Wright, the writer is much
indebted for many valuable suggestions and criticisms. The help of
Mrs. N. P. Sivertzev-Dobzhansky in the preparation of the manuscript is gratefully acknowledged.

THEODOSIUS DOBZHANSKY

Pasadena, California
July, 1937

PREFACE TO THE SECOND EDITION

TWO PRINTINGS of the first edition of this book having been exhausted, the Columbia University Press has requested the writer to make the necessary corrections for a new edition. Population genetics has, however, progressed so rapidly in the last few years that not only substantial additions but a complete rewriting of some parts of the book have become necessary. Moreover, it seemed appropriate at this time to emphasize the existence of certain unsolved problems in population genetics and in related fields, and to outline some working hypotheses which may be useful to students engaged in active research on these problems. Speculations and hypotheses are barren if they lead to no experiments and are dangerous when confused with facts; they are, however, useful if they direct the attention of investigators toward facts which may otherwise be ignored or not noticed at all.

The writer takes pleasure in expressing his appreciation of the many suggestions and criticisms contributed by Dr. L. C. Dunn, and of the help of Natalie P. Sivertzev-Dobshansky who has shared the work of the preparation of the manuscript. The writer is obligated also to Drs. A. P. Blair, M. Demerec, C. Epling, S. Hughes-Schrader, B. P. Kaufmann, E. Mayr, T. H. Morgan, J. T. Patterson, M. M. Rhoades, and F. Schrader who have given advice and have furnished unpublished information on certain topics.

THEODOSIUS DOBZHANSKY

Columbia University
New York, N. Y.
March, 1941

CONTENTS

ILLUSTRATIONS

GENETICS AND THE ORIGIN OF SPECIES

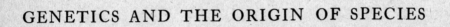

I: ORGANIC DIVERSITY

DIVERSITY AND DISCONTINUITY

FOR centuries the diversity of living beings has been a major interest of mankind. Not only are the multitude of the distinct "kinds" or species of organisms and the variety of their structures seemingly endless, but there is no uniformity within species. It is taken for granted that every human individual is unique, different from all others that live or that have lived. This is probably true of individuals of species other than man, although our methods of observation are frequently inadequate to demonstrate it. From remotest times, attempts have been made to understand the causes and significance of organic diversity. To many minds the problem possesses an irresistible aesthetic appeal, and inasmuch as scientific inquiry is a form of aesthetic endeavor, biology owes its existence in part to this appeal.

Organic diversity is an observational fact more or less familiar to everyone. It is perceived by us as something apart from ourselves, independent of the working of our minds. Individuals, although limited in existence to an interval of time, are the prime reality with which a biologist is confronted. While the uniqueness and unrepeatability of individuals are aspects falling primarily within the provinces of philosophers and artists, the scientist concentrates his attention on their similarities and differences. Indeed, a more intimate acquaintance with the living world discloses a fact almost as striking as the diversity itself. This is the discontinuity of the variation among organisms.

If we assemble as many individuals living at a given time as we can, we notice at once that the observed variation does not form any kind of continuous distribution. Instead, a multitude of separate, discrete, distributions are found. In other words, the living world is not a single array of individuals in which any two variants are connected by unbroken series of intergrades, but an array of more or less distinctly separate arrays, intermediates between which are absent or at least rare. Each array is a cluster of individuals, usually possessing some common characteristics and gravitating to a definite modal point in their variations. Small clusters are grouped together into larger secondary ones, these into still larger ones, and so on in an hierarchical order.

The discontinuity of organic variation has been exploited to devise a scientific classification of organisms. Evidently the hierarchical nature of the observed discontinuity lends itself admirably to this purpose. For the sake of convenience the discrete clusters are designated races, species, genera, families, and so forth. The classification thus arrived at is to some extent an artificial one, because it remains for the investigator to choose, within limits, which cluster is to be designated a genus, family, or order. But the classification is nevertheless a natural one in so far as it reflects the objectively ascertainable discontinuity of variation, and in so far as the dividing lines between species, genera, and other categories are made to correspond to the gaps between the discrete clusters of living forms. Therefore the biological classification is simultaneously a man-made system of pigeonholes devised for the pragmatic purpose of recording observations in a convenient manner and an acknowledgment of the fact of organic discontinuity. A single example will suffice to illustrate this point.

Any two cats are individually distinguishable, and this is probably equally true of any two lions. And yet no living individual has ever been seen about which there could be a doubt as to whether it belongs to the species-cluster of cats (*Felis domestica*) or to the species-cluster of lions (*Felis leo*). The two clusters are discrete because of the absence of intermediates, and therefore one may safely affirm that any cat is different from any lion, and that cats as a group are distinct from lions as a group. Any difficulty which may arise in defining the species *Felis domestica* and *Felis leo*, respectively, is due not to the artificiality of these species themselves, but to the fact that in common as well as in scientific parlance the words "cat" and "lion" frequently refer neither to individual animals nor to all the existing individuals of these species, but to certain modal points toward which these species gravitate. The modal points are statistical abstractions having no existence apart from the mind of the observer. The species *Felis domestica* and *Felis leo* are evidently independent of any abstract modal points which we may contrive to make. No matter how great may be the difficulties encountered in finding the modal "cats" and "lions," the discreteness of species as naturally existing units is not thereby impaired.

What has been said above with respect to the species *Felis domestica* and *Felis leo* holds for innumerable pairs of species, genera, and other groups. Discrete groups are encountered among animals as well as plants, in those that are structurally simple as well as in those that are very complex. Formation of discrete groups is so nearly universal that it must be regarded as a fundamental characteristic of organic diversity. An adequate solution of the problem of organic diversity must consequently include, first, a description of the extent, nature, and origin of the differences between living beings, and, second, an analysis of the nature and the origin of the discrete groups into which the living world is differentiated.

The true extent of organic diversity can only be surmised at present. In 1758 Linnaeus knew 4,236 species of animals. The recent estimates of described species (Pratt 1935) are as follows:

Arthropoda	640,000	Total of Column 1	794,500
Mollusca	70,000	Annelida	6,500
Chordata	60,000	Plathelminthes	6,000
Protozoa	15,000	Echinodermata	4,800
Coelenterata	9,500	All others	10,965
		Total	822,765

The number of plant species is smaller than that of animals. The following estimates have been kindly furnished by Professor Carl Epling:

Angiosperms	150,000	Total of Column I	259,000
Fungi	70,000	Liverworts	6,000
Mosses	15,000	Bacteria	1,200
Algae	14,000	Gymnosperms	500
Pteridophytes	10,000		
		Total	266,700

That the above totals fall short of the actually existing numbers of species is clear enough. For although in some groups, such as birds and mammals, most species are already known, in other groups

—notably among insects, which make up more than half of the species of animals—many new species are described every year, and large additions may be expected in the future. A million and a half species of animals and plants combined is a conservative estimate. Of course, this does not take into account the intraspecific variation, which is commensurate only with the number of living individuals.

MORPHOLOGICAL AND PHYSIOLOGICAL METHODS

A scientific study of organic diversity may proceed in two methodologically distinct ways. First, one may describe the diversity by recording as accurately as possible the multitudinous structures and functions of the beings now living and of those preserved as fossils; the descriptions are then catalogued and the regularities revealed in the process are formulated and generalized. Second, an analysis of causes which underly the diversity and determine its properties may be made. These two methods are known, respectively, as the generalizing and the exact induction (Hartmann).

At the beginning of its existence as a science, biology was forced to take cognizance of the seemingly boundless variety of living things, for no exact study of life phenomena was possible until the apparent chaos of the distinct kinds of organisms had been reduced to a rational system. Systematics and morphology, two predominantly descriptive and observational disciplines, took precedence among biological sciences during the eighteenth and nineteenth centuries. More recently physiology has come to the foreground, accompanied by the introduction of quantitative methods and by a shift from the observationalism of the past to a predominance of experimentation. The great significance of this change is readily apparent and has been stressed in the writings of many authors, some of whom have gone to the length of ascribing to the quantitative and experimental methods almost magical virtues. Another characteristic of modern biology, which has been emphasized perhaps less than its due, is the prevalence of interest in the common properties of living things instead of in the peculiarities of separate species. This attitude is important, for it centers the attention of investigators on the fundamental unity of all organisms.

The problem of organic diversity falls within the provinces of morphological as well as of physiological biology, but it is treated differently by the two. Morphology is predominantly an order-creating and historical discipline. It is concerned first of all with the recording of the fact of organic diversity as it appears to our senses, and with the description of this diversity in terms of ideal prototypes (the modal points of the species, genera, families, etc.). Next, morphology traces the development of individuals (ontogeny) and of groups (phylogeny), striving to secure an understanding of the present status of the living world through a knowledge of its past. Genetics, being a branch of physiology concerned in part with the problem of organic diversity, is a nomothetic (law-creating) science. To a geneticist organic diversity is one of the most general and fundamental properties of living matter; diversity is here considered, so to speak, as an aspect of unity through a study of the mechanisms which may be responsible for the production and maintenance of variation, an analysis of the conflicting forces tending to increase or to level off the differences between organisms. The aim of the present book is to review the genetic information bearing on the problem of organic diversity, and, as far as possible, to correlate it with the pertinent data furnished by taxonomy, ecology, physiology, and other related disciplines; this book is not concerned with the purely morphological aspect of the problem.

EVOLUTION

Since Darwin, any discussion of organic diversity unavoidably involves a consideration of the theory of evolution, which represents the greatest generalization advanced in this field. Here again morphological and physiological biology are interested in different aspects of the matter.

The theory of evolution asserts that (1) the beings now living have descended from different beings which have lived in the past; (2) the discontinuous variation observed at our time level—the gaps now existing between clusters of forms—have arisen gradually, so that if we could assemble all the individuals which have ever inhabited the earth, a fairly continuous array of forms would emerge; (3) all these changes have arisen from causes which now continue to be in operation and which therefore can be studied experimentally. The evolution theory was arrived at through generalization and inference from a body of predominantly morphological data and may be regarded as one of the most important achievements of morphological biology. However, the evolutionists of the morphological school have concentrated their efforts on proving the correctness of the first and second of the three assertions listed above, leaving the third rather in abeyance. They have been interested primarily in demonstrating that evolution has actually taken place, and in "bridging the gap," in filling up the discontinuities between the existing groups of organisms, in understanding the relationships between the branches of phylogenetic trees, and not so much in elucidating the nature of the discontinuities themselves or of the mechanisms through which they originated. As a matter of fact, Darwin was one of the very few nineteenth-century evolutionists whose major interests lay in studies of the mechanisms of evolution, in the causal rather than the historical problem. It was exactly this causal aspect of evolution which toward the close of the last century began to attract more and more attention, and which has now been taken up by genetics and related sciences. In this sense genetics rather than evolutionary morphology is heir to the Darwinian tradition.

How neglected were the studies of the mechanisms of evolution is apparent from the fact that in 1922 Bateson was able to write: "In dim outline evolution is evident enough. But that particular and essential bit of the theory of evolution which is concerned with the origin and nature of species remains utterly mysterious." To most biologists these views seem unduly pessimistic. Be that as it may, the fact remains that among the present generation no informed person entertains any doubt of the validity of the evolution theory in the sense that evolution has occurred, and yet nobody is audacious enough to believe himself in possession of the knowledge of the actual mechanisms of evolution. Evolution as an historical process is established as thoroughly as science can establish a fact witnessed by no human eye. The mass of evidence bearing on this subject does not concern us in this book; we take it for granted. But the understanding of causes which may have brought about this evolution, and which can bring about its continuation in the future, is still in its infancy. Much work has been done already to secure such an understanding, and undoubtedly more remains to be done. In the following pages an attempt will be made to evaluate the present status of knowledge in this field.

THE BEARING OF GENETICS ON EVOLUTION

It should be reiterated that genetics as a discipline is not synonymous with the evolution theory, nor is the evolution theory synonymous with any subdivision of genetics. Nevertheless, it remains true that genetics has so profound a bearing on the problem of the mechanisms of evolution that any evolution theory which disregards the established genetic principles is faulty at its source.

Every individual resembles its parents in some respects but differs from them in others. Taken as a group—a population—every succeeding generation of a species resembles but is never a replica of the preceding generation. Evolution is a process resulting in the development of dissimilarities between the ancestral and the descendant populations. The mechanisms that determine the similarities and dissimilarities between parents and offspring constitute the subject matter of genetics. Genetics is physiology of inheritance and variation. This is the reason why the quest for an understanding of the mechanisms of evolutionary continuity or change has devolved upon genetics. But inheritance and variation may be studied on their own account, as general physiological functions, without reference to their bearing on the problem of organic diversity in any of the ramifications of the latter.

The signal successes of genetics to date have been in studies on the mechanisms of the transmission of hereditary characteristics from parents to offspring, that is, on the architectonics of the germ plasm of the sex cells. The germ plasm has been shown to be essentially discontinuous, composed of discrete particles known as genes. Quantitative and qualitative characters; fluctuating variability as well as discontinuous differences between individuals, normal and pathological; intraspecific and interspecific, "superficial" and "fundamental" characters of organisms—these are determined by the genes carried in the sex cells, or, to be more exact, in the chromosomes of these cells. Chromosomes as carriers of genes have been studied in detail, with the result that the physical basis of hereditary transmission has been revealed. The transmission of hereditary characters has been brought under human control, in the sense that in organisms which have been well studied genetically the characteristics of the offspring are frequently predictable, with a rather high degree of accuracy, from a knowledge of the characteristics of the parents. In *Drosophila melanogaster,* and to a lesser extent in certain other forms, hereditary types possessing a desired set of characteristics may, within limits, be synthesized at will, and the schemes of such "syntheses" worked out in theory are almost always realized in minute detail in the actual experiments.

The elegance and precision of methods devised by genetics to control the results of experiments involving crosses of individuals differing in many hereditary characteristics have led to claims that the problem of heredity has been solved. Although a large amount of work still remains to be done in this field, it is indeed fair to say that the laws of the transmission of hereditary characters are, by and large, understood now. But the problem of heredity is much wider. Knowing the rules governing the distribution of the hereditary characteristics of an organism among the sex cells, one is in a position to predict what constellations of genes are likely to be present in the zygotes coming from the union of such sex cells. Between the genes of a fertilized egg and the characters of the adult organism arising from it there lies, however, the whole of individual development during which the genes exert their determining action. The mechanisms of gene action in development constitute the central problem of the second major subdivision of genetics: this has been variously labeled as the genetics of the realization of the hereditary characters, phenogenetics, or developmental genetics.

The problem of gene action is far from having been solved. It is known in some instances that the formation of adult characteristics, such as size or coloration of the body or its parts, is preceded by the appearance in the developing organisms of chemical substances of the hormone type which are operative in the processes that produce the adult characters. The great interest of such information is self-evident, although a physiologically minded biologist always would have taken it for granted that such chemical agents must be active in development. In any case, data of this sort permit no insight into the gene action proper. A gene is a particle located in a chromosome in the cell nucleus. Its action must of necessity start with intracellular processes, which may subsequently be translated into more or less long chains of reactions, culminating in the appearance of visible characters. Regarding these intracellular processes—interactions between the constituent parts of the chromosomes and their nuclear and cytoplasmic surroundings—practically nothing is known at present. Are all genes continually active, or does each gene exert its determining function at a certain period of development and remain quiescent at other periods? Is the gene action merely a by-product of the self-reproduction of the genes in the course of cell division? Are genes specialized, in the sense that each is concerned with a single reaction or with a few reactions which take place in the body, or is their action of a more general sort? What are the relations between gene specificity and the specificity of chemical substances, particularly proteins, composing the organism and manifested especially in serological reactions? Biophysical and biochemical work of recent years has revealed an hitherto unsuspected complexity of cellular organization on the ultramicroscopic level of molecular aggregates. To a geneticist it seems certain that genes must at the same time be a part of and determining agents of this "molecular morphology," but the problems here involved have not been touched as yet.

The genetics of the transmission, and the genetics of the realization, of hereditary materials are concerned with individuals as units. The former establishes the rules governing the formation of the gene constellation in individual zygotes, and the latter deals with the mechanisms of gene action in ontogeny. The third subdivision of genetics has as its province the processes taking place in groups of individuals—in populations—and therefore is called the genetics of populations. A population may be said to possess a definite genetic constitution, which is evidently a function of the constitutions of the individuals composing the group, just as the chemical composition of a rock is a function of that of the minerals entering into its make-up. The rules governing the genetic structure of a population are, nevertheless, distinct from those governing the genetics of individuals, just as rules of sociology are distinct from physiological ones, although they are in fact merely integrated forms of the latter. Imagine, for example, that some factors have arisen in the environment which discriminate against too tall or too short individuals of a species. From the standpoint of an individual, some growth genes would have acquired lethal properties, and the effects of these genes might be described adequately by stating the precise nature of the physiological reactions leading to death. From the viewpoint of population genetics, death of this category of individuals is merely the beginning of a complex chain of consequences: the relative frequencies of individuals homozygous and heterozygous for certain growth genes and for genes located in the same chromosomes would be altered; some genetic factors which previously were being eliminated because of their harmfulness might become neutral or even favorable; after some generations the genetic constitution of the whole species may be changed.

Since evolution is a change in the genetic composition of populations, the mechanisms of evolution constitute problems of population genetics. Of course changes observed in populations may be of very different orders of magnitude, from those induced in a herd of domestic animals by the introduction of a new sire to phylogenetic changes leading to the origin of new classes of organisms. The former are obviously trifling in scale compared with the latter, and it may not be convenient to have all of them subsumed under the name "evolution." Experience seems to show, however, that there is no way toward an understanding of the mechanisms of macroevolutionary changes, which require time on a geological scale, other than through a full comprehension of the microevolutionary processes observable within the span of a human lifetime and often controlled by man's will. For this reason we are compelled at the present level of knowledge reluctantly to put a sign of equality between the mechanisms of macro- and microevolution, and, proceeding on this assumption, to push our investigations as far ahead as this working hypothesis will permit.

EVOLUTIONARY STATICS AND EVOLUTIONARY DYNAMICS

Since the middle of the last century the organic diversity observed in nature has been considered a result of the evolutionary process. The principal tenet of the evolutionary doctrine is that the living world as seen by us at present has not always been as it is now; what we study at our time level is a cross section of the phylogenetic lines, the beginnings of which are lost in the dim past. But evolution is a process of change or movement. Description of any movement may be logically and conveniently divided in two parts; statics, which treats of the forces producing a motion and the equilibrium of these forces, and dynamics, which deals with the motion itself and the action of forces producing it. Following this scheme, we shall discuss, first, the forces which may come under consideration as possible factors bringing about changes in the genetic composition of populations (evolutionary statics), and second, the interactions of these forces in race and species formation and disintegration (evolutionary dynamics).

In bare outline, the mechanisms of evolution as seen by a geneticist appear as follows. Gene changes, mutations, are the most obvious source of evolutionary changes and of diversity in general. Next come the changes of a grosser mechanical kind involving rearrangements of the genic materials within the chromosomes. It seems probable at present that such rearrangements may at least occasionally entail changes in the functioning of the genes themselves (position effects), since the effects of a gene on development are determined not only by the structure of that gene itself but also by that of its neighbors. Combining chromosome complements of different species to produce a single new one (allopolyploidy) is an important evolutionary method among plants; reduplications and losses of whole chromosome sets (autopolyploidy), as well as of individual chromosomes (polysomy), take place in certain special groups of organisms. Finally, there is an insufficiently studied field of changes in extra-genic structures, usually associated with the cytoplasm. Whether all plasmatic changes are indirectly induced by changes in the genes is unclear at present; some of them, especially in the plastids of plants, seem to be autonomous.

Mutations and chromosomal changes arise in every sufficiently studied organism with a certain finite frequency, and thus constantly and unremittingly supply the raw materials for evolution. But evolution involves something more than origin of mutations. Mutations and chromosomal changes are only the first stage or level of the evolutionary process, and are governed entirely by the laws of the physiology of individuals. Once produced, mutations are injected into the genetic composition of the population, where their further fate is determined by the dynamic regularities of the physiology of populations. In generations immediately following its origin, a mutation may be lost or increased in frequency and this (in the case of recessive mutations) without regard to the beneficial or deleterious effects of the mutation. The influences of selection, migration, and geographical isolation then mold the genetic structure of populations into new shapes, in conformity with the secular environment and the ecology, especially the breeding habits, of the species. This is the second level of the evolutionary process, on which the impact of the environment produces historical changes in the living population.

Finally, the third level is a realm of fixation of the diversity already attained on the preceding two levels. Races and species as discrete arrays of individuals may exist only so long as the genetic structures of their populations are preserved distinct by some mechanisms which prevent their interbreeding. Unlimited interbreeding of two or more initially different populations unavoidably results in an exchange of genes between them and a consequent fusion of the once distinct groups into a single variable array. A number of mechanisms encountered in nature (ecological isolation, sexual isolation, hybrid sterility, and others) guard against such a fusion of the discrete arrays and the consequent decay of discontinuous variability. The origin and functioning of the isolating mechanisms constitute one of the most important problems of the genetics of populations.

In the following chapters an attempt will be made to summarize the available evidence bearing on these three levels of the evolutionary process. Variation-producing agents (gene mutation, chromosomal changes) are known from laboratory experiments. But it is not a priori certain that these agents observed under laboratory conditions have been effective in nature and are responsible for the organic diversity empirically observable out-of-doors. We assume this to be the case because no other equally satisfactory working hypothesis has been proposed. Nevertheless, the validity of the working hypothesis must be rigorously tested by examining whether the differences between forms encountered in nature can be resolved into the elements whose origin is known in experiments. Thus evolutionary statics will be covered in Chapters II–IV. Next the dynamic stage, the evolutionary process in the strict sense, comes under consideration in Chapters V–XI. Here one must necessarily proceed by inference, for, with very few important exceptions, the experimentalist is still not in a position to reproduce in the laboratory the historical processes that have taken place in nature. Nonetheless, a rapidly growing body of both observational and purely experimental evidence gives at least a promise that an adequate analysis of evolutionary dynamics will be possible in a not too distant future.

II: GENE MUTATION

HEREDITY AND ENVIRONMENT

OUR knowledge of the living world is acquired primarily through observations of individuals. The properties of an individual—its size, bodily proportions, physiology, and behavior—can be measured and recorded with a requisite degree of accuracy. The resulting data may be superimposed on those pertaining to other individuals, and conclusions may be drawn regarding similarities and differences between them. The information so gained is generalized to become an ordered system of classification. A modern biologist is, however, no longer satisfied with the terse statement of Cuvier, according to whom the task of an investigator is to "nommer, classer, et décrire." He wishes to know something about the causes which make an individual what it is, and which make different individuals similar in some respects and different in others. Such a causal analysis is based on two fundamental concepts formulated by Johannsen, namely those of the phenotype and the genotype.

The phenotype is what we measure and describe in our direct observations and experiments, the organism's structures and functions—in short, what a living being appears to be to our sense organs. The genotype is the genetic constitution, the sum total of the hereditary factors received by the organism from its ancestors. The genotype of an individual cannot be perceived directly; one can infer its properties only by examining the individual's pedigree or progeny or both. The relation between the genotype and the phenotype is a dynamic one, since the former determines the reactions of the organism to its environment. A phenotype is always the resultant of the interactions between a genotype and an environment. Different genotypes may react in a given environment to produce similar phenotypes; hence, similarity of phenotypes under identical environments is not always proof of the similarity of genotypes. On the other hand, the same genotype may react in different environments to produce dissimilar phenotypes; hence, dissimilarity of phenotypes is not necessarily proof of the dissimilarity of genotypes. Phenotypic differences between individuals which have developed in the same environment demonstrate the existence of genotypic differences; and phenotypic differences between individuals which possess identical genotypes prove that these individuals have developed in different environments.

Much discussion has centered around the question of the relative importance of genotype and environment, nature and nurture, in determining the phenotype of organisms. Most of this discussion is futile: in its general form the question is meaningless. In similar environments certain genotypic differences may loom large, but a great environmental change may induce alterations in the phenotype compared to which the genotypic variants would seem trivial. Thus, the appearance of the plant *Limnophila heterophylla* grown under water is so different from that of the same plant grown on land that it seems almost inconceivable that the two belong to the same species. The males of the parasitic wasp *Trichogramma semblidis* may be winged or wingless and may possess different structures of the body and appendages, depending upon the host in which they develop (Salt, 1937). Since the realization of any genotypic character takes place in the individual's development through a chain of physiological reactions, treatments may be discovered which suppress or enhance its effects. Goldschmidt (1938) asserts that the effects of any genetic change may be copied by means of environmental influences. This is true in theory but difficult to realize in practice. Nevertheless, attempts of medical science to "cure" hereditary diseases may be based on just such an approach, and eugenists should at least consider it as a possibility.

The genotype of an individual can be transmitted without change to its offspring and is potentially capable of being reincarnated in any number of individuals. In asexually reproducing organisms, large colonies may consist of genotypically identical specimens (Anderson, 1936a, in *Iris*). Figuratively speaking, every genotype exerts a pressure on the environment, tending to take possession of all the available space. Conversely, the environment exerts a constant pressure on the genotypes of the organisms residing in it, tending to modify them in various ways. The hereditary materials possess however, tremendous self-regulatory powers and can withstand unchanged the impact of most environmental agencies. It is vastly easier to render an organism sterile or to destroy it altogether than it is to produce the slightest change in the genotype.

Inheritance of acquired characters—a reflection of phenotypic changes in the structure of the genotype—apparently does not take place. The few remaining believers in this contingency, epigones of Lamarckism, can adduce no critical evidence in support of their convictions; at any rate up to the present their speculations have proved barren as working hypotheses. Unfortunately, in the heat of the polemics against Lamarckism some statements have been made by geneticists which do not contribute to a clarification of the issues: to this class belongs the assertion that the genotype is not influenced by the environment. It is true that the genotype tends to reproduce its like indefinitely in all environments in which the life of its carrier is possible. Nevertheless, genotypic changes do occur in which the environment plays at least the role of a trigger mechanism. More important still, any genotype is the result of agelong processes of evolutionary development, in which the environment, through natural selection, has been a force of paramount importance. The structure of the genotype and hence the kind of changes it is capable of producing are in the last analysis environmentally determined. The "determining environment" is, however, not merely the one prevailing at the moment, but rather it is the sum of the historical environments to which the organism had been exposed in its phylogeny.

Owing to the inherent stability of the genotype, heredity is essentially a conservative agent. Evolution is possible only because heredity is counteracted by another agent opposite in effect—namely, mutation. In genotypically homogeneous populations, hereditary variation sooner or later arises *de novo*. One of the best examples of mutation in genetically pure populations has been reported by Blakeslee, Morrison, and Avery (1927) in the Jimson weed *Datura stramonium*. Haploid individuals of this plant have in their cells twelve chromosomes, instead of the twenty-four present in the normal diploid. A certain proportion of the egg cells and pollen produced by the haploid contain all the twelve chromosomes (nonreduction). As a result of selfing, some diploid offspring may be produced.

Diploids derived from a haploid, as well as the progeny of these diploids, must be strictly identical as to genotype. The presence of residual heterozygosity, not eliminated by inbreeding, is here excluded. Nevertheless, among 173 diploid plants tested, four proved to be heterozygous for mutant genes showing Mendelian segregation.

DEFINITION OF MUTATION

The mutation concept has had a tortuous history. Not only has the term changed repeatedly in meaning, but even now it is being used in at least two different senses. Alternatives to the term "mutation" have been proposed, but all of them have failed of adoption. Many years ago Waagen (1869) designated as mutations the smallest perceptible changes in the temporal series of forms in a species of ammonites; these changes have a definite direction, and their gradual accumulation with the passage of time leads to the appearance of types progressively more distinct from the progenitor. To what extent Waagen's mutations correspond to the mutational steps observed by geneticists is an open question.

The creators of the mutation theory were Korjinsky and De Vries. The latter (De Vries 1901) defines it as follows: "As the theory of mutation I designate the statement that the properties of organisms are built from sharply distinct units. . . . Intergrades, which are so numerous between the external forms of plants and animals, exist between these units no more than between the molecules of chemistry." A mutation is, then, a change in one of the units which at present are known as genes. The comparison of genes with chemical molecules may prove to be a truly prophetic one. Thus far De Vries's statements have a decidedly modern ring. De Vries proceeds, however, to define the distinctions between his mutation theory and Darwin's selectionism: "The latter [selectionism] assumes that the usual or the so-called individual variability is the starting point of the origin of new species. According to the mutation theory the two [individual and mutational variabilities] are completely independent. As I hope to show, the usual variability cannot lead to a real overstepping of the species limits even with a most intense steady selection. . . ." On the other hand, each mutation "sharply and completely separates the new form, as an independent species, from the species from which it arose." Since De Vries's "species" are evidently not identical with the usual, or Linnaean, ones, an attempt was made to introduce the term "elementary species" for the former. This attempt has met with little sympathy, not only because the word species was here used in an entirely new sense, but especially because in sexually reproducing organisms one would have to consider almost every individual an elementary species. Furthermore, it is clear at present that the individual variability, in so far as it is hereditary at all, is due to the fact that the populations of most species are mixtures of types differing from each other in one or in several genes. Finally, the mutants obtained by De Vries in his classical investigations with *Oenothera* proved to be an assemblage of diverse changes, including gene alterations, segregation products due to a hybridity of the initial material, and chromosomal aberrations.

The studies begun by Morgan in 1910 on mutability in the fly *Drosophila melanogaster* constitute a turning point in the history of the mutation theory. Although mutations occur as sudden changes, in the sense that no gradual passage through genetic conditions intermediate between the original and the mutant types is observed, the distinction which De Vries has attempted to draw between individual and mutational variability does not exist. The amount of change produced by a mutation, as measured by the visible departure from the ancestral condition in the structural and physiological characters, varies greatly. Since mutants which are recognizable even to an untrained eye are most useful in experiments, such mutants are preserved while the slight ones are generally discarded; this has created a false impression among some biologists that all *Drosophila* mutants show striking visible alterations. Slight mutants, falling well within the normal range of individual variability, have been observed by Johannsen (1909) in beans, and Morgan (1918) has repeatedly emphasized that they occur in *Drosophila* as well. Baur (1924) found small mutations to be very common in the snapdragon (*Antirrhinum majus*). Small and large mutations are not distinct classes as some writers have implied.

From the very beginning of the work on *Drosophila* it has become clear that most mutations behave as changes in single Mendelian units (Morgan 1911, 1913). Simple segregation is observed in crosses between the ancestral and the mutant type. Since Mendelian segregation and recombination constitute the twin bases on which the existence of genes is inferred, the conclusion is drawn that most mutations represent gene changes. The nature of these changes is, however, a different problem. If a gene is a self-reproducing unit in a chromosome endowed with a definite chemical structure, alterations of this structure which permit the changed particle to retain its autosynthetic functions might be a source of the mutational variability. It would seem reasonable to restrict the term "mutation" to apply to this, and only to this, kind of change. Such a restriction leads, however, to grave difficulties in practice, since no methods are available for a direct comparison of the chemical structures of the ancestral and the mutated genes. The sole evidence of the occurrence of a change in the gene is the appearance of a phenotypic variant, a mutant, which follows Mendel's law in inheritance. Yet a loss (deficiency) or a reduplication of a part of a chromosome likewise results in phenotypic alterations that show Mendelian inheritance. Similar effects may be produced by rearrangements of the genic materials within the chromosomes (inversion, translocation). Finally, reduplications and losses of whole chromosomes may simulate Mendelian units.

Mutational changes fall, consequently, into two large classes: those presumably caused by chemical alterations in the individual genes (mutation proper, otherwise known as point mutation, transgenation, or genovariation), and those of a grosser structural kind, involving physical destruction, multiplication, or spatial rearrangement of the genes (chromosomal aberrations). An attempt to discriminate between these classes by examination of the chromosomes of the mutant types under the microscope breaks down because of the limitations of the existing cytological techniques. For example, a loss of a chromosome section may be detectable in a species with large and well-differentiated chromosomes, but not in one with small and compact ones. The giant chromosomes in the larval salivary glands of *Drosophila* and certain other flies unquestionably offer the most favorable material for such studies, but even there one cannot be certain that very small structural changes (for example, losses or additions of single discs) are not overlooked. Stadler (1932) has correctly emphasized that what is described as gene mutations is merely the residuum left after the elimination of all classes of hereditary changes for which a mechanical basis is detected.

Goldschmidt (1938, 1940) takes the extreme view that all the supposed mutations are rearrangements in the chromosomal materials. All that one can say regarding this view, which has been espoused by some earlier writers without finding many adherents, is that the postulated mechanical changes have not been shown to exist in most mutants. Admittedly, the inability to detect such changes in any one mutant is not a proof that this particular mutant is caused by a chemical, rather than a mechanical, change, but it remains nevertheless probable that many mutants do belong to this class. It would be strange indeed if the hereditary materials possessed an eternally immutable chemical constitution. Discovery of a method that would permit a separation of the intragenic from the intergenic changes is a goal for the future. For the time being the term mutation subsumes a variety of phenomena. In a wide sense, any change in the genotype which is not due to recombination of Mendelian factors is called mutation. In the narrower sense, it is a presumed change in a single gene, a Mendelian variant which is not known to represent a chromosomal aberration. Unless otherwise specified, the term will be used below in the latter sense.

TYPES OF CHANGES PRODUCED BY MUTATION

Since genes are supposedly concerned as one of the variables in all developmental processes, gene mutations may be expected to affect all parts and physiological characteristics of the organism. The available experimental evidence seems, so far as it goes, to confirm this inference.

In the vinegar fly *Drosophila melanogaster,* in which more mutations have been observed than in any other organism, the variety of characters affected is enormous. Compilation of a complete catalogue of such characters is impossible at present, since a majority of mutations have never been scrutinized from this point of view. Descriptions of mutations are made with emphasis on easily visible characteristics that may be useful for classifying flies in crossing experiments, while other, and especially physiological, traits are generally disregarded. The following list gives an idea of the diversity of mutational changes.

Some mutations affect the coloration of all external parts of the body, of the eyes, ocelli, testicular envelope, and Malpighian vessels; others, the length, diameter, and shape of the bristles—definite bristles or sets of bristles may be absent or reduplicated. Still other mutations influence the size of the eyes, antennae, legs and their parts, the form and arrangement of the ommatidia, chitinization and arrangement of body sclerites. A very interesting class of mutations causes transformation of some organs into others, revealing the homology between the two. Here belong the transformation of the balancers into a second pair of wings, of the antennae into legs, and of the mouth parts of the fly in the direction of those of lower insects. Sex organs and secondary sexual characters are affected: changes have been observed in the sexcombs, external male genitalia, number and shape of the spermathecae, number of eggstrings and egg chambers in the ovaries, shape and appearance of the eggs. Developmental stages may be changed: size, shape, and weight of the larvae, pupae, and adults. Changes in the internal organs are observed chiefly in connection with external changes; thus, the brain is changed in connection with the eye size and the presence or absence of the eyes. Purely physiological characteristics are frequently affected: reaction to light and gravity, sex-determining factors, longevity, number of eggs deposited, length of development, manner of growth, number of larval instars. Mutations are known that produce tumorlike growths in various organs and at various developmental stages. The large class of lethal mutations has not received even a fraction of the attention it deserves. It is known, however, that lethals may cause death of the organism at any stage of development, including the early embryonic ones. The causes of death are mostly obscure. Kaliss (1939) found that a small deficiency affecting the cut locus in the X chromosome permits the development of the eggs up to the stage when a larva normally hatches. In the case of the deficiency, the larva fails to hatch and its tracheal system fails to be filled with air, perhaps because of an abnormal permeability of the cuticle to water. On the other hand, Poulson (1937, 1940) has described radical changes in the course of cleavage, gastrulation, and organ formation in the eggs deficient for long sections of the X chromosome. Such data may shed new light on the general problems of developmental mechanics as well as on the role played by separate genes and gene groups. Although most mutations appear to cause losses or diminutions of organs or functions present in the wild type, certain mutations tend rather to cause hypertrophies (N. W. and K. A. Timofeeff-Ressovsky 1934). Mutants having similar phenotypes in certain environments may be modified in opposite directions by other environmental influences (Braun 1938).

A number of misconceptions exist regarding the kind of mutations observed in *Drosophila*. We are forced to give a brief consideration to some of these misconceptions, since they have figured prominently in certain discussions of the role of the mutation factor in species formation and evolution. It has been contended, for instance, that mutations involve only "superficial" characteristics, leaving the "fundamental" ones unaffected. Those making such assertions have wisely refrained from revealing their criteria for the discrimination between superficial and fundamental traits.

The presence of one pair of wings and one pair of balancers, as opposed to two pairs of wings, is one of the most striking distinguishing marks of the order of flies (*Diptera*). One may ask then, is the appearance of a four-winged *Drosophila* a fundamental or a superficial change? Is a mutation which diverts the embryonic development to a wrong course and thus causes death fundamental or superficial? Those who would like to see a mutant fly without an alimentary canal, or with the location of the heart and the nerve chain exchanged, overlook the fact that such a mutant could not survive and hence could never be detected. More important still, there is no one-to-one relationship between individual genes and separate organs. Finally, those who would call "fundamental" only a change that would transform an individual of *Drosophila melanogaster* into a representative of another species, genus, or family, fail to understand the nature of the specific differences which are due always to coöperation of many genes and hence cannot arise through the mutation of a single gene.

MUTATION AND VIABILITY

Another type of criticism advanced against the mutation theory is that the mutations observed in *Drosophila* and in other organisms produce deteriorations of viability, pathological changes and monstrosities, and therefore cannot serve as evolutionary building blocks. This assertion has been made so many times that it has gained credit by sheer force of repetition. It is true that most mutations dealt with in the laboratory decrease the viability of the fly under the environmental conditions in which *Drosophila melanogaster* is usually kept. But mutations in *Drosophila* as well as in other organisms form a spectrum, ranging from lethals to changes which are neutral or even favorable to viability. It is the middle part of this spectrum (comprising mutations producing striking phenotypic effects and from a slight to an appreciable depression of the viability) that is mainly dealt with in genetic experiments in which mutant genes are used as "chromosome markers." The great and insufficiently studied class of lethals is not a homogeneous group; some of them cause death in early developmental stages, others in relatively late ones, and still others permit the adult fly to hatch if the culture conditions are especially favorable. The last group of lethals are sometimes classed as semilethals, and semilethals intergrade with mutations that produce medium, slight, or no decrease of viability.

Timofeeff-Ressovsky (1934c, d, 1935b) has demonstrated that the effects produced by a given mutation on viability are a function both of the environmental conditions and of the rest of the genetic structure of an individual (Table 1). The mutation "eversae" in *Drosophila funebris* is at 15°–16° and at 28°–30° inferior, and at 24°–25° superior to the wild type in viability. The viability of the mutations venae abnormes and miniature is only slightly inferior to that of the wild type at 15°–16°, and much inferior at 28°–30°. On the contrary, the viability of bobbed is low at 15°–16° and approaches normal at 28°–30°. Overpopulation of the cultures decreases the relative viability in the mutations eversae, venae abnormes, and miniature, but has an opposite effect on bobbed. Combinations of venae abnormes and lozenge, each of which decreases the viability, produce a summation of the deleterious effects; combination of miniature and bobbed gives a compound which is more viable than either mutation by itself (Table 1).

Analogous results have been reported by Altschuler (1930), Csik (1935), Lüers (1935), and Brierley (1938) for *Drosophila melanogaster*. In Brierley's case the viability of some of the combinations of mutants was so much higher than that of the same mutants taken separately as to raise suspicions that the genetic uniformity of the material had not been sufficiently controlled. Kühn (1932) has found in the moth *Ephestia kühniella* mutant genes that modify the color of the eyes, wing scales, or wing pattern, and that simultaneously reduce the viability of their carriers. A combination of two of these mutants proved, however, to be equal in viability to the wild type.

The extreme rarity or even absence of mutations that improve the viability in normal strains and under normal conditions is not surprising. The structure of each gene and of the genotype as a whole is a product of a long historical process controlled by natural selec-

TABLE 1

VIABILITY OF SOME MUTATIONS AND THEIR COMBINATIONS IN *Drosophila funebris*, EXPRESSED IN PERCENTAGE OF THE VIABILITY OF WILD TYPE
(after Timofeeff-Ressovsky)

MUTATION	TEMPERATURE			COMBINATION	TEMPERATURE
	15°–16°	24°–25°	28°–30°		24°–25°
eversae	98.3	104.0	98.5	eversae singed	103.1
singed		79.0		eversae abnormes	83.7
abnormes	96.2	88.9	80.7	eversae bobbed	85.5
miniature	91.3	69.0	63.7	singed abnormes	76.6
bobbed	75.3	85.1	93.7	singed miniature	67.1
lozenge		73.8		abnormes miniature	82.7
				abnormes lozenge	59.3
				abnormes bobbed	78.7
				miniature bobbed	96.6
				lozenge bobbed	69.2

tion. Mutation is an accidental change of the gene structure, and as such it is vastly more likely to be deleterious than favorable. Furthermore, since the mutations which we can observe have taken place innumerable times in the history of the species, any mutation which constitutes an improvement over the "normal" condition has had a chance to become established. The genetic structure of the wild type with which laboratory experiments are started is presumably always fairly close to the highest level of adaptation attainable by the species in its present environment. To enhance the probability of detecting mutations favorable to the viability one must either lower the adaptive level of the initial genotype, or conduct the experiments in an environment different from that in which the species normally lives. Although no systematic experiments of this type have been made, there are certain scattered facts which suggest that favorable mutants can be observed.

The gene stubbloid in *Drosophila melanogaster* decreases the length of the bristles, and causes crumpled wings, bent legs, and decreased viability. In inbred lines of stubbloid kept in the laboratory for a long time the crumpling of the wings and the bending of legs become sometimes less pronounced as time goes on, and the general viability increases. If, however, such an "improved" line is outcrossed to an unrelated wild type strain, the stubbloid flies appearing in the F_2 generation show again the unfavorable wing, leg, and viability characteristics (unpublished observations of the writer). Similar results were obtained in other mutants by Marshall and Muller (1917) and by other observers. The best interpretation of such facts is that, in culture, mutations take place giving rise to genes which suppress the effects of stubbloid, and that the suppressors are favored by selection and the strain becomes homozygous for them. An alternative interpretation is, of course, that such suppressors are always present in heterozygous condition in any strain, and are acted upon by natural selection in stubbloid strains.

Species and strains of bacteria, yeasts, and lower fungi are characterized by definite nutritional requirements; each strain can be propagated only on media in which certain chemical components are present. It has been known for a long time that some strains may be induced to grow also on media on which they would not subsist ordinarily. This is attained either by making a very heavy inoculation of an unsuitable medium from a normal population, or by transferring the organisms from culture to culture with diminishing concentrations of the original nutrient. Growth and reproduction may start suddenly in a part of the colony, and further inoculations from that part take hold of the new food medium at once. With few exceptions (Lewis 1934), the interpretations given to this phenomenon by bacteriologists have a strong Lamarckian flavor, as indicated by the term "training" applied to it. As a matter of fact, the bulk of the available evidence may be much better accounted for on the supposition that mutations changing the food requirements of the microörganisms occur constantly, and that small numbers of mutant cells may be present in large cultures. Their occurrence is noticed only when the nature of the food medium is altered, and the "favorable" mutants are thus given an opportunity to assert themselves.

Banta and Wood (1927, 1939) observed a mutation in the water flea *Daphnia longispina,* which normally has the temperature optimum at 20° C. and which is unable to survive more than a few days at 27°. The mutant has an optimum between 25° and 30° and does not survive at 20°. This case is very suggestive when compared to that of the little fish *Crenichtys* inhabiting isolated springs in Nevada, some of which have much warmer water than others. Sumner and Sargent (1940) have shown experimentally that *Crenichtys* from warm springs may survive in cold ones, but not vice versa. Classification of mutations as favorable and harmful is meaningless if the nature of the genetic and the secular environments is not stated.

A mutation inducing changes in the structure of the mouth parts of *Drosophila* which prevents the access of food into the alimentary canal (the mutant proboscipedia) is a monstrosity, and one can scarcely imagine an environment in which such a mutation would be favorable; yet whole families exist in different orders of insects whose members have mouth parts unfit for feeding. Reduction or disappearance of the eyes is a deterioration, but many insects have no eyes. The mutation rotated abdomen has the male genitalia not in the plane of the body symmetry, so that males homozygous for the mutant gene cannot copulate and are therefore sterile. Nevertheless, twisted genitalia are one of the distinguishing characteristics of some families of flies (*Syrphidae* and others). An asymmetry of the bill is decidedly deleterious when it appears as an inheritable abnormality in the fowl and in other birds; this does not prevent its being a "normal" character in the crossbill (*Loxia*) (Landauer 1938). A mutation which prevents flowering would spell disaster to most species of higher plants, and yet plants are known that produce flowers only seldom or not at all (for example, *Elodea canadensis* in Europe). The value of anthropomorphic judgments on what constitutes a malformation is spurious.

EXTENT OF CHANGES PRODUCED BY MUTATIONS

In *Drosophila* as elsewhere, mutations form a spectrum with respect to the extent of the effects produced, ranging from drastic changes lethal to the early developmental stages to changes so minute that their detection presents a serious technical problem. This spectrum is not only similar to that of the mutational effects on viability (see above), but there is a loose correlation between the positions of a given mutation in the two spectra: namely, mutations producing great departures from the normal phenotype usually have an adverse effect on the viability, and vice versa.

To determine the relative frequency of the different types of mutations is not easy. Evidently, the greater the phenotypical change, the easier is the detection of a mutation. Since striking mutations are more valuable as chromosome markers than the weak ones, the former are picked out and studied. The published descriptions of mutations give a grossly distorted picture of the characteristics of the mutation process.

Timofeeff-Ressovsky (1934b, and especially 1934d and 1935b) has done pioneering work in attempting to clarify the situation. He treated with X-rays wild type males of *Drosophila melanogaster* from a thoroughly inbred strain, and crossed them to ClB females which previously had been repeatedly outcrossed to the same inbred strain. (The ClB females have in one of their X chromosomes a lethal gene, a marker producing a visible effect (Bar), and an inversion which eliminates crossing over between the ClB chromosome and the other X chromosome present in the same female.) In the F_1 generation, females heterozygous for the ClB chromosome were selected and outcrossed to untreated wild type males. Such females have one ClB X chromosome (untreated), and one paternal X chromosome treated with X-rays. Their sons receiving the ClB chromosome die of the lethal contained in it; the sons receiving the other X chromosome survive, provided no lethal mutation has been induced in this chromosome by the treatment. The expected sex ratio is, therefore, 2 females:1 male. If in the treated chromosome a lethal mutation is induced, the sons receiving it die of the lethal, and the offspring are females only. This is the standard method, originally proposed by Muller, and now generally used for the detection of the sex-linked lethal mutations.

If a mutation which is not lethal but which decreases the viability arises in the X chromosome, the resulting sex ratio falls between ·2 ♀ : 1 ♂ and 2 ♀ : 0 ♂ , depending upon the degree of the deleterious effect produced by the mutation. For technical reasons it was preferable to take into account only the daughters which do *not* carry the X chromosome (ClB); they form about half of all females, and can be recognized by the absence of the marking gene (Bar). The frequencies of such females and males turned out to be 1 ♀ : 0.95 ♂ if no mutation has been· induced in the treated chromosome, and 1 ♀ : 0 ♂ if a lethal mutation has been induced. The results of the experiment can be seen in Table 2, showing the sex ratio produced by individual females in form of variation series. The control series shows the ratios obtained in the progeny of males which have not been treated with X-rays.

TABLE 2

THE ♀ : ♂ RATIOS OBTAINED BY TIMOFEEFF-RESSOVSKY IN HIS EXPERIMENTS ON MUTATIONS AFFECTING VIABILITY

SEX RATIO	1.15 : 1	1.05 : 1	.95 : 1	.85 : 1	.75 : 1	.65 : 1	.55 : 1	.45 : 1	.35 : 1	.25 : 1	.15 : 1	.05 : 1	0 : 1
Control (in %)	-.1	14.1	77.1	5.5	.7	—	—	.5	—	—	—	—	—
Treated (in %)	.7	10.1	44.9	8.8	7.2	5.3	4.2	1.8	1.1	.7	1.4	.9	13.6

In the treated series, 13 percent (56 out of 432) of the cultures produced no males, indicating that mutations having lethal effects appeared. In 3 percent of the cultures, semilethal mutations were observed (sex ratios between 1 : 0.30 and 1 : 0). The most remarkable fact is, however, that a large number of cultures gave sex ratios which can be accounted for only on the supposition that mutations producing slight decreases of the viability have arisen. The exact number of such cultures in the treated series is not easy to determine, since the ratios observed in them overlap those in the cultures of the control, but they make up no less than 20 percent of the total. Timofeeff-Ressovsky repeated these experiments, varying the technique and imposing checks on the validity of his conclusions. The conclusions withstood the repeated tests. The experiments of Kerkis (1938), which were carried on independently of those of

Timofeeff-Ressovsky but with an almost identical technique, have produced astonishingly similar results.

The mutations that occur most frequently following X-ray treatments produce weak, barely perceptible effects. The same is probably true for the spontaneous mutations, and therefore the evolutionary changes are most likely a result of the summation of such small mutational steps. Prior to Timofeeff-Ressovsky's work this viewpoint was advanced by Baur (1924, 1925) on the basis of observations on small mutations ("Kleinmutationen") in the snapdragon (*Antirrhinum*), and by a number of others (Goldschmidt, Wright, Fisher, Muller, East) on more theoretical grounds. Fisher (1930) has given an interesting mathematical argument in favor of this view. These considerations agree very well with the results of the genetic analysis of the interracial and interspecific differences (Chapter III), thus demonstrating that these differences are caused by coöperation of numerous genes, each of which taken separately has only slight effects on the phenotype.

MANIFOLD EFFECTS OF GENES

Mutant genes are named according to the most prominent characteristics produced by them. In *Drosophila*, mutations of the gene "white" turn the eye color from red to white, "vestigial" makes vestigial wings, "stubbloid" causes a shortening of the bristles, and so on. This system of naming is convenient, but the names are not to be taken as complete accounts of the differences between the mutants and the ancestral form, much less as indicative of the total range of the effects of the particular gene on development. Despite the inadequate descriptions of mutations customarily given in the genetic literature (attention being centered almost exclusively on a single change or on a few easily observable ones), it is well known that many mutants, in *Drosophila* as well as in other forms, differ from the ancestral types in complexes of diversified characters. The mutation white changes not only the eye color, but also that of the testicular membrane, the shape of the spermatheca, length of life, and the general viability. Vestigial reduces wing size, modifies the balancers, makes certain bristles erect instead of horizontal, changes the wing muscles, the shape of the spermatheca, the speed of growth, fecundity, and length of life. Under favorable external conditions vestigial decreases the number of ovarioles in the ovaries while it has the opposite effect under unfavorable conditions. Stubbloid modifies the bristles, wings, legs, antennae, and viability (Dobzhansky 1927, 1930a, Saveliev 1928, Alpatov 1932).

Genes that produce changes in more than one character are said to be pleiotropic or to have manifold effects. The frequency of such genes is not well known at present. It is true that a majority of the mutations studied produce striking effects on a single character, and that their manifold effects, if any, involve changes which to our eyes appear trivial. Thus, the main characteristic of the mutant vestigial in *Drosophila* is a decrease of the wing size, and other characters mentioned above are secondary. But to conclude on this basis that vestigial is a "wing gene" rather than a "bristle gene" would be as naïve as to suppose that a change in the hydrogen ion concentration is a "color gene" because it produces a striking change in the color of certain chemical indicators. It should be kept in mind that the mutant as well as the ancestral form possesses alleles of the gene producing the mutation. The phenotype of the ancestral form is, then, determined by the gene A in coöperation with all other genes composing the genotype, while the phenotype of the mutant is due to the coöperation of the gene a with the same residual genotype. Therefore, the differences between the ancestral form and the mutant are indicative of the effects of the change $A{\to}a$, but not of the sum total of the effects of either A or a.

Today the only avenue of approach to the problem of total gene effects is through studies on physical losses, deficiencies, of genes. It is a general experience that in nonpolypoid organisms homozygous deficiencies are inviable. The work of Poulson (1940) referred to above shows that deficiencies for sections of the X chromosome of *Drosophila melanogaster* cause great disturbances in the fundamental processes of embryonic development. Moreover, most deficiencies in *Drosophila* act as cell lethals; that is, the absence of genes is fatal not only to the whole organism but also to a patch of deficient tissue surrounded by tissues in which all genes are present (Demerec 1934, 1936, 1939). There are exceptions to this rule: some deficiencies are not cell lethals, and a few cases are known in which the whole organism survives the loss of some genes (Stadler 1933, Demerec 1934, Ephrussi 1934, Muller 1935, Demerec and

Hoover 1936, McClintock 1938). The exceptions suggest either that some genes are less important in the development than others, or that some genes are normally present at more than one locus in the chromosomes. Certain geneticists are even inclined to assume special "viability genes" to account for the lethality of most deficiencies. According to this view a deficiency for, let us say, a color gene is fatal to the organism not because that gene has effects other than those involving pigment production but because of a propinquity of the color gene to a viability gene in the chromosome. This crude atomism has no foundation in fact.

Some attempts have been made to determine the frequency of manifold effects by examining a random sample of mutant genes for changes in an arbitrarily selected organ or organ system. Dobzhansky (1927) studied the shape of the spermatheca in twelve mutants of *Drosophila melanogaster* known to affect such characters as eye and body color, wing shape, and so forth; these mutants were not suspected of differing from each other in the internal anatomy in general or in the spermatheca shape in particular. Nevertheless, ten out of twelve showed differences in the shape of the spermatheca. These findings have been confirmed by Schwab (1940), who pointed out, however, that the differences in the spermatheca shape might be due to modifying genes lying in the chromosome in the vicinity of the mutant genes responsible for the externally visible changes, as well as to the latter genes themselves. Whether or not the variations in the spermatheca shape can be ascribed to manifold effects remains uncertain.

The early theorists on heredity, particularly Weismann, considered the germ plasm to be a mosaic of corpuscles, each representing an anatomically defined body part or function. This preformistic notion has become, perhaps by indirection, attached to the genes as well, and continues to influence the thinking of many geneticists. Although the corpuscular nature of the germ plasm is indeed established, there is, in the opinion of the present writer, no evidence that every gene has a circumscribed province of action, including only a single character of physiological function. This problem belongs to the field of developmental genetics, and concerns us here only in connection with the so-called neutral characters. Differences between races, species, and genera frequently involve characters whose value in the struggle for existence is uncertain. Yet the prevalence of manifold effects of genes makes caution necessary in reaching the conclusion that a given property of an organism is devoid of any adaptive significance. For a seemingly neutral character may represent only a part of the total of the effects of the gene difference; physiological properties concealed from the eye of an observer, but correlated with a neutral trait, may be important in the life of the organism.

FREQUENCY OF MUTATIONS

A living species is constantly under a pressure of the mutation process tending to produce a change in the characteristics of the organism. The magnitude of the mutation pressure is evidently a problem of prime importance for any theory of evolution. This problem is as yet unsolved, although at present the amount of available data bearing on it is far greater than was the case only a few years ago. The difficulty of obtaining accurate quantitative data on the mutation pressure is apparent. Either one tries to determine the total frequency of mutations for all the genes the organism possesses, or a particular gene is selected and its mutability measured. In the former case, mutations producing minute changes present an insuperable obstacle, for no known experimental procedure permits the detection of all such mutations, and they are suspected to be the most frequent class. If a single gene is selected, the mutation frequency is usually so low that accumulation of accurate data is technically difficult, slight mutations may be overlooked, and there is no assurance that all mutations of the gene in question produce changes in the same character (due to manifold effects).

A great amount of data has been collected by various authors on the frequency of lethal mutations in the X chromosome of *Drosophila melanogaster*. The detection of such mutations is easy and accurate: a female carrying in one of its X chromosomes a newly arisen lethal produces a sex ratio of 2 : 1 in its offspring. If such a female is heterozygous for the ClB chromosome, the detection of the lethal appearing in the normal X chromosome is simpler still, for such a female produces only daughters and no sons (see p. 30). Data involving at least 100,000 females tested with the aid of this

method have accumulated in the genetic literature; between 0.1 and
0.2 percent of these females proved to contain sex-linked lethals.
That is to say, from one to two X chromosomes out of every thousand contain a newly arisen lethal in every generation. The corresponding figure for the second chromosome is close to 0.4 percent
(17,572 chromosomes tested, Muller 1928b). The rate of origin of
lethals in the third chromosome of Drosophila pseudoobscura is
approximately 0.3 percent (21,171 chromosomes tested, Dobzhansky and Wright 1941). Timofeeff-Ressovsky (1937) surmises that
in Drosophila melanogaster close to 1 percent of the flies acquire a
new lethal in one of the chromosomes in every generation.

TABLE 3

SPONTANEOUS LETHALS IN THE X CHROMOSOME OF DIFFERENT STRAINS
OF Drosophila melanogaster (after Demerec)

STRAIN	CHROMOSOMES TESTED	NUMBER OF LETHALS	FREQUENCY OF LETHALS (IN %)
Florida	2,108	23	1.09 ± 0.15
Wooster, Ohio	1,266	8	0.63 ± 0.15
Formosa, Japan	2,054	8	0.39 ± 0.09
Oregon-R	3,049	2	
Swedish-B	1,627	3	
California-C	708	2	
Huntsville, Texas	938	—	
Urbana, Illinois	1,016	1	
Canton, Ohio	922	—	0.10 ± 0.02
Amherst, Massachusetts	572	1	
Woodbury, New Jersey	1,159	1	
Tuscaloosa, Alabama	545	1	
Seto, Japan	1,236	—	
Kyoto, Japan	875	1	
Lausanne, Switzerland	955	2	

The above estimates of the order of magnitude of the mutation
pressure for a certain selected class of changes, namely lethals, are
the best available for Drosophila or for any other organism. Too
much reliance should not be placed on them, since it is known at
present that mutation rates may differ in different strains of the
same species, and it is at least probable that the same is true for
different species. Intraspecific differences in mutation rates were
suggested by certain data of Muller (1928b), and confirmatory

evidence has been published more recently by Dubovskij (1935) and Shapiro and Volkova (1938). Demerec (1937) found that strains of *Drosophila melanogaster* coming from different geographical sources may show unlike mutation rates for lethals in the X chromosome (Table 3). Thus, the Florida strain, and perhaps also the Formosa and the Wooster, are more mutable than the rest. By making appropriate crosses, Demerec has ascertained that the difference in mutability between the Florida and the Swedish-B strains is due to the effects of a gene, or genes, located in the second chromosome. Aside from the lethals, a large number of mutations producing visible effects were observed in the Florida strain, indicating that the increase of mutability in that strain is not confined to lethals but is a general one.

It follows that the mutability, like all other characteristics of organisms, is to a certain extent under the control of the genotype. The nature and extent of this control are as yet very little known, although some very significant facts are on record. Thus, Berg (1937) has reported data which suggest that the frequency of lethal mutations per unit of chromosome length is greater in the second than in the X chromosome of *Drosophila melanogaster,* while mutations producing sterility show the reverse relation. Sturtevant (1937c) supposes that the mutability in any one strain, species, or race is controlled by a complex of genes, and that these gene complexes may be unlike in different forms. On the basis of this assumption one might expect the mutability to be affected by hybridization. Indeed, Belgovsky (1937) has observed some increase of the mutability in the hybrids of *Drosophila melanogaster* and *Drosophila simulans* as compared with that in the pure species, and Sturtevant (1939) has found evidence of a very striking increase in the hybrids of race A and race B of *Drosophila pseudoobscura.* A belief that hybridization enhances the mutability is, in fact, an old one, but until recently it has been unsupported by exact evidence.

The time factor must also be considered in connection with mutation frequencies. Every gene has an average "duration of life," meaning by this the interval of time between the successive mutational steps. The importance of this factor has been demonstrated especially clearly by Rajewsky and Timofeeff-Ressovsky (1939). The sperms of *Drosophila melanogaster* males which were allowed to copulate immediately after they had reached sexual maturity contained 0.104 ± 0.008 percent of sex-linked lethals, while in the sperm of twenty-day-old males this frequency rose to 0.254 ± 0.012 percent. The duration of the development from the egg to the adult stage is, at the temperature used, about fourteen days; the mutation frequency is, therefore, proportional to time. The increases in the frequencies of chromosomal, and possibly genic, mutations caused by the aging of seeds and pollen in *Datura, Antirrhinum,* and *Crepis* (Cartledge, Murray, Blakeslee 1935, Stubbe 1936, Nawashin and Gerassimova 1937) may be ascribed in part to the time factor. An interesting speculation is possible on the basis of these facts. The development of *Drosophila* takes days, while in other organisms it takes years or even decades. If the mutability per unit time were the same in these other organisms as it is in *Drosophila,* their chromosomes would be riddled with lethals within a few generations; mutation rates are probably not equal in all organisms (Muller 1928b).

RATE OF MUTATION OF INDIVIDUAL GENES

The spontaneous mutability of individual genes is important because it may prove to be a limiting factor in the evolutionary process. Are all genes equally mutable? In other words, is the process of mutation essentially a random matter, affecting now one and now another gene, or are some genes more predisposed to change than others? The latter assumption is undoubtedly correct. In well-studied organisms, mutations in some genes have been observed to occur repeatedly, while other genes have mutated only once. Moreover, so-called unstable or mutable genes are known (reviews have been published by Demerec 1935, and by Stubbe 1933) which mutate especially frequently, in the sex cells as well as in the somatic tissues. Somatic mutations give rise to individuals showing mosaicism, that is, a part of the tissues has a genetic constitution different from other parts.

The maize plant is well suited for studies of mutation rates because changes in genes determining the endosperm characters can be easily observed in very large numbers of individuals. Stadler (quoted in Demerec 1933) obtained the following data for seven endosperm genes (Table 4).

Differences in mutation rates of different genes are far greater than could be accounted for by chance; the gene R for example, changes more frequently than others. No comparable data exist for *Drosophila*, but the general experience has been that some genes (white, cut, yellow, forked) give spontaneous mutations much more frequently than certain others.

Patterson and Muller (1930), and especially Timofeeff-Ressovsky (1929, 1931, 1933, a, b, c) have devoted a great deal of attention to the problem of mutability to and from a given allele. The gene A mutates with finite frequencies to alleles a^1, a^2, a^3, . . . a^x. Each of these may, in turn, mutate back to A or to any other member of the series. The mutation process is potentially reversible ($A \rightleftarrows a$), but

TABLE 4

FREQUENCY OF SPONTANEOUS GENE MUTATIONS IN MAIZE (after Stadler, from Demerec)

GENES	NUMBER OF GAMETES TESTED	MUTATIONS OBSERVED	MUTATION RATE PER 1,000,000 GAMETES
R (color factor)	554,786	273	492
I (color inhibitor)	265,391	28	106
Pr (purple)	647,102	7	11
Su (sugary)	1,678,736	4	2.4
Y (yellow)	1,745,280	4	2.2
Sh (shrunken)	2,469,285	3	1.2
Wx (waxy)	1,503,744	0	0

the data show that mutation pressures to and from each allele are likely to be different, making the mutability in a sense directed. The gene W (normal red eye color) in *Drosophila melanogaster* changes to white (w), eosin (w^e), apricot (w^a), and to other states producing eye colors of varying intensities. In comparable experiments, where flies received similar amounts of the X-ray treatment, Timofeeff-Ressovsky (1933b) obtained results summarized in Table 5.

The wild type (W, red), apricot (w^a), and eosin (w^e) mutate most frequently to the extreme member of the series, namely white. It is not clear, however, whether the different whites, which are indistinguishable from each other for our eyes, may not be in reality a composite group (Timofeeff-Ressovsky 1933c). The reverse mutation from white directly to red has not been observed at all, although white may mutate to eosin, and eosin derived from it may in turn mutate to red, the reversion from white to red being thus accomplished in two steps. The mutation from the wild type to forked (forked bristles) has been observed 11 times in 43,000 chromosomes, and the reversion from forked to wild type 15 times in 44,000 chromosomes, the X-ray treatment being similar in both cases (Patterson and Muller 1930, Timofeeff-Ressovsky 1933a). Here the mutation seems to be about equally frequent in either direction.

TABLE 5

MUTABILITY TO AND FROM VARIOUS ALLELES OF THE GENE WHITE IN
Drosophila melanogaster (after Timofeeff-Ressovsky)

	w	w^{bf}	w^e	w^a	w^b	w^x	W	NUMBER OF CHROMOSOMES TESTED
Wild (W)	25	1	3	1	2	5	—	48,500
w^{co}	1	—	—	—	—	—	—	6,000
w^b	3	—	1	—	—	—	—	12,000
w^c	1	—	—	—	—	—	—	5,000
w^a	2	—	1	—	—	—	—	11,000
w^e	13	—	—	—	1	2	2	39,000
w^{bf}	1	—	—	—	—	—	—	5,500
w^t	1	—	—	—	—	—	—	7,000
w	—	1	1	—	1	—	—	54,000

The frequency as well as the kind of mutations occurring in any one gene are, like the mutability in general, controlled in part by the genotype of the organism. Timofeeff-Ressovsky (1932) has reported an especially interesting case where "normal" alleles of the same gene found in different strains have different mutation rates. Two strains of *Drosophila melanogaster,* one from America and the other from Russia, were given identical X-ray treatments. In the former, 55 mutations at the white locus were observed among 59,200 chromosomes; and in the latter, 40 mutations among 75,000 chromosomes. In addition, the "Russian allele" changes mostly to white and the "American" one to white and to intermediates (eosin, and so forth) with about equal frequency. Through special experiments Timofeeff-Ressovsky proved that the difference in the behavior of the Russian and the American strains was due to different mutability of the white gene itself, and not to an influence of modifying genes at other loci. Demerec (1929a) has established that both influences may be effective. The gene miniature in *Drosophila virilis* produces mutant alleles which modify the size and texture of the wings. Some of these alleles are about as stable as the ancestral gene; others are very unstable and revert to the wild type or change into each other with considerable frequencies. Some are mutable only in somatic cells, producing mosaic patches of normal and mutant tissues; others undergo changes mainly in the sex cells. Some mutate early and others late in development. In addition to the properties inherent in the miniature locus itself, the mutability of the locus is influenced by at least four other genes located in different chromosomes; the mutability modifiers by themselves produce no visible effects.

Rhoades (1936, 1938) has described an instance of genotypic control of the mutability which is both unusually clear and favorable for further investigation. The gene A_1 is one of the factors responsible for the production of the anthocyanin pigmentation in maize. Several alleles of this gene are known, some of which give varying degrees of coloring, while the a_1 allele causes absence of anthocyanin. Under normal conditions all these alleles mutate very infrequently. The gene "dotted" lies in a chromosome different from that in which A_1 is located; it has two alleles, Dt and dt. By itself, the dotted gene has no visible effects; but the gene a_1 becomes highly unstable in the presence of Dt, and changes to A_1 both in the somatic and in the germinal tissues. As a result, the a_1 Dt plants have dots or streaks of anthocyanin pigmentation. The number of these dots or streaks is proportional to the frequency of mutation, while their size indicates the developmental stage at which the mutations take place. The frequency of mutation in a given plant or tissue is, other things being equal, directly proportional to the number of the a_1 genes it carries. Thus, seeds may be obtained having one, two, or three a_1 genes in their aleurone tissue; the numbers of colored dots formed on such seeds approach the ratio $1 : 2 : 3$. Similarly, seeds may be obtained with one, two, or three doses of Dt; the number of dots on these seeds shows an exponential relation to that of the Dt genes. The effect of the dotted gene on the mutability is highly specific: the mutability of the a_1

gene is increased manifold, while that of the other alleles at the A_1 locus, or of the genes at other loci, is unaffected. The direction of the mutations is also determined: in the presence of Dt the allele a_1 mutates to A_1 about a thousand times more frequently than it does to still another allele, namely a^p_1. Furthermore, the mutability of a_1 in combinations with Dt is modified by the gene, or genes, designated M.

The mutability modifiers discovered by Demerec and Rhoades are agents inducing specific mutations in specific genes. An elucidation of the mechanisms of action of such factors may prove to be of utmost importance for an understanding of evolutionary changes. Perhaps equally important is the problem of the relation between the mutation rates of genes and the position of the latter in the chromosomes. To date the only information bearing on this problem is that published by Sitko (1938) and Heptner (1938). The mutability of several genes in the normal X chromosomes of *Drosophila melanogaster* was compared with that of the same genes lying in X chromosomes which had been broken by translocations and inversions (cf. Chapter IV). Statistically significant increases of the mutability in the broken chromosomes were found. Sitko concludes that the mutability is enhanced in genes lying in the proximity of breakage points. Sitko's data are not entirely convincing, but if the relation alleged by him were confirmed, it would follow that the evolutionary courses of races and species differing in gene arrangement (Chapter IV) are likely to diverge owing to the modification of the rates, and possibly of the direction, of mutation in certain genes. Kaufmann (1940a) found no change in the breakability of chromosomes that had suffered a gene rearrangement, but this does not necessarily contradict Sitko's findings.

The phenomena of genetic control of mutability may throw a new light on observations made by systematists and palaeontologists to the effect that the pace of evolution is not alike in all organisms. Some groups evolve rapidly while others undergo little change in geological epochs. A classical example of evolutionary conservatism is the brachiopod *Lingula,* which has not visibly changed since Palaeozoic time. The insect fauna of the Baltic amber (Tertiary, Oligocene) contains about 900 species, many of which are still in existence (although occurring chiefly in the Tropics), while the genera are almost all modern. On the other hand, mammals have undergone rapid changes, most of the families having developed since the early Tertiary. A systematic study of mutation rates in different organisms would give unquestionably interesting results.

INDUCTION OF MUTATIONS BY RADIATION

It is customary to distinguish spontaneous and induced mutations. The former are those which arise in strains not consciously exposed to known or suspected mutation-producing agents. Since the name "spontaneous" constitutes only a thinly veiled admission of the ignorance of the phenomenon to which it is applied, the quest for the causes of mutation has always occupied the attention of geneticists.

A general knowledge of the mutation process permits certain inferences regarding its causes. Mutations arise at all stages of the developmental cycle: at gametogenesis, in mature gametes, and in somatic tissues. Mutants are on the whole rare, and they appear as single individuals among masses of unchanged representatives of a strain. Although the distances between the adjacent genes in a chromosome are ultramicroscopically small, mutation affects only a single gene at a time (a few, perhaps doubtful, exceptions to this rule are on record). Whenever a mutation takes place in a diploid cell, only one chromosome of a pair is affected. Since a diploid cell has at least two genes of each kind, the causes of mutation must be so highly localized that only one of the two presumably exactly similar units falls within the field of action.

For years the attempts to find external agents capable of inducing mutations remained desultory and the results inconclusive. The announcement by Muller in 1927 that X-ray treatments induce both gene mutations and chromosomal changes constitutes a turning point in the history of the mutation theory and of genetics in general. An imposing amount of literature has accumulated since 1927 dealing with the effects of X-rays and other short-wave radiations on the mutation process. Excellent reviews of the subject have been published by Schultz (1936), Timofeeff-Ressovsky (1937), Stubbe (1937, 1938) and others. It will suffice to give here a condensed summary of only the most important findings and conclusions.

Timofeeff-Ressovsky (1939c) lists 39 plant and 25 animal species in which mutations under the influence of X-ray have been observed by various authors. The forms included range from fungi to flowering plants and from protozoans to mammals. What may be described as mutations was obtained also in filterable viruses. In no organism have negative results been reported. Mutations are induced only in chromosomes directly exposed to radiation; no effect is obtained in gametes developing in an irradiated body if the gonads are protected from the rays, nor are chromosomes influenced by being placed in an irradiated cytoplasm. If no mutations arise in a zygote coming from an irradiated gamete, none appear in subsequent generations: radiation has no delayed effects (the data of Helfer, 1941, suggest, however, that chromosome breakage may become effective one or two cell generations after irradiation). It is known that spontaneous mutation rates vary from gene to gene (p. 38). In *Drosophila,* X-ray induced mutations seem to be similar to spontaneous ones, qualitatively as well as quantitatively, in the sense that those mutants which most frequently appear spontaneously are also those which most frequently follow irradiation, and vice versa; irradiation merely increases the frequency of mutations. On the other hand, in maize there are indications that the mutability of certain loci is enhanced more than that of others (Stadler 1932 and personal communication). Mutations to and from a given allele are obtained with the aid of radiation, so that the mutation process is reversible.

Fairly satisfactory information is now available regarding the effects of radiations of different wave lengths on mutability. All the ionizing radiations are effective, from very soft X-rays ("Grenzstrahlen") to the hard X-rays and the gamma rays of radium (wave lengths from 2.6 to 0.01 Å), and to neutron bombardments. There is no doubt that cosmic rays are also effective, although, owing to the low intensities of these rays available for experimentation, studies in this field have not progressed very far (Jollos 1939a, Rajewsky and Timofeeff-Ressovsky 1939). The ultraviolet shows an interesting differentiation with respect to mutation inducing power, the wave lengths shorter than 3022 Å being generally effective and those longer than 3130 Å ineffective (Stadler and Sprague 1936).

A very important fact is that the frequency of mutations induced by X- or gamma rays is directly proportional to the amount of treatment expressed in r-units. These units measure essentially the amount of ionization, which is equivalent to the total amount of energy delivered by the radiation. Thus, the mutation frequency is independent of the wave length applied, as well as of the time factor (whether the treatment is administered during a long or a short time period, continuously or intermittently, provided only that the total radiation absorbed adds up to the same sum of ionizations). This, on purely physical grounds, seems to suggest that the gene change constituting an induced mutation follows a single ionization or excitation of an atom within a certain "sensitive volume." The sensitive volumes vary somewhat from gene to gene, but the order of magnitude is the same as that of the physical volumes which, on basis of other evidence, the genes are likely to possess. It should be kept in mind that the sensitive volume as above defined may be equal to or greater or smaller than the gene volume; in other words, it is unknown whether the atomic excitation anywhere in the gene, or in a definite part of the gene or in the medium surrounding the gene, is followed by mutation. The "spontaneous" mutations, in so far as they are not produced by ionizing radiation present in nature, may be due to the thermic excitations of atoms which can occasionally exceed the energy of atomic cohesion. Such thermic excitations, although very rare, must occasionally take place in any atomic structure. (For a more detailed presentation and discussion of this theory, see Timofeeff-Ressovsky, Zimmer, and Delbrück 1935, Timofeeff-Ressovsky 1937 and 1939c.) Mutations produced by ultraviolet rays are supposedly caused by the photochemical reactions which set in following absorption of the energy of the radiation.

PRODUCTION OF MUTATIONS BY AGENTS OTHER THAN RADIATION

Despite the great importance of the work on induction of mutations by radiation, the problem of mutation remains far from having been solved. Since the frequency of mutations is proportional to the amount of ionizing radiation reaching the cell nuclei, it is possible to compute what part of the "spontaneous" mutability may be accounted for by the radiation present in nature. Such computations, made independently by several investigators, agree in that much less than one percent of spontaneous mutations can be attributed to this cause. The ultraviolet, at least in *Drosophila* and maize, is even less important than the shorter wave lengths. Accordingly, the quest for mutation-inducing agents must be continued, the more so since the theory of mutation is at present based mainly on study of the radiation-induced mutants and, consequently, may prove to be one-sided.

Some observations on the influence of temperature on the mutation process are available. Even before the discovery of X-ray mutations, Muller (1928b) had demonstrated in *Drosophila* that the frequency of spontaneous mutations rises with increase of the temperature. This has been confirmed by Timofeeff-Ressovsky (1935), who found that, the time factor being taken into consideration, the frequency of sex-linked lethal mutations is multiplied about five-fold per 10° raise in temperature. These experiments were conducted at temperatures which are more or less normal for *Drosophila melanogaster* (14°–28°C.). Goldschmidt (1929b) and Jollos (1931, 1934, 1935) believed that so-called temperature shocks—that is, brief exposures of the larvae to sublethal high temperatures between 36°C. and 40°C.—result in spurts of mutability far greater than could be expected from the knowledge of the normal temperature coefficients. The repetition and extension of these experiments by various authors (Rokizky 1930, Plough and Ives 1935, Lawrow 1935, Buchmann and Timofeeff-Ressovsky 1935, and others) show that although temperature shocks do increase the mutability, the increment observed is not very high. Brief exposures to very low temperatures (0° or lower, so-called "cold shocks") seem to enhance the mutability to about the same extent as do heat shocks (Gottschewski 1934, Birkina 1938, Kerkis 1939). Finally, Zuitin (1937, 1938a, b) believes that temperature fluctuations during the development of *Drosophila* result in an increase of the mutation rates compared with the rates obtaining at constant temperatures. The published preliminary data are, however, unconvincing.

It is very probable that mutability can be influenced, if not caused, by chemical agents. It is difficult to conceive of other than chemical mechanisms for the modification of the mutability of genes by genes, such as that produced by the "dotted" gene in maize

(p. 40). Nevertheless, attempts to induce mutations by known chemicals have so far led to results which can be described at best as only suggestive. Perhaps the greatest handicap in this field is the lack of assurance that a sufficient concentration of the chemical substance used actually reaches the chromosomes of the cells in which an induced mutation can be detected. A substance present in the ambient medium or ingested with food perhaps does not pass freely into the body cavity, much less into the nuclei of the germ cells.

Baur and Stubbe (reviews in Stubbe 1938 and 1940) have treated seeds and seedlings of the snapdragon with immersion in solutions of organic and inorganic compounds. Changed individuals appeared in F_1 and F_2 after treatments with chloral hydrate, potassium bichromate, copper chloride, chloroform, and other substances, but the statistical significance of the results, as well as the exact nature of the changes obtained, are not free from doubt. A group of workers, mostly in Russia, has published a series of communications describing attempts to induce mutations in *Drosophila* by a number of chemicals. The techniques used were immersion of eggs in aqueous or alcoholic solutions of various concentrations of the substances tried, ingestion with food, and injection into the body cavity (Law 1938). Sex-linked and autosomal lethals and visibles were detected in treated and control series with the aid of refined genetic methods. Taken at their face value, the results were clearly positive in some cases, on the borderline of statistical significance in others. Sacharov (1935, 1936), Samjatina and Popowa (1934), and Kondakowa (1935), but not Law (1939), obtained increased mutation rates with solutions of iodine and potassium iodide. Copper sulphate appears to be definitely effective (Magrzhikovskaja 1938, Law 1938). Suggestive results were obtained with ammonia (Lobashov and Smirnov 1934, Lobashov 1935), potassium permanganate (Naumenko 1936), sublimate (Kosiupa 1936), lead salts (Ponomarev 1937–1938), asphyxia (Lobashov 1935), and negative results with hydrochloric (Goldat and Beliaieva 1935) and acetic acids (Lobashov 1935). Tarnavsky (1939) and Gershenson (1940) have obtained several changes resembling the mutants bithorax and beadex after treatment with nucleic acid; they realize that it would be premature to claim that this treatment is a specific inductor of these mutations. One can only hope that all these experiments will be repeated and extended. It has been well established by several investigators that the use of X-ray treatments following the introduction of salts of heavy metals into the organism results in increased mutation rates as compared to X-ray treatments alone; but since the presence of heavy atoms increases the absorption of the rays, the mutations so obtained cannot be classed as "chemical" ones.

Finally, a highly controversial topic, namely the so-called mass mutation, must be dealt with. It is well known that De Vries believed that the frequency of mutation in an organism does not remain constant, and that mutating periods alternate with periods of a relative or complete stagnation of the germ plasm. No evidence for this view was found by later investigators, and it was abandoned. As stated above, Goldschmidt described in 1929 a tremendous increase of the mutability in *Drosophila* which he believed to be due to temperature shocks. More recently Goldschmidt (1939, 1940) has reinterpreted his results to mean that a period of spontaneous mass mutation had fortuitously occurred in flies that happened to be exposed to temperature shocks, the shocks having had nothing to do with the mutation. Goldschmidt states that since 1929 similar spurts of mutability have occurred in certain of his cultures which were not exposed to any treatments. According to him, not only the appearance of several mutations at once in an experiment of Plough and Holthausen (1937), but also the increase of the mutability in a strain of *Drosophila* observed by Demerec, are instances of mass mutation. In the latter case, however, Demerec has shown that increased mutability is due to a genetic modifier (see p. 36). Although the genotypic control of the mutability is now rigorously established by Demerec, Rhoades, and others (see above), the idea that such a phenomenon exists appears absurd to Goldschmidt.

THE TRANSFORMATIONS OF PNEUMOCOCCI

Griffith, Dawson, Heidelberger, Avery, and many other bacteriologists, biochemists, and immunologists have in the last twenty years worked out a fascinating story of diversity and protean instability in the pneumonia microörganisms, pneumococci (a review in White, Robinson and Barnes 1938). The species *Diplococcus pneumoniae* is subdivided into at least thirty-two types distinguishable chiefly through immunological, physiological, and biochemical tests. Each of these types is supposed to preserve its identity when reproducing in infected hosts or on artificial culture media which give optimum growth. The core of the pneumococcus cell consists of nucleoproteins, lipids, complex polysaccharides and other substances, which, as far as the present data go, appear to be essentially similar in all the types. The surface of the cell has, however, an envelope consisting chiefly of polysaccharides which are chemically specific for each type and which are presumed to be responsible for the differences in the behavior of these types. In the process of reproduction each type of cells is able to synthesize its proper polysaccharide envelope, which is, hence, an hereditary trait by definition.

If, however, the bacteria are cultivated on media containing homologous immune sera, or on media which are otherwise unfavorable to their growth, they undergo what is described as "degradation" or "dissociation." Their normal virulence is largely lost, and the shape of the colonies growing on agar plates is changed from the normal "smooth" to a degenerate "rough." The most important fact is, however, that the polysaccharide envelope, which is present in the "smooth" form, is not detectable in the "rough" state, and with its loss the specificity of the thirty-two types likewise disappears. Immunization by the rough phase causes the formation of "antirough" antibodies, which are absorbed by the rough as well as by the smooth cells, while immunization by the smooth phase develops the "antirough" as well as the type-specific "antismooth" antibodies. A reversal of degradation can be accomplished by a passage through a susceptible host, or by addition of the antirough serum to the culture medium. The speed of this reversion is greater if the process of degradation has not been completed; it seems, however, not to have been thoroughly established whether a reversion from rough to smooth can be accomplished by these methods if a rough clone is used to start with.

With the exception of a single feature, the phenomena so far outlined are not unduly surprising from the standpoint of genetics. Mutations from smooth to rough and vice versa may take place at all times with finite low frequencies; depending on the environment in which a strain lives, one of the phases is selected and displaces the other. The unique feature is the convergence observed in the rough phase resulting in an apparent loss of the distinctions between the types. The mutations from smooth to rough seem to be physical losses of the distinctive features of the cells expressed in the polysaccharide envelope, as though the germ plasm of this organism contained a certain stable nucleus and a variable periphery which may be disposed of altogether. Still more extravagant, and yet conclusively proved, phenomena are enacted if a culture of the rough phase is added to a vaccine consisting of dead cells of the smooth phase with a trace of the antirough serum. For in this case rough reverts to smooth of the same type to which the cells in the vaccine had belonged. Thus, if a small amount of the rough culture derived from the normal (smooth) line of Type II is added to a suspension of smooth cells of Type III devitalized by heating, a smooth line of Type III, not of Type II, is produced. By this method it seems to be possible to convert at least many of the thirty-two types of the pneumococci into many other types. The transformation of the rough into the smooth of the same type from which the rough had been originally derived is, of course, also accomplished by the same method, if a vaccine of that type is used. The vaccines lose their transforming effectiveness after being heated to the boiling point, but cell suspensions heated to 60°C. and subsequently frozen and thawed are effective.

The strains "transformed" from one type into another retain their new properties after cultivation on suitable media or after passage through animal hosts. Hence, they acquire not merely a temporary polysaccharide envelope of a kind different from that which their ancestors have had, but are able to synthesize the new polysaccharide indefinitely. If this transformation is described as a genetic mutation—and it is difficult to avoid so describing it—we are dealing with authentic cases of induction of specific mutations by specific treatments—a feat which geneticists have vainly tried to accomplish in higher organisms. Admittedly, there are many obscurities in the situation which ought to be cleared up. For example, it seems to be unknown whether the transformation affects every cell in the culture or whether only some cells mutate and others are destroyed; whether the mutation takes place in connection with the division of the cells or can be accomplished without reproduction taking place; and whether all the possible transformations of the types can be induced with equal ease. Nevertheless, geneticists may profit by devising experiments along the lines suggested by the results of the pneumococcus studies.

III: MUTATION AS A BASIS FOR
RACIAL AND SPECIFIC DIFFERENCES

STATEMENT OF THE PROBLEM

ORGANIC diversity may be described simply in terms of the observable morphological and physiological differences between individuals of a race, races of a species, species of a genus, and so on. But a genetic analysis must ascertain first of all to what extent these differences are hereditary and what part of them is due to modifications induced by environmental influences during development. Next, the genetic basis of the hereditary differences must be analyzed to determine whether these can be resolved into genic differences. The only known method of origin of genic differences is through mutation; in fact, any change of the gene structure is, by definition, a mutation. It follows that any difference between individuals and populations which can be expressed as a function of gene differences is to that extent due in the last analysis to mutational changes.

Attempts to evade the above reasoning have, of course, been made. Lotsy (1916 and later work) denied that gene mutation takes place, or at any rate that it plays a role in evolution. Instead, he assumed that diverse genes and gene alleles have always existed in nature and have tenaciously maintained their identity, somewhat in the style of chemical elements. Each species carries a certain constellation of these gene elements. Races, species, and even genera occasionally cross and produce hybrids; in accordance with the second law of Mendel all possible gene combinations arise in the offspring of hybrids. Most of the recombinations are ill adapted to the environment and perish, while some favorable ones survive and form new species. Although Lotsy's theory is formally logical, the problem of the origin of the large supply of immutable gene alleles is merely pushed back into the obscure past and becomes a tantalizing puzzle.

Since mutation is an established fact, creation of this puzzle is gratuitous.

Osborn (1927) denied the importance of mutation in evolution on different grounds: "Speciation is a normal and continuous process; it governs the greater part of the origin of species; it is apparently always adaptive. Mutation is an abnormal and irregular mode of origin, which while not infrequently occurring in nature is not essentially an adaptive process; it is, rather, a disturbance of the regular course of speciation." Variations of this statement have been made into professions of faith by a number of writers. The source of the difficulty here is a profound misunderstanding of the genetic conception of the mechanisms of evolution.

It is true that the formation of species is a continuous process, but its components are the numerous discontinuous steps, mutations. Mutation changes one gene at a time; simultaneous mutation of masses of genes is unknown. On the other hand, species differ from each other usually in many genes (see below); hence, a sudden origin of a species by mutation, in one thrust, would demand a simultaneous mutation of numerous genes. Assuming that two species differ in only one hundred genes and taking the mutation rate of individual genes to be as high as $1 : 10,000$, the probability of a sudden origin of a new species would be 1 to $10,000^{100}$. This is not unlike assuming that water in a kettle placed on a fire will freeze, an event which is not altogether impossible, according to the new physics, but nevertheless improbable in the extreme. Although the integration of mutational steps into genotypes of races and species is probably always an adaptive process, it does not follow that every component step in this process is always adaptive from the start. To suppose that the organism is endowed with the ability to produce adaptive mutations—or whatever other name one may choose to apply to the elementary evolutionary changes—and to believe that these changes arise just where and when needed, amounts to a belief in miracles.

Practically the same objection applies to the theory of Goldschmidt (1940), which is, in a sense, the antithesis to Osborn's views. According to Goldschmidt, all that evolution by the usual mutations—dubbed "micromutations"—can accomplish is to bring about "diversification strictly within a species, usually, if not exclusively, for the sake of adaptation of the species to specific conditions within the area which it is able to occupy." New species, genera, and higher groups arise at once, by cataclysmic saltations—termed macromutations or systemic mutations—which bring about in one step a basic reconstruction of the whole organism. The role of natural selection in this process becomes "reduced to the simple alternative: immediate acceptance or rejection." A new form of life having been thus catapulted into being, the details of its structures and functions are subsequently adjusted by micromutation and selection. It is unnecessary to stress here that this theory virtually rejects evolution as this term is usually understood (to evolve means to unfold or to develop gradually), and that the systemic mutations it postulates have never been observed. It is possible to imagine a mutation so drastic that its product becomes a monster hurling itself beyond the confines of species, genus, family, or class. But in what Goldschmidt has called the "hopeful monster" the harmonious system, which any organism must necessarily possess, must be transformed at once into a radically different, but still sufficiently coherent, system to enable the monster to survive. The assumption that such a prodigy may, however rarely, walk the earth overtaxes one's credulity, even though it may be right that the existence of life in the cosmos is in itself an extremely improbable event.

The above arguments against the views of Lotsy, Osborn, and Goldschmidt may or may not be convincing to everyone. Fortunately, the problem of the role of mutations in evolution need not be settled by rhetoric, since it is open to experimental attack. If mutations are the building blocks of evolution, it must be possible to demonstrate (1) that racial, specific, and other differences can be resolved completely into genic differences; (2) that these genic differences are of the same kind and magnitude as the observable mutations, and (3) that any kind of difference encountered between species may be present, at least as a rudiment, within species as well. To what extent the available information satisfies these requirements the reader will be able to judge for himself from this and the following chapters.

Although more mutants have been obtained in laboratory cultures of *Drosophila* than in all other organisms combined, the flies found in nature appear superficially more uniform than insect species customarily are. Since biologists in general are unaware of the fact that visible external differences between good species of *Drosophila* are, as a rule, also less striking than those found between insect species at large, a misapprehension has become current that laboratory mutants have no counterpart in nature. This is certainly not the case; mutants were recorded to occur in natural populations very early in the history of *Drosophila* studies (Lutz 1911 in *D. melanogaster*, Sturtevant 1915a in *D. repleta*). Spencer (1932) recorded a population of *D. hydei* in which 6.5 percent of the males were vermilion eyed, and more recently (1938) he found a number of populations of this species containing several percent of individuals showing the mutant bobbed. A remarkable variety of alleles at the bobbed locus was discovered, and their frequencies appeared to vary from locality to locality. Dubinin, Romashov, Heptner, and Demidova (1937) examined almost 130,000 wild specimens of *D. melanogaster* from several localities in southern Russia, and found in this material more than 2,800 "aberrant" individuals. A part of the latter contained noninheritable abnormalities, but others were mutants, for the most part identical with well-known laboratory types (among them, extra bristles, ebony, sepia, yellow). The relative frequencies of different mutants vary from locality to locality and from year to year; most of the mutants are recessives, although a few semidominants are recorded; mutants that produce slight changes in the appearance and viability of the flies are more common than more drastic and deleterious variants. At one collecting station—a deep pit with decomposing fruit—many individuals were found to be homozygous for the gene divergent which makes its carriers flightless.

No matter how carefully and extensively one may examine the phenotypes of wild individuals of a given species, the information thereby gained regarding the variability in natural populations of this species will be incomplete. It is well known that a majority of mutations that arise in the laboratory are recessive and, when homozygous, affect adversely the viability of their carriers. An individual may be heterozygous for one or more mutants and yet preserve a "normal" phenotype. A population may consist of mutant heterozygotes, but, so long as each mutant type is so rare that mating of the carriers is unlikely to occur, no mutant homozygotes appear, and the mutant genes remain concealed. These considerations, which are as simple as they are important, were first enunciated by Tschetwerikoff (1926, 1927), who drew from them the obvious conclusion that a genetic analysis of natural populations is necessary to reveal the concealed variability. Several techniques are used for such analysis. Taking, for example, females which have already been fertilized in nature, one may discover in their immediate offspring (F_1 generation) whether each particular female was heterozygous for any sex-linked mutant genes, and whether she or her mates carried autosomal dominants. Inbreeding F_1 individuals will permit the detection in F_2 and F_3 generations of the recessive autosomal mutants. Wherever practical, more refined methods should be used. In principle, these methods consist of crossing individuals collected in nature to laboratory strains having known mutant genes which serve as "chromosome markers." This is the start of a series of crosses so designed as to produce in the end individuals homozygous for the chromosome to be tested. If the "wild" chromosome in question contains any recessive genetic variant, such as a lethal, a semilethal, or a gene producing visible external characters or physiological modifications, its effects will be detectable in the homozygotes. Exact quantitative studies of the frequencies of definite mutants or of mutants of a given type can be undertaken.

Such studies have been carried out by Tschetwerikoff (1926, 1927), Timofeeff-Ressovsky (1927), Dubinin and collaborators (1934, 1936), Gordon (1936), Olenov and collaborators (1938, 1939), Muretov (1939), Plough, Ives, and Child (1939) in *Drosophila melanogaster;* Sturtevant (1937a), Dobzhansky and Queal (1938b), Dobzhansky (1939a) in *D. pseudoobscura;* Gordon (1936), Gordon, Spurway, and Street (1939) in *D. subobscura;* Balkaschina and Romaschoff (1935) in *D. phalerata, D. transversa* and *D. vibrissina* (a review in Dobzhansky 1939b). In a general way, the results of all these studies are so consistent with each other that one or two examples will suffice to describe the situation.

A summary of the data of Dubinin and collaborators is given in

Table 6. These investigators have analyzed samples of populations of *Drosophila melanogaster* collected in various localities in Russia, chiefly in the Caucasus. Not only is a large proportion of the wild flies "infected" with recessive mutants producing visible external changes, but many are heterozygous for recessives which are lethal when homozygous. Only one among eleven populations studied ap-

TABLE 6

FREQUENCY OF MUTANT GENES IN WILD POPULATIONS OF *Drosophila melanogaster* (after Dubinin and collaborators)

LOCALITY	YEAR	NUMBERS OF CHROMOSOMES II AND III TESTED	LETHALS IN CHROMOSOME II	VISIBLE AUTOSOMAL MUTANTS
Essentuki	1931	187	20	78
"	1932	120	15	25
Piatigorsk	1931	81	8	16
"	1932	142	11	35
Vladikavkaz	1931	165	32	35
"	1932	115	13	6
Mashuk	1931	180	19	103
"	1932	178	15	30
Erivan	1931	102	16	25
"	1932	81	7	5
Kislovodsk	1931	144	13	68
Batum	1931	101	14	23
Armavir	1932	42	9	22
Delizhan	1931	92	not studied	0
Tambov	1931	120	not studied	44
Gelendzhik	1933	877	70	226
"	1934	616	78	470
"	1935	797	70	410
Total		4,140	410	1,621

pears to have been free of lethals; in the other ten the frequency of lethals varied from 7.7 percent to 21.4 percent. Population samples taken in the same locality on successive years show fairly pronounced fluctuations in the frequencies of mutants. Some of the mutants thus detected in the wild state were identical with well-known laboratory mutants (the recessives sepia, ebony, scarlet, black, purple), others were new. The mutants "extra bristles" and "comma" were found in most populations studied, and in some instances up to 50 percent of the flies carried these mutants in heterozygous or homozygous condition. Other mutants were discovered in a single locality, but some of them were common where they did occur; thus, 7.9 percent of the chromosomes from Batum carried the gene ebony, and as many as 3.5 percent from Vladikavkaz contained a certain lethal. In contrast with the abundance of autosomal recessives, lethals as well as visibles, no autosomal dominants or sex-linked mutants were encountered among seven thousands flies tested in Dubinin's experiments. A few such mutants have, however, been found in the much smaller sample from Berlin examined by Timofeeff-Ressovsky. This is not unexpected, since dominants and sex-linked genes are not sheltered from natural selection by being concealed in heterozygotes, and are, therefore, promptly eliminated from the population if they affect adversely the viability of their carriers. The population sampled by Timofeeff-Ressovsky might have developed under a temporary relaxation of selection, caused, perhaps, by overabundance of food.

TABLE 7

FREQUENCY OF LETHALS AND SEMILETHALS IN THE THIRD CHROMOSOMES OF WILD POPULATIONS OF *Drosophila pseudoobscura*

REGION	NUMBER OF POPULATIONS SAMPLED	CHROMOSOMES TESTED	PERCENT WITH LETHALS	PERCENT WITH SEMILETHALS
Death Valley, California and Nevada	10	849	11.9	3.1
San Jacinto, California	9	1,883	11.0	1.9
Mexico and Guatemala	16	120	20.8	9.2

In *Drosophila pseudoobscura* the third chromosome (an autosome) has been extensively analyzed. Lethals (genes preventing the survival of any homozygotes) were distinguished from semilethals (which permit a few homozygotes to survive), although in nature both of these classes are probably eliminated with equal rapidity. No population sample of sufficient size was found to be free of lethals. In populations inhabiting Mexico and Guatemala the infestation with lethals was significantly greater than in those from more northern localities. Comparison of Tables 6 and 7 suggests that the concentration of lethals in natural populations of *D. pseudoobscura* is higher than in *D. melanogaster* (here one must take into consideration the fact that the second chromosome of *D. melanogaster* is twice as large as the third chromosome of *D. pseudoobscura;* on the other hand Plough, Ives, and Child [1939] seem to find very high concentrations of lethals in some *D. melanogaster* populations). Preliminary data (unpublished) show that, in natural populations of *D. pseudoobscura,* about 23 percent of the second and 11 percent of the fourth chromosomes (191 and 46 chromosomes tested, respectively) contain lethals and semilethals. Since a fly carries each of these chromosomes in duplicate, it follows that certainly more than half of the individuals of *D. pseudoobscura* found outdoors are heterozygous for one or more autosomal lethals. Mutant genes producing visible external effects are likewise common; for example, in wild flies collected in various parts of the distribution area of the species, each of the recessive eye-color mutants orange and purple have been encountered in heterozygous condition more than a dozen times. The extent of the mutational variability concealed in natural populations appears to be far greater than one would have suspected even a few years ago.

SMALL MUTATIONS IN DROSOPHILA

It may be taken as established that mutants producing striking phenotypic changes and pronounced depressions of viability are common both in "natural" and in "laboratory" populations. We may now inquire whether "small" mutations, which are likely to prove the main source of the raw materials of evolution, are abundant outdoors. Dubinin and collaborators (1934) have made three experiments to secure data bearing on this problem. First, ten strains of flies obtained each from a single female caught in nature were bred, and the number of certain bristles (sternopleurals) was studied in the flies from these strains. The number of bristles is a variable character, and laboratory strains of *Drosophila* frequently show heritable differences in this respect. Statistically significant differences were found also between strains derived from separate wild females. Moreover, the average number of the bristles proved to be different in groups of strains coming from different localities. Second, strains of flies coming from nature were outcrossed to flies with the dominant gene Dichaete, whose manifestation has been shown previously (Sturtevant 1918) to be sensitive to the effects of modifying genes present in various lines. Pronounced differences in the manifestation of Dichaete were observed also in outcrosses to wild strains from various localities in the Caucasus. Third, the manifestation of one of the commonest major mutations (extra bristles) found in a number of wild populations was studied quantitatively, and found to be different in nearly every strain. This suggests that genes modifying the effects of this mutation are common in the population studied.

Sturtevant (1937a), Dobzhansky and Queal (1938b), and Dobzhansky (1939a) in *Drosophila pseudoobscura* and Muretov (1939) in *D. melanogaster* adopted a somewhat different approach to the problem of small mutations. As stated above (p. 55), quantitative studies on mutation frequencies in natural populations involve series of crosses designed to produce flies homozygous for individual wild chromosomes. With the aid of a requisite system of genetic markers, the homozygotes are made distinguishable from the heterozygous sibs developing in the same culture bottles, and the various classes of the flies are expected to appear in definite Mendelian ratios. Now, Mendelian expectations are predicated on the assumption that all the classes are alike in viability; if a wild chromosome contains a recessive or a semidominant gene or genes reducing the viability of the carier, some of the homozygotes die, and the ratios become distorted. If no homozygotes appear in a sufficient sample of flies, the wild chromosome contains a lethal; if very few homozygotes develop, a semilethal is present; if the homozygotes are somewhat less or somewhat more numerous than expected, minor modifiers, respectively reducing or increasing the viability, are involved. Likewise, if a wild chromosome contains modifiers speeding up or slowing down the development of the flies, most of the homozygotes hatch respectively before or after their heterozygous sibs have hatched. The frequency of such modifiers in natural populations proved to be enormous. Dobzhansky estimated that about 40 percent of the third chromosomes in *D. pseudoobscura* contain viability modifiers. Modifiers of the development rate and of fertility are common, but no frequency estimates are yet available. Preliminary data indicate a similar situation in the second and fourth chromosomes. All in all, it may be doubted that any two individuals in natural populations are alike in genetic constitution.

NATURAL MUTATIONS IN ORGANISMS OTHER THAN DROSOPHILA

It is evidently very difficult to detect mutations in organisms unsuitable for laboratory experiments, and which therefore have been only superficially studied, or not studied at all, from the point of view of genetics. Nevertheless, many scattered observations are available to show that *Drosophila* is at least not alone in the living world in producing mutants under natural conditions. Biological literature is full of records of appearance of aberrant individuals among masses of normal representatives of a species in nature. They are sometimes described as aberrations, phases, monstrosities, and sometimes are merely recorded without much detail. Naturalists of the old type were prone to assume that these unorthodox-looking creatures are due to developmental accidents, to fortuitous coincidences of external conditions. That developmental accidents occur in nature, and may produce teratological specimens, is not doubted by anyone. But in a number of cases it has been established with varying degrees of certainty that aberrations of this sort are in reality hereditary types, mostly recessive to the normal condition, and represent rare instances when recessive genes, long carried in the population in heterozygous state, emerge as homozygotes because of the occasional mating of two carriers.

Dunn (1921) was the first to apply the above genetic interpretation to the aberrant individuals in wild species of rodents (albinism, pink eyes, yellow, black, or white-spotted specimens among the agouti-colored normals). The aberrations found in nature resemble well-known breeds of domestic species (rabbits, mice, and guinea pigs), in which these characteristics are inherited as Mendelian recessives.

Storer and Gregory (1934) have made a special study of exceptional individuals in the western pocket gopher *Thomomys bottae*. They record at least seven exceptional types, all analogous to the familiar varieties of the domesticated rodents. One of them, with black fur, is especially interesting. In California the black specimens of the pocket gopher are very rare, the normal coloration being agouti (black is recessive to agouti in genetically studied species).

But in *Thomomys townsendi* from Idaho (Nampa) black individuals are no great rarity, and *T. niger* from Oregon is normally black. Black and spotted individuals occur as rare freaks throughout the distribution area of the hamster *Cricetus cricetus*. At the northern boundary of the species area, in the Ufa district of the western Ural Mountains, the blacks are very common, and in certain localities displace the wild type entirely (Kirikov 1934). Among crickets many species are dimorphic with respect to wing length, the long-winged and the short-winged specimens being sometimes found in the same population, and sometimes restricted to different localities. *Pteronemobius heydeni* in southern France is normally short winged, but Chopard and Bellecroix (1928) have shown that long-wingedness exists in the population in heterozygous condition. Further examples of this kind may be found in Timofeeff-Ressovsky (1939a, 1940), Goldschmidt (1940), and Stresemann (1926).

Recessive genes producing various structural and physiological changes, some of them lethal or semilethal, are common in populations of man and of domestic animals (a short review by Mohr, 1939). That a similar situation obtains in populations of wild species as well is shown by the appearance of "mutants" after a few generations of inbreeding the progeny of individuals taken from nature. Experiments of this kind have been described by Sumner (1932) in the mouse *Peromyscus* and by Spooner (1932) and Sexton and Clark (1936) in the crustacean *Gammarus chevreuxi*. H. Timofeeff-Ressovsky (1935) obtained a mutation in the beetle *Epilachna chrysomelina,* which resembled a type of this species previously recorded in some localities. Similar data exist for cross-fertilizing plants. Jenkins (1924) examined 3,750 lines of commercial maize and found 18.1 percent of them to be heterozygous for chlorophyll defects in seedlings and 6.1 percent for chlorophyll defects in mature plants; Hayes and Brewbaker (1924) obtained similar results. According to Mangelsdorf (1926), approximately 3 percent of maize plants are heterozygous for lethal or semilethal genes producing, when homozygous, defective seedlings. Chlorophyll defects, dwarf plants and other variants appeared in inbred progenies of the grasses *Festuca pratensis, Dactylis glomerata,* and *Phleum pratense* (Nilsson 1934), and of the white mustard *Synapis alba* (Saltykovsky and Fedorov 1936). Nilsson records also numerous structural variations in the inbred lines of the above named grasses, which suggest that the populations of these species carry recessive genes of the "small mutations" type.

The increase of the variability observed in many species of domesticated animals and plants as compared with their wild progenitors may be explained in part by the inbreeding to which these forms are subjected in captivity. Recessive mutant genes concealed in wild populations are likely to be disadvantageous in the state of nature, and the homozygotes may be eliminated rapidly. Some of these mutants may, however, be selected by man to suit his purposes and fancies, and consequently may be perpetuated as homozygotes. In this respect the well-known fact that the characteristics of domestic breeds are mostly recessive to the normal or wild-type condition may be significant. "Effects of domestication" is a phrase frequently used in a manner bordering almost on mysticism, especially in the older literature dealing with the origin of the domesticated animals and plants. Granting that there is much yet to be learned about these phenomena, it is at least worth while to consider them in the light of what is known about the genetic variability concealed in natural populations and the effects of inbreeding in uncovering this variability. If it were established that hybridization frequently results in an increase of the mutation rates of genes (see p. 36), that would be another agent enhancing the genetic variability in the process of domestication. It seems to be true that many of the species of domestic animals and plants have descended each from more than one geographic race, if not from more than one species, of wild ancestors. Inbreeding and hybridization are also prominent among methods used for the improvement of the existing cultivated forms, and it may not be amiss to reexamine them in the light of modern population genetics.

INDIVIDUAL AND RACIAL VARIABILITY

An enormous, and hitherto scarcely suspected, wealth of genic diversity has been detected in wild populations of *Drosophila*. The fragmentary information available suggests that the same situation obtains in other organisms as well. From a systematist's viewpoint this store of variability is more potential than actual, since it is caused mainly by recessive genes carried in heterozygous condition.

But the phenotypic manifestation of recessive germinal changes is merely a question of their frequency in the population, for as soon as they become so frequent that matings of the heterozygous carriers are likely to occur, homozygotes showing the effects of the genes involved will be produced. This is exactly what is observed. The "exceptional" individuals, the aberrations discussed above, are such outcroppings on the morphological surface of the concealed genic variability.

Since mutations in any one gene may occur, and presumably do occur, in every part of the species population, mutant individuals may be encountered throughout the species area. As we shall see in the following chapters, their frequencies depend on the mutation rates, on their being favored or opposed by natural selection, and on other causes. If a mutant occurs very rarely, it is classed as an aberration, monstrosity, or as an "individual variant." If it is common and its frequency is more or less uniform everywhere, the species is said to be polymorphic (Ford 1940). Finally, if the frequency of an hereditary type varies in different parts of the species area, we are dealing with racial differentiation. It is evident that these distinctions are arbitrary, since all kinds of intermediate conditions are encountered. One may doubt that the frequency of any mutant is ever completely uniform throughout a species, except, perhaps, in species approaching extinction or represented by very small total numbers of individuals. The black specimens of gophers and hamsters (p. 61) are rare mutants in some localities, common in others, and in still others they are the typical representatives of their species. The concealed mutants in *Drosophila* populations are by no means uniformly distributed geographically, and colonies of these flies separated by less than a mile may differ in at least the frequencies of various mutant genes (p. 179). The same mutant may be a rare aberration in one species, a common phase of another, a species character in a third, and even a generic character elsewhere. An instructive example of this sort has been described by Zimmermann (1933): the absence of the second cubital cross vein in certain bees behaves in the manner just indicated.

Racial subdivision is a name which subsumes a great number of diversified phenomena. The term "race" is used quite loosely to designate any subdivision of a species consisting of individuals which have certain hereditary traits in common and which differ from other subdivisions in the incidence of certain genetic characters. Formation of geographical races is probably the most usual method of differentiation of species in at least the nonmarine representatives of the animal and plant kingdoms. The zoological literature on this subject has been reviewed by Rensch (1929). A geographical race can occupy an area ranging from a fraction of a square mile to hundreds of thousands of square miles, and many races are subdivided into secondary and tertiary races. Populations of *Drosophila* inhabiting parts of the same forested valley and populations of land snails residing on two sides of a foot path bisecting a meadow are races by definition, provided they differ, as they frequently do, in the incidence of certain genes. The same name is correctly applied to the great subdivisions of mankind. In many plants the species population is split into numerous "ecotypes" adapted to living in definite ecological stations and found wherever the proper environment exists in the distribution area of the species (Turesson 1922–1931 and others). Costal, dune, forest, swamp, alpine, and other ecotypes are distinguished. Ecotypic differentiation is known among animals as well as among plants (see pp. 202–206). Ecological races may be superimposed on, or may merge into, the geographical ones. The term "race" is applied also to breeds of domestic animals and plants, although these artificially created populations maintain their identity in many cases only by man's effort to prevent their free interbreeding and consequent amalgamation.

The individual variability, in so far as it is hereditary, may be likened to a store of building materials; the process of race formation consists in arranging the materials in definite patterns. An excellent illustration of this situation is provided by the snail *Partula otaheitana* which inhabits the radially arranged valleys of the island of Tahiti (Crampton 1916). Individuals of this snail vary in many characters: the spiral of the shell may be dextral or sinistral; size, shape, and color of the shell may differ. In one of the valleys (Fautaua) a population is found in which all the characters and combinations of characters present in the species as a whole may be encountered in separate individuals. Other valleys harbor distinct races each restricted to a single valley or to a few adjacent ones.

Every race is characterized by a definite combination of traits found in the Fautaua population, but in no case are any distinctive traits added to the Fautaua complex. Such reservoirs of phylogenetic potentialities are quite familiar to paleontologists. Three families, seven genera, and seventeen species of primitive horselike animals described from a certain Eocene stratum in South America by early investigators have been more recently shown to belong to a single greatly variable species—*Henricosbornia lophodonta* (Simpson 1937). The reason for so extreme a change of evaluation lies in that the differences between the intraspecific variants in *H. lophodonta* are analogous both in kind and degree to those distinguishing groups of a much higher rank—species, genera, and families—among the later representatives of the horse tribe.

THE SIMPLEST FORM OF GEOGRAPHICAL VARIABILITY

It has been customary to contrast discontinuous and continuous variability. Since no intermediates exist between the dextral and sinistral shell forms in certain molluscs, every individual may be without hesitation recognized as a member of one or the other class. Contrariwise, all the intergrades occur between dwarf, average, and giant stature in man. As far as the hereditary variability is concerned, the distinction between the discontinuous and the continuous types parallels that between the large and the small mutations; both distinctions have no more than a descriptive significance. In either case the basic phenomenon is the presence of more than a single allele of a certain gene. Where the members of the allelic series differ greatly in their phenotypic effects, the genetic analysis is simple, variation is discontinuous, and the population is split into clear-cut phases. Where the phenotypic expression of the genic diversity is not striking or is obscured by environmental influences, the genetic analysis encounters technical obstacles, variation is continuous and most easily describable in terms of mean values and variances of measurements.

The dextrality and sinistrality of the molluscan shell have been quoted above as an example of discontinuous variability. Table 8, extracted from the mass of data of this sort published by Crampton (1916, 1932), shows the frequency of the dextral and sinistral spirals in the shells of *Partula suturalis vexillum* in some valleys of the island of Moorea. Each valley has a characteristic frequency of shells of either kind; in some places the population is purely dextral or purely sinistral, in others a mixed population is found. In the water snail *Limnaea* the direction of coiling of the shell is determined by a single gene (Diver, Boycott, Garstang 1925, Sturtevant 1923). It is very probable that in *Partula* the mode of inheritance is the same as in *Limnaea,* and hence the variation shown in Table 8 is probably due to different frequencies of the gene which determines the direction of the coiling of the shell in various colonies.

TABLE 8

THE FREQUENCY (IN PERCENTS) OF DEXTRAL AND SINISTRAL SHELLS IN *Partula suturalis* IN MOOREA (after Crampton)

LOCALITIES	DEXTRAL	SINISTRAL	NUMBER OF INDIVIDUALS
Atimaha	100.0	0	277
Vaianai	100.0	0	369
Oio	98.7	1.3	612
Haapiti	93.0	7.0	241
Uufau	12.5	87.5	303
Moruui	0.1	99.9	537
Maraarii	0	100.0	788
Varari	0	100.0	578

The British Trust for Ornithology has conducted a coöperative study of the guillemot *Uria aalge* (Southern 1939). The "bridled" phase of this cliff-dwelling sea bird has white "spectacles" around the eyes, the unbridled phase lacks this adornment. The difference is probably due to a single gene. On Heligoland and the coasts of Brittany and southern England less than 1 percent of the population are bridled; northward, the frequencies of bridled individuals increase, reaching percentages of 2 to 12 in Scotland, 23 to 26 in the Shetland Islands, 34 on the Faroes, and about 40, 50, and 70 on Novaya Zemlya, North Cape, and Iceland, respectively. The "simplex" structure of the third upper molar tooth in the mouse *Microtus arvalis* is recessive to normal. According to Zimmermann (1935), more than 85 percent of the population in southern Denmark and adjacent parts of Germany are "simplex." The frequencies of "simplex" diminish southward, reaching almost zero in central and southern Germany. Such regular geographical gradients or "clines" (Huxley 1938a, 1940) in the frequencies or in the expression of variable characters are a common situation in many animal and plant species.

The geographical distribution of the blood groups in man has been studied in more detail than any other instance of geographical variability (a summary in Boyd 1939). The inheritance of the blood groups is slightly more complex than that of the characters discussed

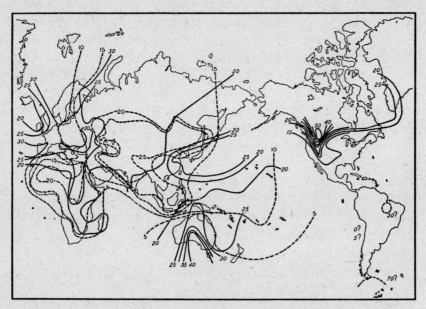

FIG. 1. The frequencies of the blood group genes A (solid lines) and a^B (broken lines) in the human populations. The figures for the Americas refer to the native (Indian) populations. (After Boyd.)

above, since it is determined by a gene having three, or even four, distinguishable alleles denoted a, A, and a^B respectively. The interaction of these alleles produces four blood groups—the group O consists of individuals homozygous for a (aa); the group A has the gene A in homozygous or heterozygous condition (AA or Aa); the group B carries the gene a^B ($a^B a^B$ or aa^B), and the group AB has both A and a^B (Aa^B). The relative frequencies of the four blood groups in various populations have been determined, and from these data the relative frequencies of the three alleles have been deduced. The frequencies of the genes A, a^B, and a are usually denoted as p, q, and r, respectively.*

Fig. 1 shows the frequencies p and q of the alleles A and a^B in the populations of different countries. The data for the Americas pertain to the Indian, not the white, populations, but since considerable hybridization has taken place throughout this territory the validity of this part of the data is open to some doubt. The lines connect the localities in which a given concentration of the genes was observed; such lines may, perhaps, be termed isogenes. The racial differences with respect to the blood groups are quantitative. On the great Eurasiatic continent the frequency of a^B increases from west to east, but drops again southward, reaching a low value among the Australian aborigines. The gene A (p) is common in Europe and in northern Asia (Ainus), but relatively rare in southern Asia and Africa. Certain North American Indian tribes (Blackfeet) have very high, and South American very low, frequencies of A. We need not consider here the speculations concerning the history of human migrations which are made on the basis of the blood group distribution; it is, however, evident that when the distributions of other human genes are better known than is the case at present, anthropology and history will have been enriched by a new source of evidence for their theories.

GEOGRAPHICAL VARIABILITY DUE TO SEVERAL GENES

The Asiatic beetle *Harmonia axyridis* (a ladybird beetle) is extremely variable with respect to the color pattern of the elytra and of the pronotum (Fig. 2). The numerous patterns known in this species can be divided into five groups, intermediates between which are absent or very rare. Individuals with yellow—or yellow spotted with black—elytra form one group, within which the variation is due to minor genetic and also to environmental factors (Fig. 2 a–c). This pattern behaves as a recessive; other patterns are due either to interactions of several genes (Tan and Li 1934), or to a series of alleles of a single gene (Hosino 1940). The geographical distribution of the color classes is shown in Table 9.

* The formulae used for this deduction are: $p = 1-\sqrt{O+B}$, $q = 1-\sqrt{O+A}$, and $r = \sqrt{O}$.

West-central Siberia (Altai, Yeniseisk) is occupied by a race manifesting nearly always the pattern *axyridis* (Fig. 2 e). In central Siberia the yellow forms appear and rapidly displace *axyridis,* which on the Pacific Coast of Siberia and in China is very rare or is absent. *Spectabilis* and *conspicua* are found in the Far East only, the latter apparently reaching a high frequency in Japan. Aulica is nowhere frequent, but is found almost everywhere in the Far East (Dobzhansky 1933c). The variation in this species could be expressed in terms of frequencies of the genes determining the various patterns

TABLE 9

FREQUENCIES OF COLOR PATTERNS (IN PERCENTS) IN *Harmonia axyridis* FROM DIFFERENT REGIONS

REGION	SUCCINEA, FRIGIDA, 19-SIGNATA	AULICA	AXYRIDIS	SPECTABILIS	CONSPICUA	UNCLASSIFIED	NUMBER EXAMINED
Altai Mountains	0.05	—	99.95	—	—	—	4,013
Yeniseisk Province	0.9	—	99.1	—	—	—	116
Irkutsk Province	15.1	—	84.9	—	—	—	73
West Transbaikalia	50.8	—	49.2	—	—	—	61
Amur Province	100.0	—	—	—	—	—	41
Khabarovsk	74.5	0.3	0.2	13.4	10.7	—	597
Vladivostok	85.6	0.8	0.8	6.0	6.8	0.1	765
Korea	81.3	—	—	6.2	12.5	—	64
Manchuria	79.7	0.5	—	11.2	8.6	—	232
North China (Peiping)	83.0	0.4	—	8.8	7.3	0.5	9,676
West China (Szechwan)	42.6	2.9	0.01	28.8	25.1	0.8	1,074
East China (Soochow)	66.6	0.6	—	16.5	16.1	0.2	6,231
Japan	27.2	—	11.0	14.3	47.4	—	154

just as well as in terms of frequencies of the patterns themselves. The contradictory results of Tan and Li on the one side and of Hosino on the other make such calculations meaningless for the time being.

The case of *Harmonia axyridis* is by no means unique. In several species of ladybird beetles (*Coccinellidae*) the writer (Dobzhansky 1933c) has found similar situations, and they are quite common in most diverse forms, animal as well as plant. Quantitative data on the frequencies of variants in different localities were already being collected by Bateson in 1895; subsequently this subject has been rather neglected, but recently there has been a resurgence of interest toward it (for example Barulina and Dombrovskaya 1937, Welch 1938, Diver 1939, 1940, Gregor 1938, 1939, Howard 1940). Some species are regularly polymorphic, and the frequencies of the different types composing the population are similar in all parts of the area inhabited by the species. In other species all the types are present throughout the distribution area, but their relative frequencies are not alike in different regions (the variation of the blood groups in man is a good example of this situation). In still further

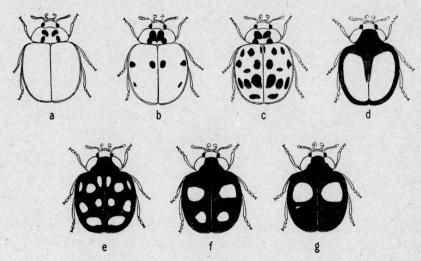

FIG. 2. Color patterns in varieties of *Harmonia axyridis*. (a) var. succinea; (b) var. frigida; (c) var. 19-signata; (d) var. aulica; (e) var. axyridis; (f) var. spectabilis; (g) var. conspicua.

differentiated species the distribution area is subdivided into regions each of which is inhabited by a definite form, or a definite set of forms, which do not occur elsewhere, but mixed populations exist in the intermediate zones. The intermediate zones may be wide, or may be so narrow that mixed populations practically no longer exist.

Dr. Ernst Mayr has called my attention to the geographic races in the bird *Pachycephala pectoralis* (Table 10). It inhabits some of the South Sea islands, each island or a group of neighboring islands having a race of its own, characterized in part by alternatively varying characters (Mayr 1932). The exchange of individuals between the populations of different islands is probably very rare. The remarkable feature of this case is that at least eight combinations of the five alternative characters are known, and that the same combination may occur in races found on rather remote islands (i.e., New Britain, New Hebrides, and the southern part of Fiji, Table 10). On any one island the character combination is nearly constant, the population apparently being genetically almost pure with respect to these characters. Two exceptions from this rule have been found.

TABLE 10

ALTERNATIVELY VARYING CHARACTERISTICS IN GEOGRAPHIC RACES OF
Pachycephala pectoralis (after Mayr)

RACE	DISTRIBUTION	THROAT		BREAST BAND		COLOR OF BACK		FORE-HEAD		WING	
		Yellow	White	Present	Absent	Olive	Black	Yellow	Black	Colored	Black
dahli	New Britain ⎱										
chlorura	New Hebrides ⎰		+	+		+			+	+	
vitiensis	So. Fiji ⎰										
bougainvillei	No. Solomon ⎱	+		+		+			+	+	
torquata	N.E. Fiji ⎰										
melanota	S.W. Solomon	+		+			+		+		+
melanoptera	So. Solomon	+		+		+			+		+
sanfordi	N.E. Solomon	+			+	+			+	+	
ornata	Santa Cruz		+	+			+		+	+	
bella	S.W. Fiji ⎱	+		+		+		+		+	
optata	Central Fiji ⎰										
graeffii	N.W. Fiji	+			+	+		+		+	

Three little islands of the Solomon group are inhabited by a hybrid (or mixed) population in which yellow-throated as well as white-throated individuals occur. In another case a single individual having an unusual combination of characters has been found in an otherwise homogeneous population. Varieties of cultivated and wild plants are best described as having different combinations of a limited number of alternative characters (Vavilov 1922, 1928), and the same is true for species of some genera (for example the Neuropteran genus *Cyrnus*, Klingstedt 1937).

CONTINUOUS GEOGRAPHICAL VARIABILITY

Since large mutations as a class are less frequent than genic changes with small visible effects, one could expect that geographical races may be encountered in which the differences between the component types are far less striking than those in races discussed above. Indeed, continuous geographical variation is a commonly observed phenomenon. The lady beetle *Coccinella septempunctata* may serve as an example. The geographical distribution of this species includes Europe, northern Asia, and north Africa. Throughout this area it has seven black spots on the red elytra, but the

FIG. 3. Geographical variation in the size of the spots on the elytra of *Coccinella septempunctata*. The size of the circle is proportional to the diameter of the discal spot.

size of the spots is variable. In central and southwestern Asia a race with very small spots occurs (Fig. 3). Northern Europe and especially the Far East are inhabited by races with large spots. In any locality the population is variable with respect to the size of the spots, but the variability forms a normal probability curve, and it is futile to attempt to classify the individual variants in any other than arbitrary classes. Likewise, there is no clear line of separation between the races with large and those with small spots. The populations coming from geographically remote localities are often strikingly different, but intermediate populations are found in the intervening localities, forming a continuous chain of intergradations between the extremes. The racial variability of stature, of cephalic index, and of many other characteristics used by anthropologists for the description and classification of the human races is continuous. Remarkably regular geographical clines have been described in the honey bee by Alpatov (1929), and numerous examples of this type of variation may be found in the reviews by Rensch (1929, 1937, 1939), Reinig (1938, 1939), and in monographic treatments of various animal and plant genera.

The genetic analysis of continuous variability is technically difficult. The same obstacles are met with here that are encountered in studies on small mutations. Interracial crosses produce in the F_2 generation continuously varying arrays of individuals instead of a clear segregation into discrete classes. Laborious progeny tests are necessary to reveal the Mendelian segregation obscured by the individual variability which is mostly environmental in origin. These difficulties led some writers to a sort of a defeatist attitude; continuous variability was declared different in principle from the discontinuous one. It was said that only the latter is clearly genic, while the former was alleged to be non-Mendelian and to be due to some vague principle which assiduously escapes all attempts to define it more clearly. The sharp distinction between the continuous and the discontinuous variability is, however, gratuitous. All sorts of intermediate situations occur. The variations of human eye color and hair color are good examples. Moreover, and this is decisive, we are fortunate in having several published accounts of genetic analyses of continuous variation; these accounts agree in showing that the genetic basis of continuous variation is similar in principle to that of discontinuous variation.

The classical studies of Nilsson-Ehle on the genetics of cereals first established the principle of multiple factors, which was later applied to the inheritance of quantitative characters in general. An inherited difference between two individuals or races can be due to coöperation of several genes each modifying the character by a certain more or less small value. The effects produced by the different genes involved may be approximately equal, or some genes may be more effective than others. In the latter case we speak of a "main" factor and its modifiers. The heterozygotes are frequently intermediate between the two homozygotes, so that every genotype has its own phenotype, of course modified by environmental factors. The differences between the phenotypes are, however, not absolute; rather, they are relative, differences of degree. The situation may be further complicated if one or both of the ancestral races are themselves not homogeneous for some of the genetic factors causing the interracial distinction. For instance, the interracial distinction may be due to five pairs of genes producing cumulative effects; one race is predominantly *AABBCCDDEE* and the other *aabbccddee,* but some individuals of the constitution *aaBBCCDDEE* are encountered in the population of the first, and some *AAbbccddee* individuals in the population of the second race.

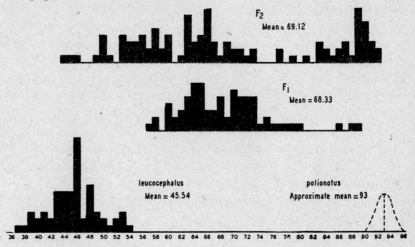

FIG. 4. Inheritance of the extent of the colored area of the pelage in the cross *Peromyscus polionotus* × *P. leucocephalus.* (After Sumner.)

Sumner (1923, 1924a, 1929, 1930, 1932, Sumner and Huestis 1925) has made a painstaking investigation of the geographical variability of some species of deer mice, *Peromyscus.* The geographical races differ here in such characters as size of body; length of tail, feet, and ears; the extent of the colored portion of the pelage; coloration of the pelage; proportionate number of different types of hairs, and so on. The result of interracial crosses is usually that the F_1 generation is intermediate between the parents, and about as variable as each of the parental races themselves. In the F_2 generation the mean values of the characters are likewise intermediate, and mostly similar to those of the F_1 generation. The variability is, however, greater, so that the extreme variants fall within the range of the normal variation of the ancestral races. Backcrosses to the ancestral races cause shifts of the mean values in the direction of the parents. Fig. 4 shows the inheritance of the extent of the colored area of the pelage in the cross *Peromyscus polionotus polionotus* × *P. polionotus leucocephalus*. The former is a dark animal, the extent of the colored area having a mean value of about 93. *Leucocephalus* is light, the mean value of the colored area being 45.54. The F_1 and the F_2 generations are almost exactly intermediate between the parents, mean values being 68.33 and 69.12 respectively. The variability in F_1 is however smaller (the standard deviation, $\sigma = 6.46$) than in F_2 ($\sigma = 13.87$).

The increase of variability in the F_2 was supposed to be evidence of the occurrence of Mendelian segregation. Taking the theoretical example of the two races differing in five genes (see above), the F_1 will consist of a single genotype ($AaBbCcDdEe$), or at most of a few genotypes (if the ancestral races are not homogeneous). But in F_2 the number of genotypes is much greater; for a character determined by five genes this number equals 3^5, or 243. Moreover, only a small fraction of the offspring will be identical in genotype with either of the parents; for the case of five genes this fraction is 4^{-5}, or 1:1,023. Evidently, the difficulty encountered in the analysis of a character determined by multiple factors will vary depending upon the number of genes involved, the equal or unequal effectiveness of these genes in modifying the character, and the absolute size of the effect—other things being equal. Sharp differences are easier to analyze than the small ones. Crosses involving some of the racial characters in *Peromyscus* have given such small increases of the variability in F_2 generation that in his earlier work Sumner believed them to be non-Mendelian. Only the accumulation of further data and improvements in technique finally convinced Sumner that the multiple gene hypothesis is adequate to account for his data; in fact his work is a good example of the applicability of this hypothesis. Muller (1936) has pointed out that the increase of the variability in the F_2 generation of crosses is not strictly necessary if multiple genes are involved, for the variability due to the interracial hybridization may sometimes be canceled by the intraracial variability present in the parental strains.

Tedin (1925) has analyzed the differences between lines of the plant *Camelina sativa* from various localities in Sweden. Characters distinguishing the lines are leaf shape, hairiness, height of the plant, shape of the pods, the angle between the main axis of the inflorescence and the pod stalks, seed weight, and others. Throughout, the inheritance was traceable to multiple genes. In some cases Tedin was able to isolate single Mendelizing factors causing the quantitative differences, in other cases the number of the factors remained unknown. As a whole, Tedin's work remains one of the best examples of a successful application of the multiple gene hypothesis. Equally good results were obtained by Philiptchenko (1934) on quantitative differences between strains of the cultivated species of wheat.

A very extensive series of investigations on the continuous geographic variation in the moth *Lymantria dispar* has been published by Goldschmidt. Races of this moth are often widely different in such characters as the strength of the sex factors (Goldschmidt, Seiler, Poppelbaum 1924, Goldschmidt 1932a), color of the caterpillars (Goldschmidt 1929a), duration of the winter rest of the eggs (1932c), speed of the development (1933a, b) and others (1934b). For each character Goldschmidt finds several determining genes, one of which, according to his interpretation, produces a major effect while others act as plus and minus modifiers.

The genetic basis of continuous variation is probably similar to that of discontinuous variation. The extremes of the two races (for instance, the Japanese and the central Asiatic populations of *Coccinella septempunctata*, Fig. 3) may be supposed to differ, respectively, in a number of genes, $AABBCCDDEE$ . . . and $aabbccddee$ . . . The intermediate populations may be $AAbbccddee$, $AABBccddee$, $AABBCCddee$, $AABBCCDDee$, or mixtures of these genotypes. The characteristics of the intermediate races will, then, be determined by the average number of the multiple genes present in the population in a given locality.

GENETIC CONCEPTION OF A RACE

So many diverse phenomena have been subsumed under the name "race" that the term iself has become rather ambiguous. Sometimes any subdivision of a species which is genetically different from other subdivisions is called a race. A "geographical race" has somewhat more definite implications: it is a group of individuals which inhabits a certain territory and which is genetically different from other geographically limited groups. This is the meaning of the term race as used in the taxonomic literature, with the important reservation that the hereditary nature of the racial characteristics is more often assumed than empirically known. The amount of attention which the problem of races has attracted in genetics is very small, altogether out of proportion to its theoretical and practical importance. This explains the abuses which the race concept has suffered, especially in recent years.

In classical morphology and anthropology, races are described usually in terms of the statistical averages for characters in which they differ from each other. Once such a system of averages is arrived at, it begins to serve as a racial standard with which individuals and groups of individuals can be compared. This simple method of racial studies is unquestionably convenient for some practical purposes. The difficulty is, however, that from the point of view of genetics such an attempt to determine to which race a given individual belongs is sometimes based on an unmitigated fallacy. The fact which is very often overlooked in making such attempts is that racial differences are more commonly due to variations in the relative frequencies of genes in different parts of the species population than to an absolute lack of certain genes in some groups and their complete homozygosis in others. Examples quoted above show that gene frequencies in different races of a species may vary from o percent to 100 percent, these being no more than limiting values. Individuals carrying or not carrying a certain gene may sometimes be found in many distinct races of a species.

The difficulty is enhanced by the genetically complex nature of most racial differences. Blood groups are certainly not the sole difference between human races; populations of *Partula* vary with respect to size, shape, color, and other characters, as well as in the direction of coiling of the shells; *Harmonia* exhibits variation in size, shape, and coloration of the body and its parts. The geographical distributions of the separate genes composing a racial difference are very frequently independent. In fact, the distribution of the blood group genes in man does not resemble that of the genes for the skin color or the cephalic index (although the related racial groups are more likely to be similar in each of these characters than the unrelated ones). Goldschmidt (1934b) has made especial efforts to correlate the geographical distributions of the various genes differentiating the *Lymantria* races, only to find them largely independent. The result is that with respect to some genes an individual or a population A may be more similar to B than to C, but in other genes the same individual or population A may be more like C than B. In fact, individuals of the same race may differ in more genes than individuals of different races.

The fundamental units of racial variability are populations and genes, not complexes of characters which connote in the popular mind a racial distinction. Much confusion of thought could be avoided if all biologists would realize this fact. How important it is may be illustrated by the following analogy. Many studies on hybridization were made before Mendel, but they did not lead to the discovery of Mendel's laws. In retrospect, we see clearly where the mistake of Mendel's predecessors lay: they treated as units the complexes of characteristics of individuals, races, and species, and attempted to find rules governing the inheritance of such complexes. Mendel was first to understand that it was the inheritance of separate traits, and not of complexes of traits, which had to be studied. Some of the modern students of racial variability consistently repeat the mistakes of Mendel's predecessors.

An endless and notoriously inconclusive discussion of the "race problem" has been going on for many years in the biological, anthropological, and sociological literature. Stripped of unnecessary verbiage, the question is this: is a "race" a concrete entity existing in nature, or is it merely an abstraction with a very limited usefulness? To a geneticist it seems clear enough that all the lucubrations on the "race problem" fail to take into account that a race is not a static entity but a process. Race formation begins when the frequency of a certain gene or genes becomes slightly different in one part of a population from what it is in other parts. If the differentiation is allowed to proceed unimpeded, most or all of the individuals of one race may come to possess certain genes which those of the other race do not. Finally, mechanisms preventing the interbreeding of races may develop, splitting what used to be a single collective genotype

into two or more separate ones. When such mechanisms have developed and the prevention of interbreeding is more or less complete,
we are dealing with separate species. A race becomes more and more
of a "concrete entity" as this process goes on; what is essential
about races is not their state of being but that of becoming. But
when the separation of races is complete, we are dealing with races
no longer, for what have emerged are separate species.

Racial variability must be described in terms of the frequencies
of individual genes in different geographical regions or in groups of
individuals occupying definite habitats. Such a description is more
adequate than the usual method of finding the abstract average
phenotypes of "races" because it subsumes not only an account of
the present status of a population, but to a certain extent also that of
its potentialities in the future (e.g., presence of certain genes in
heterozygous state which, if increased in frequency, may change the
phenotype of the race). The geography of the genes, not of the
average phenotypes, must be studied. To date, only a few attempts
to apply this method in practice have been made. The most successful one among them is that concerning the blood groups in man
(Figure 1). The scarcity of similar data for other organisms is due
less to any difficulty in obtaining such data than to a lack of appreciation of their importance

MENDELIAN INHERITANCE IN SPECIES CROSSES

Hybrids between species, and sometimes between genera, have
been obtained and studied before as well as after the rediscovery of
Mendel's laws. A rather unwieldy mass of data has resulted from
these studies; an attempt to account for inheritance in all species
crosses in Mendelian terms is at first sight hopeless. Some of the
early geneticists took it almost for granted that Mendel's laws are
applicable only to intraspecific crosses, the interspecific ones being
governed by some other principles, and Goldschmidt (1940) has recently come out squarely in favor of such a view. He believes that
mutational gene changes are responsible only for differences between
individuals and races of the same species, and that evolution proceeds mainly through "systemic mutations" which transform one
species at once into a different one. Systemic mutations are by their
very nature not resolvable into analyzable genic differences, and it

is their property to disrupt the crossability of the new species to its ancestor or to make the hybrids between them sterile.

We need not consider here the fact that systemic mutations have never been observed, and that it is extremely improbable that species are formed in so abrupt a manner. Sufficient evidence for a rebuttal of Goldschmidt's and kindred views is available. It must be remembered that the existence of genes is inferred primarily through observations on the Mendelian segregation of traits distinguishing the parental forms in the second and the following generations of hybrids. Normal chromosome pairing and disjunction in the gametogenesis of a hybrid are prerequisites for the occurrence of Mendelian segregation. To assert that where differences are analyzable in Mendelian terms they are not species differences and vice versa, and then to use the unanalyzable cases as a proof of the existence of changes other than gene mutations is begging the question. Indeed, many species cannot be crossed and others produce sterile hybrids or hybrids with disturbances of chromosome pairing. The classical studies of Federley (1913) on the hybrids between the species of the moth *Pygaera* have demonstrated that in those crosses in which no segregation was observed no chromosome pairing had taken place in the gametogenesis of the hybrid, and Mendelian segregation was preceded by formation of at least some chromosome bivalents.

The interspecific hybrids in which a straightforward genetic analysis can be made constitute, therefore, only a residue left after the elimination of the sterile and the chromosomally abnormal hybrids. The difficulties do not end here. As we have seen, even in interracial crosses the isolation and study of the individual genes are often very difficult on account of the large number of genes involved. The species differences are likely to be determined by more numerous genes than the racial ones, making the segregations in F_2 and later generations from interspecific crosses correspondingly more complex.

The results obtained by Baur (1924, 1930, 1932) and Lotsy (1911) in crosses between species of snapdragons (*Antirrhinum*) may be regarded as typical for fertile hybrids between closely related plant species differing in clearly visible characters. In the cross *Antirrhinum majus* $\times$ *Antirrhinum molle*, the F_1 generation is in most respects intermediate between the parents. The variability of the F_1 is about as great as that of the more variable parental species, in this case *Antirrhinum molle*. The second generation obtained by selfing the F_1 is enormously variable in all characteristics. Among hundreds of plants no two identical individuals can be found, and many siblings differ in a most striking manner. A majority of plants carry various recombinations of the parental characteristics, and may be therefore loosely described as intermediates. Some individuals resemble one or the other of the parents in one or more characters, such as flower or leaf shape, color, height, or manner of growth, but, according to Baur, none can be mistaken for a pure *majus* or pure *molle*. Moreover, many individuals possess characteristics present neither in the parents nor in the F_1 generation, but encountered in other species of *Antirrhinum* or even in other genera of the family *Scrophulariaceae*. These owe their origin to the formation of new combinations of the ancestral genes, which interact in such a manner as to produce apparently novel characteristics.

The rarity of segregation products completely identical with the parental species indicates that the number of genes making up the species differences is in most cases large. Exactly how large, has been determined neither in the *Antirrhinum* hybrid just discussed nor in any other. It is beyond doubt that certain, mostly qualitative, characters show simple Mendelian segregation in many interspecific crosses where hybrids are fertile. Occasionally several pairs of differentiating genes may be isolated and studied one by one. Hybrids between species of *Mirabilis* (Correns 1902), *Dianthus* (Wichler 1913), *Nicotiana* (East 1916, Brieger 1935), *Canna* (Honing 1923, 1928), *Crepis* (Babcock and Cave 1938), *Antirrhinum* (Kühl 1937), cotton (see below), guinea pigs (Detlefsen 1914) and birds (Phillips 1915, 1921) may be cited as examples. But there is left a residue of differences between the parental species which is not easily dissolved into constituent genes. What is this residue, and does it in any way resemble the postulated systemic mutations?

The behavior of the residual part of the species difference is identical with that of the ubiquitous quantitative differences between individuals and races. There is observed an increase of the variability in F_2 as compared to that in F_1, and, hence, evidence is available that more or less numerous complementary genes are at work. In neither case is it possible to isolate individual genes, to determine exactly their number, and to study their properties one by one. The fact that such a feat of analysis has never been accomplished is an undeniable loophole in our knowledge of evolution. It must be noted, however, that Goldschmidt (1940) does not stress the quantitative characters, the genetic analysis of which is technically so difficult, as a basis of his views. As a matter of fact, he attributes the origin of at least a part of them to "micromutations" (the gene mutations of other authors), not to systemic mutations. Regarding the traits which show clear Mendelian segregations in the species crosses, Goldschmidt insists on the necessity of proving that these are due to differences at specific loci in the chromosomes rather than to chromosomes as wholes. In this insistence Goldschmidt is probably justified; evidence that a given difference is caused by a chromosome does not solve the problem of the number of the genes involved. The technical difficulties confronting an investigator in this field are great. Species and races have different gene arrangements in their chromosomes, and differences of this kind are known to inhibit crossing over and recombination (see Chapter IV). It must be admitted that in no case have all the differences between two good species been completely resolved into gene changes. The view that they are so resolvable is, nevertheless, a working hypothesis so far not contradicted by any facts, and has far more evidence in its favor that any of the alternative hypotheses ever proposed.

ORGANIZED SYSTEMS OF GENE DIFFERENCES

If the above working hypothesis is accepted, the question may be raised in what manner the gene differences combine to form species genotypes. Do species differ simply in a certain number of more or less unrelated genes each taking care of a given character or function, or are the differentiating genes somehow arranged into interdependent systems? It may seem that, in view of the unsatisfactory status of our knowledge of species genetics, raising such a question is premature. It happens, however, that species of cotton, *Gossypium*, are peculiarly suited for investigation of this problem, and Harland (1932a, b, 1935, 1936), Hutchinson (1934, 1937), Silow (1939a, b), and their collaborators have published much pertinent information. The genus *Gossypium* consists of a series of sharply defined wild and cultivated species living in the Tropics of both the Old and the New World. Some of the species are diploid, others apparently allopolyploid (see Chapter VII). Despite the clear-cut differences between them, some of the species having the same numbers of chromosomes can be crossed and produce fertile offspring with few or no disturbances of chromosome pairing. Within a species there is frequently considerable variation, caused partly by gene changes giving simple Mendelian segregations and partly by minor modifying genes giving the blending type of inheritance in crosses. Parallel variations in different species are common, as they so frequently are in other animals and plant groups (Vavilov 1922). This is merely an indication of the presence of homologous genes in related species producing similar mutant types. Sometimes a gene allele which is the prevailing form in one species occurs in another as a more or less rare aberration (a similar situation has been described in *Silene maritima* and *S. cucubalus* by Turrill, 1940). With respect to sixteen genes analyzed in both *Gossypium hirsutum* and in *G. barbadense,* the prevailing forms of the two species are alike in eight genes and different in the other eight.

The simple situation just outlined proves deceptive when the interspecific hybrids are studied. For the same mutant types which, when tested within a species, give clear-cut Mendelian segregation ratios, display a blending type of inheritance in the species hybrids. Thus, both in *Gossypium barbadense* and in *G. hirsutum* there exist variants with and without purple spots on the petals. Within either species the presence of this spot is a simple dominant compared to its absence. In the *G. barbadense* $\times$ *G. hirsutum* hybrids, the F_1 has a small spot, and in F_2 there occur plants with very large spots, without spots, and with intermediate spots of all sizes. By proper backcrossing of the hybrids to the parental species it is, however, possible to extract strains having either predominantly *G. barbadense* or predominantly *G. hirsutum* germ plasms. In such strains the presence or absence of the petal spot is again inherited in a simple manner. An analysis of this situation made by Harland has led to the following conclusions. The presence of the petal spot in either species is caused by the gene S^B and its absence by its allele s^B; moreover, in *G. barbadense* there exists a complex of modifying genes the combined effects of which is to give a large spot in the presence of S^B. In *G. hirsutum* there is a modifier complex which makes the petal spot small. In the interspecific hybrid both the gene S^B and the modifying genes undergo segregation, hence the inheritance of the petal spot is blending instead of simple.

Inheritance similar to that of the petal spot is observed for many other characters studied in *Gossypium barbadense* $\times$ *G. hirsutum* as well as in other hybrids. In fact, clear-cut Mendelian segregations prove to be an exception in these interspecific crosses. Not only complexes of modifying genes are involved, but also the "major" genes are frequently represented by different alleles in different species. The interactions of such major and minor gene complexes result, then, in development of characters "normal" for a given species. But even when the species are similar with respect to some characters, the similarity may prove illusory, since the genetic bases of these characters, as shown by the segregations in the interspecific hybrids, may be different. Harland concludes that species of *Gossypium* differ in hundreds or in thousands of genes combined to form coördinated systems, and that "the modifiers really constitute the species." Even when the end products of two or more evolutionary lines appear rather similar, the similarity may be attained by different means.

Whether differences between species of a genus are always as profound as those found in cotton is at present a moot question. According to Harland, species of *Gossypium* have been separate since the Cretaceous period, and therefore they are relatively very ancient. Anderson (1939a, b, Anderson and Whitaker 1934), working both as a geneticist and as a comparative morphologist, concludes that a situation similar to that in *Gossypium* is encountered in many plant genera: "The acknowledged discontinuity between the two species, taken in their entirety, is a discontinuity of combinations, reinforced by a few discontinuous differences in single characters." According to Anderson, "two species were made of two different materials." Goldschmidt generalizes this formula to apply it to all "true" species, and takes this to be evidence in favor of his theory of evolution by systemic mutations. He disregards, however, the fact that nowhere has a closer approach been made to a complete analysis of species differences into gene elements than in *Gossypium*, in which the orderly complexity of the genetic texture of species is most apparent. One may surmise that the process of evolutionary divergence involves a gradual accumulation of differences between the species genotypes, as a result of which the same physiological function may become subtended by different gene complexes. The importance of this process for the evolution of higher categories (families, orders, classes) needs no emphasis. For instance, Harland makes the following inference: "organs such as the eye, which are common to all vertebrate animals, preserve their essential similarity in structure or function, though the genes responsible for this organ must have become wholly altered during the evolutionary process, since there is no reason now to suppose that homologous organs have anything genetically in common." Divergence of evolutionary lines does not involve merely increase of the number of gene differences; it probably involves also changes of the developmental functions of the genes and a gradual increase of the differences between the structures of the genes which had been identical or similar in the ancestral forms. Here, however, the threshold of the unknown is crossed; speculations of this sort are useful as guiding lights for further studies, but it would be dangerous to mistake them for established facts.

SEROLOGICAL DIFFERENCES BETWEEN SPECIES

In recent years, owing principally to the work of the University of Wisconsin group of investigators (Irwin and Cole 1936, 1940, Irwin 1938, 1939, Irwin and Cumley 1940; see these papers for other references), a new tool has been added to the arsenal of genetic methods. This tool is the analysis of species and racial crosses in terms of serological reactions. The classical studies of Nuttal, Landsteiner, and others have shown that species, as well as systematic categories above and below the species, differ in the composition of their serum proteins. Haemaglutinin tests, worked out chiefly by Landsteiner and his collaborators, proved to be especially valuable for a quantitative assay of these differences in vertebrates. The magnitude of the biochemical differences is, in general, proportional to the closeness or remoteness of the forms tested in the recognized biological system.

The demonstration that these biochemical differences are determined by genes has given a *coup de grâce* to the view that gene inheritance is concerned only with superficial characteristics of organisms (an argument peculiarly impressive to biologists in whom the adjective "biochemical" evokes emotions of superstitious awe). Perhaps more important is the consideration that the antigens detected by means of immunogenetic tests are deemed likely to represent the primary products of the action of the respective genes. This consideration, advanced by Irwin and Cole (1936) and by Haldane (1938), is based on the observation that most antigens present in the parental forms are also detectable as such in the hybrids, no phenomena of dominance and recessiveness being encountered. Moreover, formation of interaction products or so-called "hybrid substances," which occurs very frequently where external characteristics of organisms are concerned, is rare among antigens. It would seem, then, that immunogenetic studies offer an opportunity to estimate the quality and quantity of the genic differences wherever two types can be crossed and a fertile hybrid is obtained.

Irwin, Cole, and their collaborators have analyzed the serological properties of the erythrocytes of various species of pigeons (*Columba*) and doves (*Spilopelia* and *Streptopelia*). These species may be crossed, and some of the hybrids obtained are fertile. A comparison of the parents with each other and with the F_1 hybrids reveals that certain antigens are present in one parent but not in the other. As already mentioned above, the F_1 hybrids have, as a rule, all the antigens present in both parents and no new ones. Less frequently, a few of the parental antigens seem to be absent in the hybrids, but the latter possess some antigens lacking in either parents. Cases of this sort are accounted for by assuming that the hybrid antigens are combination products of the missing parental ones. By backcrossing the F_1 hybrid to the parental species, it is possible to demonstrate that the antigen complexes undergo Mendelian segregation. With sufficient material one could isolate and identify the individual antigens forming the complex differentiating the species crossed. This is, naturally, a very laborious procedure; it is limited, among other things, by the possible linkage of several antigens because the genes producing them are located in the same chromosome. Nevertheless, Irwin (1939) has successfully isolated at least ten distinct antigens present in the pearlneck dove (*Spilopelia chinensis*) but not in the ring dove (*Streptopelia risoria*).

Knowing that certain antigens differentiate the species A from the species B, it is possible, by crossing the species themselves and their hybrid products to the species C, to find out which of the antigens are present in the latter. Several such comparisons were made by Irwin and Cole. For example, it has been found that a complex of antigens common to the pearlneck and ring doves is absent in the pigeons *Columba livia* and *C. guinea;* another complex is "shared" by the two doves and *C. guinea* but is absent in *C. livia;* a few antigens are common to the pearlneck and *C. livia* but are absent in the two others; still others are common for the doves and *C. livia* but absent in *C. guinea,* and so forth. Some antigens, common to all species of a genus or to those of a section of a genus, are called "group antigens," in contrast to "species antigens" present only in a single species or in few of them. Antigenic differences may occur between individuals of a single species, though the number of them is, of course, not as great as where different species are involved.

The picture of the genetic differences between species emerging from immunogenetic studies has the simplicity of a schoolroom illustration: species are merely different combinations of independent genes and of antigens produced by them. It would, however, be a mistake to stress the contrast between this simplicity and the complexity suggested by other genetic studies, particularly by those on species of cotton discussed above. The interrelations between the serological differences on one hand and those in externally visible characteristics on the other are by no means clear. For example, the blood groups in man (p. 67) are easily identifiable by immunological reactions, and yet no connection between the blood groups and visible traits has been found. It is unknown how frequently the genetic differences at large have serological equivalents. Antigens may, indeed, be the primary products of the gene action, but nothing definite is as yet known about their role in the subsequent developmental phenomena. Under such conditions, attempts to formulate generalizations regarding the genetic nature of species differences must perforce be postponed until more information is available.

MATERNAL EFFECTS AND THE NONGENIC INHERITANCE

As the genetic analysis is inexorably limited in application to forms that cross and produce at least partly fertile F_1 hybrids, there is by the very nature of things no possibility of adducing a direct experimental proof that the differences between systematically remote organisms are also genic and mutational in origin. Although it is very doubtful that the ability of organisms to cross is strictly proportional to the closeness of their relationships, a general correlation of this sort unquestionably exists.

This purely negative consideration has opened the gates for contentions that genes determine only the characteristics of the lowest systematic categories (races, species, genera), while those of the higher categories are not genic. The only kind of positive evidence on which these contentions seemed to be gaining a foothold were the results of the experimental embryologists on the early developmental stages (chiefly the type of cleavage) in hybrids between remote forms. In such hybrids the effects of the foreign sperm begin to manifest themselves not immediately after the entry of the sperm into the egg, but only after a more or less prolonged delay, and may in some cases not come to pass before the hybrid embryo dies. In a number of well-known experiments that have been for some time the subject of a lively controversy, the eggs were artificially deprived of the female pronuclei, and were fertilized by spermatozoa of unrelated animals. If such eggs develop, the development begins according to the plan characteristic for the species which has produced the eggs, not the spermatozoa. The impression is therefore gained that the development is directed by the maternal cytoplasm, and hence is nongenic.

The value of this kind of evidence for a demonstration of cytoplasmic inheritance is, however, spurious. An egg evidently cannot be regarded naïvely as a mechanical sum of two independent elements—a nucleus and a cytoplasm. On the contrary, an egg is an organized system which represents the result of a long process of development in the ovary of the mother. The structure, and hence to a certain extent the potentialities, of the egg had been determined before fertilization by the genes in the nucleus of the growing oocyte and perhaps also by the genes in the surrounding maternal tissues. The characteristics of the development which sets in after fertilization by a sperm of a foreign species need not be due to the gene complex present in the egg at that particular time; they may have been predetermined much earlier by the maternal genotype. Such a predetermination is by no means an *ad hoc* assumption invented for the refutation of cytoplasmic inheritance; on the contrary, the predetermination of the characteristics of a zygote by the maternal genotype is observed in many intraspecific, as well as interspecific, crosses, and is usually described as "maternal effect." Three examples of the maternal effect phenomenon are given below. They differ from each other in the degree of complexity of the situation and also with respect to the duration of time during which the predetermination by the maternal genotype is noticeable in the zygote.

Toyama (1912) was the first to describe several cases of maternal effects in the silkworm (*Bombyx mori*). Races of this moth frequently differ in the kind of eggs they produce. Some eggs are spindle-shaped and others round, some have brownish and others greenish or whitish coloration. The characteristics of the eggs produced by a given female always conform to those of the race to which she belongs, and are independent of the race of her mates. F_1 hybrid females from crosses between races differing in the kind of eggs they produce may lay eggs similar either to those of the maternal or to those of the paternal race (depending upon which gene is dominant and which is recessive), but in any case all eggs produced by an F_1 female are alike. Finally, in the F_2 generation three-quarters of the females produce eggs like the dominant, and one-quarter like the recessive race; here again all eggs produced by an individual female are alike and independent of the race of her mates. The explanation of this mode of inheritance is of course extremely simple: the appearance of an egg is due not to its own genetic constitution as established after fertilization, but to the genes of the mother in whose body the egg develops.

The inheritance of the direction of coiling of the shell in *Limnaea peregra* (Sturtevant 1923, Diver, Boycott, Garstang 1925) is equally illuminating. Eggs of a dextral individual fertilized by the sperm of a sinistral one develop into dextral adults. These, when inbred, give again a purely dextral F_2 generation, but in the latter, three-quarters of the individuals lay eggs developing into dextrals and one-quarter lay eggs giving rise to sinistral adults. An individual of pure sinistral parentage fertilized by the sperm of a pure dextral individual produces only sinistral progeny. This progeny however produces on inbreeding a purely dextral F_2 generation. Among these F_2 individuals, three-quarters give dextral and one-quarter sinistral F_3's. These relationships, at first sight very puzzling, are easily accounted for if one assumes that the characteristics of the shell of an individual are determined by the genotype of its mother rather than by its own genotype. The gene for dextral shells (D) is dominant over that for sinistral shells (d). The results of the crossing experiments may, then, be represented by the following scheme:

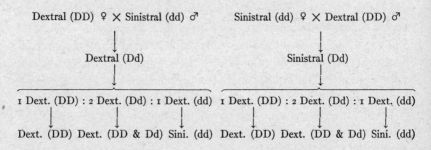

Dextral (DD) ♀ × Sinistral (dd) ♂   Sinistral (dd) ♀ × Dextral (DD) ♂

Dextral (Dd)   Sinistral (Dd)

1 Dext. (DD) : 2 Dext. (Dd) : 1 Dext. (dd)   1 Dext. (DD) : 2 Dext. (Dd) : 1 Dext. (dd)

Dext. (DD) Dext. (DD & Dd) Sini. (dd)   Dext. (DD) Dext. (DD & Dd) Sini. (dd)

In fact, the inheritance of the direction of coiling in *Limnaea* is quite analogous to that of the egg characteristics in the silkworm. The direction of coiling, which is expressed in the adult mollusc in the structure of the shell, is already laid down in the egg cell before this is fertilized. Whether the individual developing from a given egg will be dextral or sinistral is quite clearly visible in the early cleavage stages, at which the asymmetry of the embryo is revealed by the relative position of the mitotic spindles.

The hybrids between race A and race B of *Drosophila pseudo-obscura* are different, depending upon the direction in which the cross is made. The cross B ♀ × A ♂ produces in the F_1 generation sterile males having abnormally small testes. The reciprocal cross (A ♀ × B ♂) gives rise to males that are likewise sterile, but whose testes are normal in size. An analysis of this difference between the males coming from reciprocal crosses has been made by Dobzhansky (1935c), who has shown that the development of small testes is due to an interaction between the cytoplasm of the eggs deposited by a race B mother, and the chromosomes of race A brought in by the spermatozoon. Chromosomes of race B in eggs deposited by race

A mothers may permit the development of large testes (for details see Chapter IX).

There can be no doubt that many, if not most, of the alleged instances of cytoplasmic inheritance are actually due to maternal effects. Nevertheless, some authentic cases of inheritance through the cytoplasm have been recorded. Best known among them are those involving the transmission of the chlorophyll-bearing plastids in plants. The chloroplasts, or the cellular elements from which they arise, are endowed with a power of self-reproduction, and they sometimes undergo changes which are then transmitted independently from the genes and chromosomes. Thus, plants are produced with a piebald foliage, containing in their normal green parts normal plastids, and in the pale green or the white parts plastids more or less devoid of chlorophyll. Correns (1937 and earlier) and Renner (1934) have shown that the defective plastids are transmitted almost exclusively in the maternal line, in such a way that seed formed in flowers developing from the normal green parts of the plant give rise to green offspring, and seed from the chlorophyll-less branches are devoid of green plastids. Only in some plants in which plastids are transmitted through the pollen grains as well as through the embryosacs can the chlorophyll defects be inherited partly in the male line also.

It must be noted that the plastid color is by no means always independent of the genes. In many plants (a review in Correns 1937) pale-green and colorless strains are clearly gene determined, and give simple Mendelian segregations when crossed to normal green relatives. In other plants green-white variegations are produced by mutable genes, so that the white tissues differ from the green ones as a mutant from the wild type. What, if any, relation exists between the gene-determined and the autonomous changes in the plastids is obscure. May it not be that plastid changes are induced in a manner similar to strain transformations in pneumococci (see p. 47)?

Certain other instances of matroclinous inheritance appear not to be related to the plastids, leading to the inference that other self-reproducing bodies capable of transmitting heredity exist in the cytoplasm. The pertinent information has been summarized by Correns (1937), Wettstein (1937b), Michaelis (1938), and Jollos (1939b). The most important data in this field are those of Wettstein (1924, 1928, 1937b) on mosses. The intraspecific variation in these forms (*Funaria hygrometrica*) is purely gene determined, but some of the interspecific differences are not. The F_1 hybrids of *F. hygrometrica* and *F. mediterranea* are intermediate between the parents in some respects, but mostly resemble the species which served as a mother. Some characters show clear segregations after meiosis, and hence are gene determined. But the influence of the cytoplasm remains clear, since the offspring of the hybrid retain many peculiarities of the maternal species after many generations. In the intergeneric hybrids *Funaria hygrometrica* × *Physcomitrium piriforme*, *Physcomitrium eurystomum* × *Physcomitrella patens*, and others the plasmatic differences between the parents are still more important. The spores formed after meiosis in the hybrid are in part inviable, and it is possible to prove that the spores which receive a major part of the chromosomes of the maternal species survive, while presence of chromosomes of one species in the cytoplasm descended from the other acts as a lethal. No gradual reconstruction of the cytoplasm by the foreign genes is observed; some of the hybrid lines have been kept for as long as fifteen years, and repeated backcrossing to the paternal species or genus produces no drift toward making the incongruent gene-cytoplasm combinations more compatible. In general, the farther the parental forms are removed taxonomically, the greater is the absolute and the relative effectiveness of the plasmatic differences. Wettstein and others propose to distinguish three components in the germ plasm: the genome which is the sum total of the chromosome-borne genes, the plastidome which is composed of the autonomous properties of the plastids, and the plasmon covering the genetically effective portion of the cytoplasm.

Observations on cytoplasmic inheritance are available also in certain other forms. Hybrids between species of *Epilobium* have been the subject of many experiments and of much polemics (literature references in Correns 1937, Michaelis 1933, 1938). The hybrid obtained from the cross *Epilobium hirsutum* × *E. luteum* is different from that resulting from the reciprocal cross. By pollinating these hybrids by *E. hirsutum* pollen in several successive generations, one should be able to obtain a pure *hirsutum* genome in *hirsutum* cytoplasm in one case, and a *hirsutum* genome in *luteum* cytoplasm in the other. If the cytoplasm is genetically ineffective, or if the plasmon can eventually be rebuilt by a foreign genome, the two kinds of plants should become alike. It appears that they do not converge entirely, although there is no agreement as to the details of this process. L'Héritier and Teissier have described a situation in *Drosophila melanogaster* which suggests either a plasmatic inheritance or transmission through the cytoplasm of symbiontlike microörganisms. A strain has been found which is extremely sensitive to exposure to atmosphere of carbon dioxide; where normal flies are merely narcotized and recover without sustaining much harm, the flies of the susceptible strain are killed. A susceptible female crossed to a normal male produces susceptible offspring; continuous backcrossing of hybrid females to normal males produces sooner or later a mixture of normal and susceptible individuals, which, however, do not appear in any definite proportions. The cross normal × susceptible gives in F_1 a mixture of normals and susceptibles in ratios varying from 1:10 to 9:10. The normals breed true, the susceptible males produce only normals, while the susceptible females produce again both classes of offspring. By introducing suitable genetic markers it has been shown that the phenotype of an individual has nothing to do with what combination of chromosomes of the two strains it possesses.

In the present status of our knowledge of plasmatic inheritance it is futile to attempt to evaluate the role of the plastidome and the plasmon in evolution. How widely these phenomena are distributed, what are the mechanisms of the transmission of heredity of these kinds, and above all what is the mode of origin of such variations is not clear. Judging from the information now available, plasmatic inheritance is on the whole a rare phenomenon. Where, as in the mosses and in *Epilobium,* this form of inheritance is most firmly established, plasmatic differences occur between species and genera which do not normally cross in nature, but do not occur within a species.

IV: CHROMOSOMAL CHANGES

CHROMOSOMES AS GENE CARRIERS

AMONG the constituents of the cell, chromosomes have attracted a lion's share of the attention of investigators. The demonstration that chromosomes are the physical carriers of heredity had been achieved by the nineteenth-century exponents of cytology and experimental biology before the rebirth of Mendelism. The next historically decisive step was taken by Sutton (1903) and Boveri (1904) who pointed out that the transmission of genes can be understood only if they are borne in the chromosomes. The architectonics of the germ plasm has been revealed in great detail partly by direct cytological observation, but mainly through inference from genetic data. Boveri, and especially Morgan, Bridges, Sturtevant, and Muller, have demonstrated that every chromosome is an individual carrying a definite set of genes as well as that the genes are geometrically arranged within the chromosomes in a fixed linear order. A crucial proof of the correctness of the theory of the linear arrangement of genes in the chromosomes has been afforded by Muller, Painter, Dobzhansky, Stern, McClintock, and others through observations on chromosomes broken by X-ray and other causes and through concurrent genetic experiments. These observations and experiments have also shown that, in the chromosomes rebuilt through fragmentation and reunion, the genes do not lose either their powers of self-reproduction or their distinctive properties, thus proving the essential discreteness of the genes. A limitation on this discreteness is, however, imposed by the functional interdependence of the neighboring genes, as shown by the phenomena of position effects investigated by Sturtevant, Dobzhansky, Dubinin, Muller, and others. The apparent antinomy of the genes being discrete and yet interdependent bodies has misled Goldschmidt (1937, 1938) into denying the very existence of the genes (a critique of this standpoint is given on page 109).

The cells of each tissue in a species or biotype have, at a given stage of the mitotic cycle, a definite number of chromosomes with fixed gene contents, gene arrangement, volume, length, shape, and morphological features such as primary and secondary constrictions and trabants. These constants make up the karyotype of the organism. A chromosome, as well as a gene, is a self-reproducing body, and is potentially able to give rise to an indefinitely large number of exact copies. Nevertheless, the stability of the karyotype, like that of the genotype, is subject to certain limitations. The relationships between the genotype and the karyotype must be made clear. Is the chromosome structure determined ultimately by the genetic composition of the organism, or is the karyotype in a sense superimposed on the genotype? The answer is that the relation between them partakes of both possibilities. The gene contents of and the gene arrangement in the chromosomes display a far greater fixity than the other properties of the karyotype, although in neither case is the fixity absolute.

In different tissues of the same individual the size and shape, and occasionally the number, of chromosomes vary within wide limits. There is nothing surprising in such variations, since during the mitotic cycle the chromosomes execute not only a series of amazingly complex visible manoeuvres but perform physiological and chemical functions which are, we have reason to believe, even more intricate. The thing which is to be wondered at, and which has made genetic theories seem incredible to some biologists, is not that chromosomes vary but that despite these variations they preserve the fundamental constancy of the structure of each component gene and gene association. That constancy is, of course, an essential attribute of the germ plasm, and is a property of the living matter. Yet, the sole avenue of gene action in development is physiological change in the cells containing the genes; only secondarily can such intracellular changes initiate reactions on intercellular and supracellular levels. Hence, mutational changes in the gene necessarily alter the physiology of the cells, and may alter the visible characteristics of the chromosomes. Such phenomena, subsumed under the name "genotypic control" of the chromosomes are actually known (a review in Darlington 1932b and 1937b).

Nawashin (1934) has described changes in the chromosome morphology following hybridization of species in *Crepis*. As a rule, the chromosomes in the hybrids have the same relative sizes, shapes, constrictions, and trabants which they have in the respective parental species. Occasionally the appearance of certain chromosomes is modified in the cells of a hybrid. Strains of *Matthiola incana* fall into two classes, some having much longer meiotic chromosomes

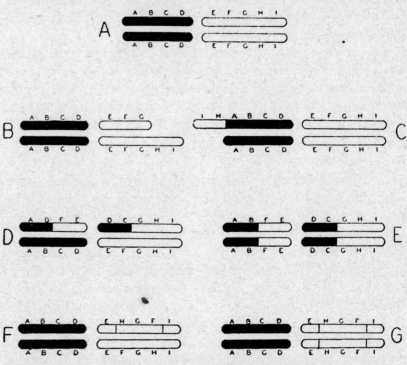

Fig. 5. (a) Normal chromosomes; (b) deficiency; (c) duplication; (d) heterozygous translocation; (e) homozygous translocation; (f) heterozygous inversion; (g) homozygous inversion. (From Dobzhansky.)

than others; Mann and Frost (1927) have found the differences between these classes to be due to a single gene. Hybrids between a strain with long and one with short chromosomes have short chromosomes in F_1, while in F_2 long-chromosomed and short-chromosomed plants appear in a 1:3 ratio. Geographical races of the gypsy moth (*Lymantria dispar*) vary in the size of their chromosomes; Goldschmidt (1932b) showed these variations to be due to a series of multiple genes. McClintock (1934) found genetic conditions in maize modifying the production of the nucleoli by the chromosomes.

Aside from the alterations in the appearance of chromosomes induced by genic changes, there exists a large group of alterations of an entirely different kind. Chromosomes may be reduplicated or lost, giving rise to individuals with an excess or a deficiency of certain genes. Blocks of genes located normally in one chromosome may become detached from their normal position and be transposed to different chromosomes. The relative positions of genes within a chromosome may be changed (Fig. 5). Alterations of this sort may or may not result in a visible modification of the chromosome morphology, but they cause permanent transformations of the karyotype, and may acquire the role of a racial or a specific characteristic. These are chromosomal changes proper, as distinguished from changes induced in the chromosomes by genes. The chromosomal changes are clased aṣ mutations in the wide sense of that term (see above), but they differ from gene mutations in that they represent modifications of the gross structure of chromosomes rather than of the structure of individual genes. Two organisms may possess exactly the same genes arranged in a different fashion in a different number of chromosome aggregates. It is expedient to treat the chromosomal changes as a phenomenon separate from gene mutation, although in recent years we have learned that they may not be quite as completely independent as was formerly supposed (see the discussion of position effects).

CLASSIFICATION OF CHROMOSOMAL CHANGES

Two main classes of chromosomal changes may be distinguished. Numerical changes involve variations of the number of chromosomes, but leave the gene contents and arrangements within the chromosomes unmodified. Structural changes alter the number or the distribution of genes in separate chromosomes. The further subdivisions of these classes may be gathered from the following synopsis:

I. Numerical changes—affecting the number of chromosomes
   A. Change in the number of sets of chromosomes present in the nucleus
      a. Haploidy. Higher organisms are mostly diploid during a major

part of the life cycle, that is, they possess two chromosomes of each kind in the nuclei of most cells. Gametes, and gametophytes (in plants), are haploid, and carry one chromosome of each kind. Some diploid organisms have produced under experimental conditions haploid aberrants, which have a single set of chromosomes in the tissues that are normally diploid. Such haploids are known in *Datura, Crepis, Oenothera, Triticum, Nicotiana, Solanum,* and several other plants.

b. Polyploidy. Normally diploid organisms may give rise to forms with more than two sets of homologous chromosomes. Such forms are known as polyploids. Triploids (three sets), tetraploids (four sets), pentaploids (five sets), hexaploids (six sets), and higher polyploids are encountered. Autopolyploids and allopolyploids are usually distinguished. The former arise from diploids that have the two members of each pair of chromosomes more or less similar in the gene contents and gene arrangement. Reduplication of the chromosome complement of a diploid hybrid, which consequently has two different sets of chromosomes, gives rise to an allopolyploid. The boundary between the auto- and the allopolyploids is not sharp, owing to the gradations which exist with respect to the similarity and the dissimilarity of chromosomes. Some species, especially among plants, are normally polyploid.

B. Change in the number of separate chromosomes of a set (Heteroploidy)

a. Monosomics arise through a loss of one of the chromosomes, giving rise to individuals which are diploid except for the lack of one of the chromosomes of the normal complement. Inbreeding monosomics may result in appearance of some zygotes that lack one of the chromosomes entirely; such zygotes are as a rule inviable. Monosomics are known as karyotypical aberrants in *Drosophila, Datura,* and in other species.

b. Polysomics are individuals having one of the chromosomes represented three (trisomics) or more times. They are obviously the reciprocal of monosomics. Monosomics and polysomics may be derived from polyploids as well as from diploids.

II. Structural changes—affecting the gene contents of chromosomes

A. Changes due to a loss or a reduplication of some of the genes located in a chromosome

a. Deficiency (deletion). A section containing one gene or a block of genes is lost from one of the chromosomes (Fig. 5B). If a normal chromosome carries genes *EFGHI*, the deficient chromosomes are *EFG, GHI,* etc. An organism may be heterozygous or homozygous for a deficiency. A short deficiency, producing no cytologically visible reduction of the size of a chromosome, may be mistaken for a gene mutation. In fact, at least some of the lethal mutations in *Drosophila* are due to deficiencies.

b. Duplication. A section of a chromosome may be present at its normal location in addition to being present elsewhere (Fig. 5C). If normal chromosomes have genes *ABCD* and *EFGHI*, the duplication may be *IHABCD, EFGHI* or the like. An individual may therefore have some genes represented three times (heterozygous duplication) or four times (homozygous duplication). Studies on chromosomes in the salivary gland cells of *Drosophila* and *Sciara* have shown that in the "normal" chromosomes certain sections are represented two or more times in the haploid set. Such "repeats" are duplications which have become established in the phylogeny.

B. Changes due to an alteration of the normal arrangement of genes

a. Translocation. Two chromosomes, *ABCD* and *EFGHI*, may exchange parts, giving rise to "new" chromosomes *ABFE* and *DCGHI* (Fig. 5D). An individual may be heterozygous or homozygous for a translocation (Figs. 5D and 5E). Genes which in one species lie in the same chromosome may in another species lie in different ones. Such differences between species are probably due to the occurrence of translocations in the phylogeny. Translocations have been produced experimentally in *Drosophila*, in maize, and elsewhere. Their genetic detection is based on the fact that individuals heterozygous for translocations produce gametes containing deficiencies and duplications for chromosome sections (see Chapter IX for more detail). Thus, at least four types of gametes may be produced in an individual having the constitution represented in Fig. 5D: (1) *ABCD, EFGHI*, (2) *ABFE, DCGHI*, (3) *ABCD, DCGHI*, and (4) *ABFE, EFGHI*. Gamete (1) is normal; gamete (2) carries the translocation but has every gene represented once; gamete (3) is deficient for *EF* but has *DC* twice; gamete (4) is deficient for *DC* but has *EF* twice. Since gametes carrying deficiencies or duplications normally die or give rise to inviable or abnormal zygotes, an apparent linkage is produced between the chromosomes involved in a translocation. The cytological methods of the detection of translocations are discussed below.

b. Inversion. The location of a block of genes within a chromosome may be changed by a rotation through 180°. The resulting chromosome carries the same genes as the original one, but the arrangement of the genes is modified from *EFGHI* to *EHGFI*, or *EGFHI*, or others (Fig. 5F). In individuals heterozygous for an inverted section (Fig. 5F), the frequency of the detected crossing over in the chromosome involved is markedly lowered, both within and outside of the limits of the inversion. Homozygosis for an inversion (Fig. 5G) restores the normal frequency of crossing over, but the linkage relations between the genes are altered.

The occurrence of structural chromosome changes in natural populations is discussed in the following paragraphs. Among the numerical changes, polyploidy presents some problems *sui generis* which will be dealt with in Chapter VII. Monosomics and polysomics as independent phenomena seem to play a very subordinate role in the evolution of most groups of organisms, except in as much as sex determination is accomplished by representatives of one sex having a certain chromosome in duplicate which the opposite sex carries only once (cf., however, Chapter X).

ORIGIN OF CHROMOSOMAL CHANGES

Chromosomal changes, like gene mutations, became known at first as spontaneous outbreaks of germinal variability. De Vries has described spontaneous mutants in *Oenothera* some of which proved to be chromosomal changes. The first deficiencies, duplications, translocations (Bridges 1917, 1919, 1923), and inversions (Sturtevant 1917, 1926) detected in *Drosophila melanogaster* have either arisen spontaneously in laboratory cultures, or else had been present in the natural populations whence the experimental flies originated. Polysomics, monosomics, polyploids, haploids, and translocations were observed in *Datura stramonium* by Blakeslee (1922). The discovery of the induction of gene mutations and chromosomal changes by X-rays (Muller 1928a) has given a tremendous impetus to the investigations of both phenomena. In forms which are favorable for genetic or cytological studies, chromosomal aberrations can now be induced and detected in virtually unlimited numbers. During the decade that has elapsed since the discovery of the influence of X-rays on the chromosomes, induced chromosomal changes have been extensively and successfully studied and used as tools in many genetic experiments. *Drosophila, Sciara, Zea,* and *Tradescantia* are favorite materials for such work.

Numerical chromosome changes arise owing to occasional breakdowns of the mitotic mechanism of cell division, giving rise to cells having an excess or a deficiency of certain chromosomes. The frequency of such breakdowns is, in most species, rather low. Thus, nondisjunction of the X chromosomes in *Drosophila melanogaster* takes place once in about 1,500 to 2,000 eggs. Some environmental changes, such as X-ray treatments and temperature shocks, as well as certain genetic conditions increase the frequency of chromosome abnormalities to a considerable extent. Polyploidy may be induced rather regularly by mechanical and chemical treatments (Chapter VII). Structural chromosome changes seem to involve more recondite processes than numerical ones, since the former necessitate breakage of the chromosomes and reconstitution of new ones from the resulting fragments. A great deal of work has been devoted in recent years to the elucidation of the mechanisms of such changes. Two hypotheses have been put forward in this field. One of· them, known as the "contact hypothesis," was originated by Belling (1927) and elaborated especially by Serebrovsky (1929) and Dubinin (1930). It assumes that chromosomes occasionally undergo "illegitimate crossing over" between nonhomologous sections. If two different chromosomes are involved in such a process, an interchange of blocks of genes may result, and a translocation may be produced. Loop formation in a chromosome with a subsequent establishment of new connections at the point of overlapping of the chromatids may give rise to inversions, deficiencies, and duplications. According to this view, the chromosome breakage and the reunion of the fragments occur simultaneously and are parts of the same process. The alternative viewpoint, known as the "breakage first" hypothesis (Stadler 1932), is that chromosomes suffer fragmentation, owing perhaps to the destruction of a gene or genes somewhere in the linear series or to a severance of an intergenic connection. Subsequent to this, the fragments may either remain loose, or become reattached to restore the original gene arrangement, or may unite with other fragments to form new aggregates.

The task of discriminating between the two hypotheses proved to be a difficult one. Nevertheless, experimental and analytical work of Bauer, Demerec, and Kaufmann (1938), Bauer (1939), Catcheside (1938), Sax (1938, 1940), Muller (1940b), and of many others has shown that the breakage first hypothesis is the more likely to be correct. The occurrence of chromosome fragments in cells treated with X-rays has been known for a long time. Sax and his collaborators, as well as Fabergé (1940), succeeded in analyzing such chromosome fragments in *Tradescantia*, a plant with large chromosomes. Some of the fragments are due to single breakages; their frequency, like that of the X-ray induced gene mutations, is directly proportional to the amount of treatment expressed in r-units, and hence, presumably, to the number of ionizations produced by the passage of the rays (Table 11). Again, as with the gene mutations, the frequency of single breaks is independent not only of the wave length of the radiation applied, but also of the duration of treatment, and whether it is continuous or intermittent (Muller 1940b, Kaufmann 1941). Similar results were obtained by Carlson (1941) who studied the frequency of single breaks induced in chromosomes of neuroblast cells of grasshoppers.

TABLE 11

FREQUENCY OF SINGLE FRACTURES INDUCED IN THE CHROMOSOMES OF *Tradescantia* BY X-RAY TREATMENTS (after Sax)

TREATMENT IN R-UNITS	CHROMOSOMES EXAMINED	BREAKS INDUCED Number	Percentage
10	6,330	14	0.2
20	6,930	24	0.4
40	8,610	76	0.9
80	7,368	148	2.0
120	4,902	141	2.9
160	8,292	375	4.4
200	8,508	472	5.1

Occurrence of a single break in a chromosome of a nucleus may be followed by a reunion of the fragments and restoration of the original karyotype. If the reunion does not take place, the broken chromosome is usually lost in subsequent cell divisions (see below for the reasons); this results either in the production of a monosomic or in death of the cell. In order that a stable, and therefore detectable, structural change in the chromosome may arise, at least two breaks must be available in the nucleus, so that the different broken ends may unite to form new gene arrangements. The probability of two chromosome breaks in the same nucleus is, evidently, equal to the square of the probability of the occurrence of a single break (a more accurate description of the situation, especially if many breaks are induced, is given by the Poisson distribution formula). Therefore, one may expect that the frequency of detectable chromosome changes will be proportional not to the amount of

X-ray treatment expressed in r-units, but rather to the square of that amount. Indications that this expectation may be realized have already been obtained by Oliver (1932). More exact experiments performed in *Drosophila* by Bauer, Demerec, and Kaufmann (1938), Bauer (1939), and Muller (1940b), and in *Tradescantia* by Sax (1940), have demonstrated an exponential relation between the frequency of detectable chromosome changes and the amount of radiation producing them, the exponents varying between 1.5 and 2. An illustration of this may be seen in Table 12.

TABLE 12

RELATION BETWEEN THE AMOUNT OF X-RAY TREATMENT AND THE FREQUENCY OF CHROMOSOMAL CHANGES IN *Drosophila melanogaster* (after Bauer)

AMOUNT OF TREATMENT IN R-UNITS	INDIVIDUALS EXAMINED	PERCENT OF INDIVIDUALS WITH CHANGED CHROMOSOMES	NUMBER OF CHROMOSOME BREAKS FOR INDIVIDUAL
1,000	616	2.4 ± 0.6	0.055 ± 0.015
2,000	654	9.8 ± 1.2	0.237 ± 0.030
3,000	595	18.8 ± 1.6	0.492 ± 0.046
4,000	447	32.2 ± 2.2	0.955 ± 0.078
5,000	608	44.9 ± 2.0	1.441 ± 0.080

Two stages must, therefore, be distinguished in the production of structural changes: chromosome breakage and reunion of the fragments. A fracture of a chromosome produces two "injured surfaces" which are for a certain time capable of reunion with other similar surfaces anywhere in the nucleus (Sax 1940, Muller 1940b, Helfer 1941). If many reunions are possible (that is, if many breaks are induced in a nucleus), the fragments whose ends happen to be geometrically closest have the greatest chance of effecting a junction. This seems to be the explanation of the fact that inversions within a chromosome arise more frequently, and translocations between chromosomes less frequently, than would be expected on chance alone (Bauer, Demerec, Kaufmann 1938, Bauer 1939). The apparent differential susceptibility of the chromosomes in the male and female germ cells to breakage by X-ray observed in *Sciara* (Metz and Boche 1939) and *Drosophila* (Glass 1940) may conceivably be accounted for by similar considerations. Much remains, however, to be done to clarify the details of the processes involved. Thus, nothing is as yet known about the nature of the bond which establishes the "reunion" of the fragments, or about the nature of the apparent attraction which the "injured surfaces" of chromosomes exhibit toward each other. Furthermore, the mechanism of the production of small rearrangements, especially of small deficiencies, appears to be different from that of larger structural changes. The former seem to be produced by single X-ray hits, and their frequency increases in proportion to the amount of treatment (Demerec, Kaufmann, and Hoover 1938, Muller 1940b, Demerec and Fano 1941). It seems, then, that under certain conditions a single ionization or a chain of closely spaced ionizations may be responsible for more than one chromosome fracture (Sax 1940).

The freedom of the chromosome reconstruction through breakage and reunion is limited by several important factors. It has been known for a long time that every chromosome possesses an organelle —variously termed as centromere, kinetochore, or spindle attachment—which is especially concerned with the chromosome movements during mitosis. It is immaterial for our purpose whether the centromere is the locus at which a contractile fiber uniting the chromosome with the mitotic pole is attached, or whether its role in guiding chromosome movements is accomplished through some other means, such as electrostatic attractions and repulsions. The important fact is that the centromere occupies a definite position within the chromosome, being in this respect like any gene having a fixed place in the linear series. Early studies on chromosomal aberrations induced by X-ray (Painter and Muller 1929, Dobzhansky 1930b, Navashin 1932) showed that only those rearranged chromosomes having a single centromere are capable of survival, and hence that the centromere is a permanent and necessary part of the chromosome. This has been abundantly confirmed by further studies. Direct observations on the X-ray treated cells and their immediate progeny have shown that chromosome aggregates having no centromere or more than one centromere are actually formed but are eliminated due to their inability of being regularly transmitted from cell to cell during mitosis (Mather and Stone 1933, Sax 1938, 1940, and many others). McClintock (1938) has, however, found that the centromere, apparently unlike a gene, may be fractured, with each of the resulting fragments retaining the function of a complete organelle. Results similar in principle to those of McClintock were described by Upcott (1937a), Koller (1938), Darlington (1939, 1940) and Rhoades (1940), who found that a centromere may undergo a transverse division, giving rise to chromosomes with terminal centromeres; such chromosomes prove to be, however, unstable. It is important in this connection that in certain insects, notably in *Hemiptera,* there are chromosomes which either possess multiple centromeres or else the centromeric function is not localized in a single organelle (this fact has been recently emphasized by Schrader, 1935). It would be interesting to know what behavior the fragments of such chromosomes would display after treatments with X-ray; temporary unions of several chromosomes to form compound bodies are well known to exist, for example, in *Ascaris.*

The role of the free ends of chromosomes remains unclear. A single break in a chromosome produces two fragments, one having and the other lacking a centromere. The latter fragment is lost, but the former might be expected to be retained as a chromosome with a terminal deficiency. Since, at least with low doses of X-rays, cells with a single break must be more common than those with two or more breaks, terminal deficiencies should be by far the commonest class of chromosomal aberrations. This is certainly not the case: such deficiencies are very rare. Neither do chromosome fragments become attached to unbroken ends of other chromosomes; such aberrations, once labeled "simple translocations" and supposed to be the commonest type, are at least very rare. These and other considerations led Kossikov and Muller (1935) to the conclusion that genes in the middle of a chromosome are bipolar and must be connected with two and only two other genes, while the gene constituting the free end of a chromosome is unipolar and unable to form an attachment except at one point. Subsequently Muller has named the terminal genes "telomeres" and has ascribed to them the same degree of fixity and permanence as the centromeres possess. Telomeres cannot become interstitial genes, nor can the reciprocal change take place. A number of facts seem to contradict this view. In the first place, terminal deficiencies, although very rare following X-ray treatments in *Drosophila,* do occur (Demerec and Hoover

1936, Sutton 1940). Some inversions found in nature appear to be terminal (Kaufmann 1936). Finally, McClintock (1939) has shown by a series of ingenious experiments that in maize a mechanically broken chromosome may survive under certain conditions despite the loss of its normal terminal end. A loss and acquisition of uni- and bipolarity may, therefore, be observed.

Compared to the amount of information available on the X-ray induced structural changes, our information regarding their spontaneous counterparts is negligible. In *Drosophila* they seem to arise very infrequently; for example, only three spontaneous translocations are known with certainty in this material (L. V. Morgan 1939). Observations of the writer on *Drosophila pseudoobscura* show that in this species the rate of the spontaneous origin of major inversions and translocations is certainly smaller than that of the lethal mutations in the chromosomes, and it may be much smaller. By contrast with *Drosophila*, the chromosomes of *Tradescantia* are very unstable, and Giles (1940) has had the opportunity to observe numerous cases of spontaneous chromosome breakage. He has also computed that the amount of natural radiation in the environment is approximately 1,800 times too small to account for the observed frequency of the chromosome changes, and has pointed out that the existence of variations in the frequency of these changes in different strains suggests the presence of genetic modifiers. Spontaneous chromosome changes are frequent also in *Allium* (Nichols 1941).

POSITION EFFECTS AND THE VALIDITY OF THE GENE THEORY

Classical genetics conceives the hereditary materials, the germ plasm, as absolutely discontinuous. The germ plasm is a sum total of discrete particles, the genes. The genes are pictured as independent of each other, both in inheritance and in evolution. Each of them can undergo mutational changes, or can separate from its neighbors by crossing over and by chromosome breakage, without affecting the adjacent genes. A chromosome is, then, a string of genes arranged in a definite but fortuitous linear order. This crudely atomistic theory, like atomistic theories in other branches of science, possesses a high heuristic value, amply manifested by the results of its application over four decades of the history of genetics. But, again like other atomistic theories, the original gene concept proves to be an oversimplification. Evidence has accumulated that the genes are not so impervious to the influence of their neighbors as has been thought. The effect of a gene on development is a function not only of its own structure but also of its position in the chromosome. A change of the linear order of the genes in a chromosome may then leave the quantity of the gene unaffected, and yet the functioning of the genes may be changed. Only a brief summary of the evidential basis for this viewpoint can be given here. For more detailed reviews of the present status of the problem, see Dobzhansky 1936c, d.

The mutant gene Bar in *Drosophila melanogaster* produces rather frequently "mutations" to a more extreme allele, known as double-Bar, or to the wild type. Sturtevant (1925) has shown that these "mutations" are in fact due to a reduplication or a loss of a certain gene or of a group of genes, and Bridges (1936) and Muller, Prokofyeva, and Kossikov (1936) have shown that the original mutation from the wild type to Bar was also a duplication for a chromosome section containing several genes. A wild-type chromosome consequently has these genes represented once, Bar twice, and double-Bar three times. In Bar and double-Bar the homologous sections in the chromosome follow each other in tandem. Bar and double-Bar decrease the number of ommatidia, and consequently the eye size as compared to the wild type. As mentioned above, double-Bar is more extreme than Bar. Sturtevant (1925) compared the number of ommatidia in flies homozygous for Bar with that in flies heterozygous for double-Bar and wild type, and found that the former have larger eyes than the latter. Now a fly homozygous for Bar has a total of four Bar genes, two in each chromosome; a fly heterozygous for double-Bar has also four Bar genes, three in the double-Bar chromosome and one in the wild-type chromosome. The two kinds of flies have the same number of Bar genes and differ only in the position of the latter in the chromosomes. Hence the fact that their phenotypes are not identical can be due only to a position effect. Bar genes lying in the same chromosome reinforce each other's action more than the same number of Bar genes when located in different chromosomes. Rapoport (1936) has obtained "quadruple Bar," which presumably has the Bar section represented five times in the same chromosome, but no further intensification of the position effect was observed.

Translocations and inversions in *Drosophila* very often produce effects that could not be expected on the basis of the classical gene theory. Indeed, these structural changes alter merely the gene order, and the individuals carrying them must have the same genes which the ancestral type carries in its chromosomes. Alterations of linkage relationships, but no phenotypic effects, are expected in translocation or inversion hetero- and homozygotes. Yet, translocations and inversions are frequently lethal when homozygous, or else they may produce visible changes in the morphology of the flies (Bridges, Muller, Dobzhansky, Patterson, and others). The behavior of translocations and inversions is often such as would be expected if their origin were accompanied by mutation in some genes. The remarkable fact is that these apparent "mutations" occur in the immediate vicinity of the places where the chromosomes were broken or reattached in the process leading to the production of the respective translocations or inversions. For example, Dobzhansky has observed a "mutation" from the wild type to an allele of Bar, and this "mutation" arose simultaneously with a breakage of the chromosome near the Bar locus. It is now believed that in cases of this sort we are dealing not with gene mutations at all, that is not with changes in the structure of the genes themselves, but with position effects. Suppose the chromosomes *ABCD* and *EFGHI* are involved in a translocation which gives rise to the chromosomes *ABFE* and *DCGHI* (Fig. 5). The genes *B* and *C*, and *F* and *G*, were adjacent in the original chromosomes but in the new chromosomes they are far apart. The genes *B* and *F*, and *C* and *G*, were not adjacent in the original chromosomes, but they are in the new ones. If the functioning of a gene is influenced by its neighbors, the removal of the old and the substitution of the new neighbors may induce position effects, and the gene will appear changed, as though its own structure had been altered by a mutation.

There is no simple criterion to decide which of the changes associated with chromosome reconstructions are due to real mutations and which to position effects. That some of them are due to the latter cause has been proved in a series of ingenious experiments of

Dubinin and Sidorov (1935). In a translocation in *Drosophila melanogaster* one of the genes lying in the chromosome near the breakage point appeared changed. By crossing over, a portion of a normal chromosome was substituted for the translocation chromosome containing the seemingly changed gene. A fresh gene so introduced into the broken chromosome immediately underwent a change caused by its new location.

. It must be emphasized that the data now available give no basis for assuming the position effect phenomenon to be universal. Many translocations and inversions in *Drosophila* are not perceptibly different from the wild type either when heterozygous or homozygous. More important still, no position effects at all have been detected in maize, despite a diligent search and despite the large number of structural changes which are known in this plant. The meaning of this difference between *Drosophila* and maize is entirely obscure, and so is the question which of these forms is more representative of organisms at large. Nothing definite is known about mechanisms responsible for the production of position effects. Several authors, notably Sturtevant and Beadle (1939), interpret position effects as a purely developmental phenomenon. If the chemical substances produced by various genes in the same nucleus react with each other intracellularly, the geometrical proximity or remoteness of the genes from which these substances emanate may be important variables influencing the course of the reactions. Alterations of the intergenic distances might, evidently, change the outcome of the developmental processes. Very different is the interpretation of position effects given by Goldschmidt (1937, 1938, 1940). As we have seen above (p. 22), Goldschmidt believes that all gene mutations are connected with minute structural changes in the chromosomes, that is, they represent position effects. This would "point to a theory of the germ plasm in which the individual genes as separate units will no longer exist." The assumption is made that the whole chromosome is a single enormous chain molecule of complex structure. This molecule is longitudinally differentiated, since various side chains or chemical residues follow each other in a linear order. "The normal pattern has a definite genetic effect which is changed with a change of the pattern, and eventual units such as genes have nothing whatsoever to do with the effects." What has been known as a gene mutation is, then, a structural alteration which changes the function of the chromosome as a unit.

Goldschmidt's views sound iconoclastic indeed. In the opinion of the present writer, their cutting edge is, however, very much blunted if they are stripped of their revolutionary phraseology, and if the belief, which is certainly unwarranted by facts, that all mutations are accompanied or caused by structural changes in the chromosomes is rejected. It must be admitted, however, that regardless of whether position effects are to be interpreted as due to interactions of chromosome products in development or to changes in these products themselves, the genes can no longer be thought of as absolutely discrete entities. As the writer pointed out in 1932, the germ plasm may consist of genes and yet have a continuity of a higher order; Muller and his collaborators have expressed similar views. According to Goldschmidt, genes must either be separated by impregnable walls, or else they do not exist at all. If this were the only choice, his conclusions would be justified. But surely many more than these two alternatives are to be considered. Discrete entities like genes may be integrated into systems, chromosomes, functioning as such. The existence of organs and tissues does not preclude their cellular organization. Moreover, the degree of independence of cells varies from tissue to tissue; leukocytes may behave like so many amoebae, meristematic cells are associated more intimately, and in muscle fibers the boundaries between cells seem to disappear entirely. To what extent the genes in a chromosome are interrelated is an open question, the solution of which is not helped by hastily prejudging the issue.

It is important for a geneticist to have a clear idea of how the gene concept is arrived at and how the genes can be delimited. The assumption that genes exist is a corollary to Mendel's laws; Mendelian segregation and recombination attest that the germ plasm is not a continuum. A gene is a unit of Mendelian heredity. But segregation and recombination are not sufficient to divide the germ plasm into ultimate units. Deficiencies and duplications may be inherited in a manner simulating single genes, and yet they frequently involve several genes. The phenomenon of crossing over furnishes a more sensitive test, since it permits a division of the chromosome into finer blocks. There exists, however, evidence to show that between some genes crossing over is rare or absent. The gene as a unit of mutability permits a still finer analysis, but its application is limited by our inability to draw a definite boundary between gene changes proper and structural changes in the chromosomes, as well as by the complications arising from comparison of the alleles at certain loci (e. g., scute in *Drosophila melanogaster*, where mutants A and B, and B and C, but not A and C, may behave as alleles). Finally, chromosome breakage occurring spontaneously or under the influence of X-rays furnishes evidence to prove that discrete blocks of chromosome material may be physically separated from each other without loss of ability to reproduce themselves, although not necessarily without a change in developmental functions. As Darlington (1939) puts it, "this gene is a unit of heredity because it is mechanically separable from other genes in heredity, that is, in cell division." Whether or not this criterion has an unconditional validity is as yet uncertain, and it may well be doubted. Nevertheless, it is an undeniable fact that, as a rule, all of the above criteria—however imperfect each of them taken separately may prove to be in scattered cases—concur in delimiting the same blocks of chromosomal materials as discrete units, which are described as genes. Genes may prove to be separate molecules or molecular aggregates loosely held together by some relatively inert substance; or they may be merely links of an enormously long chain molecule; or they may be molecular nuclei connected with their neighbors by chemical bonds. No matter which of these possibilities, if any, will prove to be true, the existence of genes is as well established as that of molecules and atoms in chemistry. It is also virtually certain that genes are bodies of the order of magnitude of large molecules, and hence one must beware of thinking about them and their possible connections in terms of crude mechanical analogies.

TRANSLOCATION AS A RACIAL CHARACTER

It has been pointed out above that the occurrence of gene mutations in laboratory experiments does not constitute a proof that evolution is caused by them. The same statement applies equally to chromosomal changes. Some critics have hastened to remark that since mutations and chromosomal changes can be induced by so destructive an agent as X-rays, such changes bring about degeneration and not evolution. An acid test of the ideas concerning the role played by chromosomal changes in evolution must, however, come through an analysis of the differences between races, species, and other natural groups. For if these differences are similar to those observed between chromosomal aberrations obtainable under laboratory conditions, the conclusion follows that chromosomal changes are an active evolutionary agent.

An extensive series of observations on the chromosomes of the Jimson weed (*Datura stramonium*) of different geographical origins has been reported by Blakeslee (1929, 1932), Bergner, Satina, and Blakeslee (1933) and Blakeslee, Bergner and Avery (1937). This plant possesses twelve pairs of chromosomes, which normally form twelve bivalents at meiosis. In crosses between certain streams, one or more circles of four or six chromosomes appear, the remainder of the chromosomes forming bivalents as usual. Belling (1927) and Belling and Blakeslee (1926) have shown that the circle formation at meiosis is due to translocations involving two or more chromosomes. The chromosomes of two strains are shown in Fig. 6a and b respectively. The chromosome structure observed in one of these strains might arise from that in the other by means of a translocation; for instance, the chromosomes 1.2 and 3.4 (Fig. 6a) might exchange sections, giving rise to the chromosomes 1.3 and 2.4 (Fig. 6b). Since like parts of chromosomes come together and pair at meiosis, a cross-shaped configuration (Fig. 6d) will be formed in the hybrid between the two strains. At the metaphase of the first meiotic division, the cross-shaped figure will be transformed into a twisted circle shown in Fig. 6e. A translocation in which three different chromosomes have exchanged sections gives a circle of six chromosomes (Fig. 6j); two translocations between two different pairs of chromosomes produce two circles of four chromosomes each, and so on. The formation of chromosome configurations like those shown in Fig. 6d and i has been inferred on the basis of genetic data or has actually been seen cytologically in spontaneous as well as in induced translocations in *Datura,* in maize (Burnham 1930, McClintock 1931), *Drosophila* (Dobzhansky and Sturtevant 1931), and in other organisms.

Each of the twelve chromosomes of *Datura stramonium* is distinguishable from the others genetically, and some of them also cytologically. One of the strains of this plant has been arbitrarily chosen as a standard of comparison, and the free ends of each chromosome in this strain designated by numbers 1, 2, 3 . . . 23, 24. The standard strain consequently has chromosomes 1.2, 3.4, 5.6 . . . 21.22, 23.24. By means of methods which we need not describe here in detail, the structure of the chromosomes in other strains

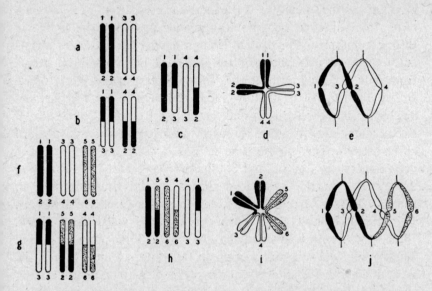

FIG. 6. Translocation between two (b-e) and between three (g-j) chromosomes. Normal chromosomes (a) and (f); (b) and (g) translocation homozygotes; (c) and (h) translocation heterozygotes; (d) and (i) chromosome arrangement at pairing stages; (e) and (j) arrangement of chromosomes at the metaphase of the meiotic division.

has been ascertained. In the strains united under the name "prime type 2," chromosomes 1.18 and 2.17 are found instead of the 1.2 and 17.18 present in the standard. The origin of "prime type 2" from the standard, or vice versa, is obviously due to a translocation involving these two chromosomes; hybrids between the standard and the "prime type 2" strains display a circle of four chromosomes and ten bivalents at meiosis. The "prime type 3" strains have chromosomes 11.21 and 12.22 instead of the standard chromosomes 11.12 and 21.22; "prime type 4" has chromosomes 3.21 and 4.22

instead of 3.4 and 21.22; other "prime types" found in nature, or induced by X-rays or radium treatments have different combinations of parts of the chromosomes of the standard line.

Datura stramonium is a weed which at present is nearly cosmopolitan in distribution, because of its involuntary transport by man with agricultural products. Its original native country is not known with certainty. In organisms so deeply influenced by man one does not generally expect to find clearly defined geographical races; even more interesting, therefore, is the fact that populations of *D. stramonium* from different geographical regions proved to be unlike in their chromosomal constitution. Plants having chromosomes apparently identical with those of the standard line have been grown from seed collected all over the United States, in the West Indies, Brazil, France, Portugal, Italy, Japan, Portuguese West Africa, and Australia. The populations from Brazil and from the United States, except along the Atlantic seaboard, seem to have only standard chromosomes. The "prime type 2" has a wider distribution; it is very common in Central and South America (except in Brazil and Argentina), on the Atlantic seaboard in the United States, in Europe, in Asia (except Japan), and in Africa (except the western Portuguese colonies). The "prime type 3" is restricted to Peru, Chile, and Central America, but has been found once in Spain. The "prime types" 4 and 7 occur in the eastern United States, the West Indies, the Mediterranean countries of Europe, South Africa, and Australia. The Peruvian and Chilean population seems to be homozygous for the chromosomes 1.18, 2.17, 11.21, 12.22 (combination of the "prime types" 2 and 3); the F_1 hybrids from standard and Peruvian or Chilean strains have therefore two circles of four chromosomes and eight bivalents at meiosis.

Translocations are known in many plant species besides *Datura* and maize. In peas (*Pisum sativum*) translocation heterozygotes have been identified by Håkansson (1929, 1931a, 1934), Sansome (1931), Pellew and Sansome (1932), and Lamprecht (1939). Gairdner and Darlington (1931) and Darlington and Gairdner (1937) observed circles of chromosomes at meiosis in *Campanula persicifolia*, J. Clausen (1931) in *Polemonium reptans*, Philp and Huskins (1931) in *Matthiola incana*, Håkansson (1931b, 1933) in *Clarkia* and *Salix*, Levan (1935a), Katayama (1936), and Levan and Emsweller (1938) in species of onions (*Allium*), Upcott (1937b) in two species of *Tulipa*, Stebbins (1938, 1939) in *Peonia*, Müntzing (1938) in *Galeopsis*, and Ganesan (1939) in *Notonia grandiflora*. Species of grasses appear· to form translocations very frequently (Katterman 1931, Müntzing 1932, 1935a, 1937a, Rancken 1934, Smith 1936. See further references in Darlington 1937b and Müntzing 1939). Individual as well as racial differences involving translocations are common in *Tradescantia* (Darlington 1929a, Sax and Anderson 1933, Anderson and Sax 1936). The extraordinary behavior of many species of *Oenothera*, which for many years was one of the outstanding riddles in genetics, has been shown to be due to translocations. Many *Oenothera* species are permanent translocation heterozygotes; in some of them, all the chromosomes form a large circle at the meiotic division (Darlington 1929b, Blakeslee and Cleland 1930, Cleland and Blakeslee 1931, Emerson and Sturtevant 1931).

Compared to plants, very few translocations have been found in natural populations of animal species, and this difference is not entirely due to lack of study. The present writer has examined the salivary gland chromosomes in the offspring of between ten thousand and twenty thousand individuals of *Drosophila pseudoobscura* taken from natural populations without finding a single translocation. In attempting to understand the reasons of this difference in the behavior of plants and animals the following considerations are relevant. Translocation heterozygotes usually (although not invariably) produce some gametes with duplications and deficiencies for certain chromosome sections (see p. 99). Such gametes may constitute 50 percent and more of the total output of gametes. Since duplications and deficiencies are frequently lethal, the unbalanced types are destroyed, and the reproductive potentials of translocation heterozygotes are lowered. In natural populations, translocation heterozygotes are, therefore, subject to a negative selection pressure tending to decrease their frequencies and eventually to eliminate them altogether. It must, however, be noted that as soon as a translocation becomes homozygous the negative selection pressure ceases to operate. In fact, in a sexually reproducing population in which the translocation is present in a majority, and the ancestral gene arrangement in a minority, of a chromosome, it is the ancestral arrangement which is subject to adverse selection. The difficulty which a translocation encounters in becoming established in a population is greatest during the period when the changed chromosomes are in a minority and occur mainly or only in heterozygotes. In organisms which reproduce, at least facultatively, by self-fertilization, apogamy, parthenogenesis, or asexually, translocations can multiply and become established somewhat more easily than in obligatorily cross-fertilizating forms. It is very suggestive that at least a majority of the plant species in which translocation heterozygotes have been found in natural populations are not obligatory cross-fertilizers.

It is an interesting fact that, despite the unfavorable conditions which translocations find in most animal populations, they are nevertheless encountered there from time to time. The clearest of all is the case of translocation in the grasshopper *Metrioptera brachyptera* described by White (1940b). An individual carrying this translocation in heterozygous condition was found in a certain locality in England in 1934; in 1937 several more translocation heterozygotes were encountered in the same locality. The translocation has, evidently, persisted in the population for at least three years. Another translocation was described in the grasshopper *Trimerotropis citrina* by Carothers (1931). The "multiple chromosomes" seen at meiosis in *Jamaicana* (Woolsey 1915), *Hesperotettix* and *Mermiria* (McClung 1917) and in the copepod *Diaptomus castor* (Heberer 1924) indicate the presence of translocation heterozygotes. What conditions enable these translocations to be retained in the natural populations has not been studied. In the following chapter (p. 184) we shall return to the discussion of this question.

INVERSIONS IN NATURAL POPULATIONS OF DROSOPHILA

The original technique used for the detection of inversions was based on the reduction of the frequency of crossing over in inversion heterozygotes and the emergence of new linkage relationships in inversion homozygotes. With the aid of this very laborious technique, Sturtevant (1931) discovered that some individuals of *Drosophila melanogaster* differ from others in the gene arrangement in their chromosomes. He was also able to show that several different gene arrangements, related to the standard one as inversions, occur in various American and European populations of this species. The rediscovery of the giant chromosomes in the larval salivary gland cells of flies by Heitz and Bauer (1933), and the application of these chromosomes as a tool of genetic research by Painter (1934), have enormously facilitated the comparison of the gene arrangements in different strains, and have at the same time rendered such comparison extremely accurate. In salivary gland cells of most flies the chromosomes increase more than a hundredfold in length as compared with their size in other tissues (gonads, nerve ganglia). They appear as cross-striped cylinders or ribbons, the cross striation forming a constant pattern that permits the identification not only of the separate chromosomes but also of their parts. The stainable discs that form the striations may or may not correspond each to a single gene, but in any event their longitudinal seriation is known to reflect accurately the gene arrangement in the chromosome. In addition, the homologous chromosomes in the salivary gland nuclei undergo a very intimate pairing, disc by disc, thus enabling one to determine the exact positions of the homologous discs in the chromosomes present in an individual. Suppose an inversion heterozygote has two chromosomes $ABCDEF$ and $AEDCBF$. The only way in which these chromosomes can pair so as to bring every homologous gene into contact with a gene in the partner chromosome is by forming a loop, shown schematically in Fig. 7 in the upper right corner. The presence of such a loop is therefore a proof of the existence of an inversion; the extent and the ends of the loop serve to discriminate between inversions in the same chromosome in different strains.

The possibilities of this method for comparisons of chromosome structure in races and species are tremendous, although its application is unfortunately restricted to the order of flies (*Diptera*) where these amazing chromosomes occur. Not only inversions but all other chromosome changes as well can be detected by this method; its accuracy is unrivaled. With inversions, it permits in certain special cases tracing the phylogeny of the chromosomal structures. Suppose the original, ancestral gene arrangement in a chromosome is $ABCD$-$EFHI$. An inversion of the section from B to E gives rise to an arrangement $AEDCBFGHI$ (Fig. 7). A second inversion may take place in this chromosome. The location of the second inversion may

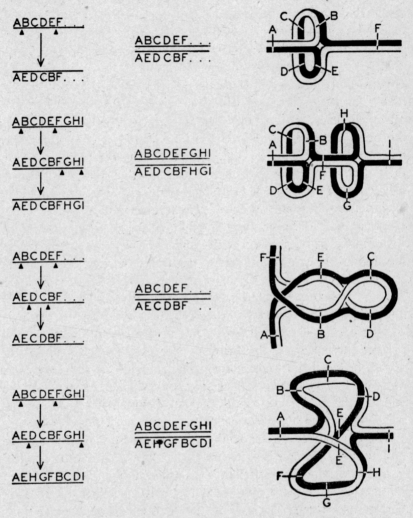

FIG. 7. Chromosome pairing in the salivary gland cells of individuals heterozygous for inversions. Upper row, a single inversion; second from the top, two independent inversions; third from the top, two included inversions; lower row, overlapping inversions.

be outside the limits of the first: $AEDCBFGHI \rightarrow AEDCBFHGI$. Such inversions may be described as independent. An individual heterozygous for the chromosomes $ABCDEFGHI$ and $AEDCBF$-HGI will have in the salivary gland nuclei a double loop in the chromosome affected (the configuration shown second from the top in Fig. 7). The second inversion may occur inside the first, forming included inversions: $ABCDEFGHI \rightarrow AEDCBFGHI \rightarrow AECDBFGHI$ (the configuration second from the bottom in Fig. 7). Finally, the second inversion may have one end inside and the other end outside the limits of the first. Such inversions are termed overlapping ones: $ABCDEFGHI \rightarrow AEDCBFGHI \rightarrow AEHGFBCDI$ (the configuration in the lower right corner in Fig. 7).

Let us consider especially the overlapping inversions. Suppose we observe in different strains the three gene arrangements ($ABCDEF$-GHI, $AEDCBFGHI$, and $AEHGFBCDI$). The first of these can arise from the second or give rise to the second through a single inversion. The same is true for the second and the third. But the third can arise from the first, or vice versa, only through the second arrangement, which therefore becomes a necessary intermediate step in the line of descent. A direct origin of the third from the first, or vice versa, is highly improbable, for it would require not only a simultaneous breakage of the chromosome in four places (between A and B, D and E, E and F, and H and I), but also a fortuitous reunion of the resulting fragments in such a way as to simulate the arrangement that is obtainable through the two-step process indicated above. If we find only the first and the third arrangements, it is possible to postulate with a high degree of probability that the second exists in some unknown strains, or at least that it existed in the past. If all three are actually observed, the probability of the first and the third being related through the second becomes almost certainty. To recapitulate, the phylogenetic relationship of the three gene arrangements indicated above is $1 \rightarrow 2 \rightarrow 3$, or $3 \rightarrow 2 \rightarrow 1$, or $1 \leftarrow 2 \rightarrow 3$, but not $1 \leftrightarrows 3$. With the independent and the included inversions, no determination of the sequence of origin is possible; they are ambiguous in this respect. This theory of inversions has been applied in practice to the study of the gene arrangements found in natural population in *Drosophila pseudoobscura* and other species.

Using the salivary gland method, Tan (1935) and Koller (1936a) have shown that the two races A and B of *D. pseudoobscura* differ from each other in four inverted sections, two of which lie in the X chromosome, one in the second, and one in the third chromosome. These two races produce, when crossed, sterile male offspring in the F_1 generation (Lancefield 1929); the cause of the sterility and the nature of these "races" will be discussed below. Tan has also found that some strains of race B have the same gene arrangement in the third chromosome as is encountered in most of the strains of race A that he had at his disposal. The gene arrangement may therefore be different not only between races but also within a race. Dobzhansky and Sturtevant (1938) and Dobzhansky (1939) have made a systematic study of the gene arrangements in strains of *D. pseudoobscura* coming from flies collected throughout the geographical range inhabited by the species. An almost bewildering amount of variation in the gene arrangement within the species was disclosed.

The gene arrangement is especially variable in the third chromosome, where a total of twenty-one different gene sequences has been recorded. All these gene arrangements can arise from each other through inversions of some sections of the chromosome, and curiously enough nearly all of them proved to be related to each other as the overlapping inversions considered above. This fact has made it possible to construct the phylogenetic chart of the gene arrangements in the third chromosome shown in Fig. 8. Each arrangement is designated in the chart by the name of the geographical locality in which it has been first encountered. Any two arrangements connected in Fig. 8 by an arrow give a single inversion loop in the heterozygote. It may be mentioned here that some of these arrangements (Santa Cruz, Tree Line) had been postulated theoretically as the necessary "missing links" between the other arrangements, and subsequently found when more strains were examined. One of the arrangements (see Fig. 8) remains hypothetical as far as the species *D. pseudoobscura* is concerned, but an arrangement possessing the essential properties of this hypothetical one has been met with in a related species, *D. miranda*.

None of the different arrangements shown in Fig. 8 occur over the entire distribution area of the species. Some of them ("Standard," "Arrowhead") have however a rather wide distribution; others

("Wawona," "Sequoia") occupy relatively restricted areas, and still others have been observed thus far in only one or a few strains from a single locality. In some localities the population is mixed, that is, two or more (up to six) arrangements occur, usually with different frequencies. Some large regions contain however a population that is nearly or completely homogeneous with respect to the gene arrangement in the third chromosome.

It is neither necessary nor desirable to discuss here the geographical distribution of each gene arrangement. Suffice it to say that all

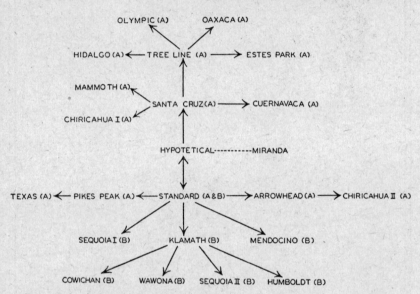

FIG. 8. A phylogenetic chart of the gene arrangements encountered in the third chromosome of race A and race B of *Drosophila pseudoobscura*.

the intermediates are found between the condition where a gene arrangement may be described as an "individual variation" in flies coming from a definite locality, and one where a definite chromosome structure becomes an established racial characteristic for a certain fraction of the species (Fig. 9). Thirteen of the arrangements shown in Fig. 8 occur only in race A; seven others solely in race B; a single one, the "standard," occurs in both races. It is, hence, probable that the "standard" arrangement is also the ancestral one, but other hypotheses are also possible. In general it must be emphasized that the method of overlapping inversions is rigorous

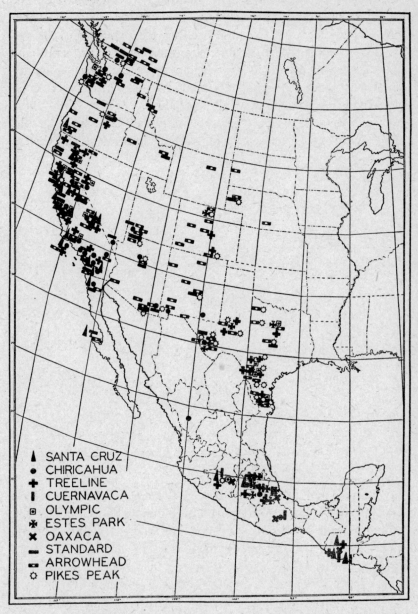

FIG. 9. Geographical distribution of the gene arrangements encountered in the third chromosome of race A of *Drosophila pseudoobscura*.

only as far as the establishment of the configuration of the branches of the phylogenetic tree, but not of the location of its root, is concerned. The phylogenetic tree shown in Fig. 8 may be read in various ways, depending upon which of the arrangements is chosen as the ancestral one. Even so, the overlapping inversion method is superior to other methods of phylogenetic study, for it does permit an exact description of the relationships between the different variants observed.

The gene arrangements in the chromosomes of *D. pseudoobscura* other than the third are relatively constant. Yet five arrangements are known in the second, two in the fourth, three in the right limb, and two in the left limb of the X chromosome. Some of the arrangements in the right limb of the X proved to be associated with a peculiar genetic condition that causes a male carrying it to produce mostly daughters in his progeny. This "sex ratio" condition has been found in from 0 percent to 30 percent of the individuals in populations from different localities, its frequency generally increasing as one proceeds from north to south (Sturtevant and Dobzhansky 1936). In some instances the overlapping inversion method proved to be applicable, and a phylogenetic chart has been traced for the second chromosome. The greater variability of the third than of the rest of the chromosomes of *Drosophila pseudoobscura* has led to a suspicion that the third chromosome, or certain parts of it, may be especially prone toward breakage resulting in formation of chromosomal aberrations of the inversion type. This suspicion is, however, contradicted by the findings of Bauer, Demerec, and Kaufmann (1938) and Bauer (1939) that the X-ray induced breakages are distributed among the chromosomes of *Drosophila melanogaster* at random, that is in proportion to the chromosome lengths. No crowding of breakages in any part of any chromosome was observed, although the recent data of Kaufmann (1939) do suggest that certain sections are broken somewhat more frequently than others. Helfer (1941) has made a similar study in *Drosophila pseudoobscura* and obtained results similar to those of Kaufmann. The importance of such facts for the construction of phylogenies of chromosome structures with the aid of the overlapping inversion method is obvious. The number of discs in the third chromosome of *Drosophila pseudo-obscura* is of the order of one thousand, and repeated origin of the same inversion requires a coincidence of chromosome breakages at exactly the same two loci. Hence, only two inversions out of a million newly arisen ones are likely to be identical.

Examination of chromosomes in salivary gland cells has led to the discovery of inversions in wild populations of several species of *Drosophila* and other flies. *Drosophila azteca* is a species encountered in Mexico, Guatemala, and, sporadically, in Arizona and California. Three chromosomes proved to be variable in this form, showing excellent examples of overlapping, as well as of independent and included, inversions. Phylogenetic charts were drawn for two of the chromosomes (Dobzhansky and Socolov 1939). One of the phylogenetic charts contained an "hypothetical" gene arrangement, which has been recently discovered (Dobzhansky 1941). The geographical relationships in this species are quite clear, in contrast to *Drosophila pseudoobscura* where they can be unraveled only with difficulty. In *D. azteca* phylogenetically closely related chromosome structures tend to occur in the same or in geographcally close regions, while remote regions are populated with phylogenetically remote structures. As in *D. pseudoobscura,* no gene arrangement can be taken as "typical" or "normal" for this species, since no arrangement is commonly encountered throughout the distribution area. Similar relations are encountered in *D. algonquin* (Miller 1939), *D. athabasca* (Novitski, unpublished), *D. miranda* (Koller 1939b), *D. funebris,* and an unnamed species related to *D. obscura* studied by Dubinin, Sokolov, and Tiniakov (1937).

In the chromosomes of *D. melanogaster* the gene arrangements known from classical laboratory experiments are by far the commonest in populations of America, Europe, and in Turkestan, but inversions in the second and third chromosomes occur in several percent of the flies in practically all the populations examined (Sturtevant 1931, Dubinin, Sokolov, and Tiniakov 1937). In this species certain gene arrangements may, therefore, be considered as normal, and others as aberrant ones. This may be due to the fact that *D. melanogaster* is not a native form, but a species associated with man in all the localities in which its populations were extensively studied. It is possible that the present nearly cosmopolitan distribution of this species is traceable back to relatively few introductions of small numbers of flies from its original home, the location of which is not known with certainty. A similar situation apparently obtains in *D. ananassae* (Kaufmann 1936, 1937, Kikkawa 1938). Inversions have been recorded also in *D. repleta, D. robusta* (Frolova 1936, Sturtevant unpublished), and, in fact, in all species of *Drosophila* which have been studied in this respect (unpublished data of Sturtevant, Dobzhansky, and others).

INVERSIONS IN POPULATIONS OF ORGANISMS OTHER THAN DROSOPHILA

The detection of inversions by examination of the chromosomes in salivary gland cells is possible only in certain favored representatives of the order of flies *Diptera*. Outside the genus *Drosophila* this method has been successfully applied in the family of midges (*Chironomidae*) by Bauer (1936). In natural populations of several species a considerable proportion of individuals proved to be inversion heterozygotes; in one of them only 18 out of 77 individuals examined showed no detectable inversions, while the remainder were heterozygous for one to four inversions each. Five different inversions were identified with certainty.

Where the detection of inversions by neither the salivary gland method nor the suppression of crossing over method is practicable, a resort may be had to examination of the meiotic divisions. We have seen that chromosomes in the inversion heterozygotes in the salivary gland cells undergo pairing by forming loops represented schematically in Fig. 7. As shown by McClintock (1933), such loops are observable also at the prophase of meiosis in inversion heterozygotes in *Zea mays*. If crossing over now takes place within the inverted section, the result, illustrated diagramatically in Fig. 10, will be the production of two normal chromatids, one chromatid with two spindle attachments, and one chromatid with no spindle attachment. At anaphase of the first meiotic division the chromatid with two attachments will form a "chromatin bridge" uniting the two daughter groups of chromosomes (Fig. 10e). A fiberless chromosome will be present lagging on the spindle. Such chromatin bridges and fiberless fragments were seen cytologically by McClintock (1933) in maize, by Stone (1933) in X-rayed *Tulipa,* by Mather (1935) in *Vicia,* and were postulated on genetic grounds in inversion heterozygotes in *Drosophila* (Sturtevant and Beadle 1936).

There can be no doubt that chromatin bridges and fiberless frag-ments at meiosis were seen in many organisms by cytologists who took them to be artifacts and failed to record them. Since the significance of the meiotic bridges and fragments has been under-stood, inversion heterozygotes are being recorded in great abun-dance in a variety of materials, both animals and plants The following, doubtless incomplete, list of references will suffice to in-dicate the wide distribution of the phenomenon. Among plants, inversion heterozygotes have been recorded in *Matthiola incana* (Philp and Huskins 1931), *Trillium erectum* (Smith 1935), rye (Lamm 1936), *Aesculus hippocastanum* (Upcott 1936), *Allium scoradoprasum* (Katayama 1936), four out of twenty-six examined species of *Fritillaria* (Frankel 1937), several species of *Tulipa* (Upcott 1937b), *Campanula persicifolia* (Darlington and Gairdner

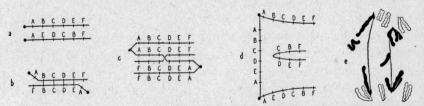

FIG. 10. Crossing over in inversion heterozygotes, leading to the for-mation of chromosomes with two and with no spindle attachments (d). (e) Chromatin bridges in the hybrid *Lilium martagon* × *Lilium hansonii*. (After Richardson.)

1937), *Lilium testaceum* (Ribbands 1937), several species of *Tradescantia* (Darlington 1937b, Swanson 1940), *Peonia* (Stebbins 1938), and *Agropyron* (Ostergren 1940). Tyrolean populations of *Paris quadrifolia* (Geitler 1938) take the palm as far as the abundance of inversions is concerned: not a single chromosome or chromosome limb of this plant is free of inversions, and it seems as though the whole species consists of complex inversion hetero-zygotes. And it must not be forgotten that inversions are here de-tected by a method predicated on the occurrence of crossing over within the inversion segments!

Among animals, inversion bridges have been seen in the grass-hopper *Chorthippus bicolor* and *Ch. biguttulus* (Darlington 1936, Klingstedt 1939), in ducks (Crew and Koller 1936) and the squir-rel *Sciurus carolinensis* (Koller 1936b). Finally, Koller (1937) records what looks like an inversion heterozygote in man, the material coming from an individual who happened to have French and Scottish ancestry. There can be no doubt, then, that formation of inversions is a very widespread method of evolution of the chromosomal apparatus, and in importance exceeds that of the translocations. In contrast to translocation heterozygotes, heterozygosis for inversions produces, except under certain special conditions, no appreciable reduction of the reproductive potential of the species (see Darlington 1936, Sturtevant and Beadle 1939).

DEFICIENCIES AND DUPLICATIONS

Deficiencies and duplications involve losses or multiplications of some genes. In this respect they are basically distinct from translocations and inversions, for the latter alter only the gene arrangement but not the number of genes. A deficiency or a duplication is therefore usually accompanied by phenotypical effects, while an individual that carries a translocation or an inversion need not be different from the ancestral form (compare, however, the position effects). We have seen that in *Drosophila* most deficiencies are lethal when homozygous, and that lethal "mutations" are not infrequently deficiencies for short chromosome sections. Duplications are in general less drastic in their effects than deficiencies, but many of the former are nevertheless lethal, or provoke structural and physiological changes of some kind in the carrier. In the genetically active parts of the *Drosophila* chromosomes, only small deficiencies are viable even in heterozygous condition. Some of the lethal "mutations" are, indeed, due to minute deficiencies (Slizynski 1938).

Drosophila pseudoobscura manifests a remarkable variation in the shape of its Y chromosome (Dobzhansky 1935b, 1937c). Some strains of this species have a large, V-shaped, slightly unequalarmed Y chromosome. In other strains, one or the other or both of the arms of the V are shortened, as though they have lost some of the material which is present in the type mentioned first. In still other strains the Y chromosome is J-shaped, and its length is barely half the length of the Y in other strains. In all, seven distinct types of Y chromosome are encountered in the species, each type being found only in populations that inhabit a definite part of the distribution area. Three of the seven types are rather widespread; the remaining four are each restricted to a fairly small region. For instance, one of the types is found only in southern California, another only in the highest part of the Rocky Mountains in northern Colorado, a third only around Puget Sound in the Northwest.

The Y chromosome of *Drosophila* is composed of an "inert" material, so described because it contains fewer genes per unit length or volume than other chromosomes. In the salivary gland nuclei the Y is much contracted relative to the others, and is in a condition not favorable for study. The lack of the whole of Y, or the presence of two Y's, produces no visible alteration in the fly morphology. These properties prevent a detailed analysis and comparison of the different Y chromosomes in *D. pseudoobscura,* but by the same token they also explain the relative ease with which a Y chromosome can be modified without disastrous consequences to the viability of its carrier. It is fairly certain that the seven types of the Y are all derived from a single prototype through either losses (deficiencies) or reduplications. Variations in the Y chromosome are known also in *D. ananassae* (Kaufmann 1936), and in *D. simulans* (Sturtevant 1929b, Heitz 1933).

The detailed study of the salivary gland chromosomes in *D. melanogaster* made by Bridges (1935) showed that sections having identical disc patterns may occur in two different parts of the same chromosome. Moreover, these sections, known as "repeats," manifest a certain amount of mutual attraction, and in some cells may be seen paired with each other. Since the similarity of the disc patterns in chromosome sections and the pairing of the latter in the salivary gland nuclei are the only criteria of the homology of blocks of genes that we have at present, Bridges concluded that the repeats are composed of similar or identical genes. If this is true, it follows that, while an ordinary diploid *D. melanogaster* carries most genes in duplicate, some genes, namely those located in the repeat sections, are present four times.

Repeats can be observed in the chromosomes of many species of *Drosophila* other than *D. melanogaster*. Production of new repeats by "mutation" has also been recorded: the Bar case is the best-known example (see p. 107); Demerec and Hoover (1939) and Oliver (1940) have described two further instances. Variants involving additions or losses of repeats have not been found, however, in natural populations of *Drosophila*. Comparison of the repeats in pairs of closely related species—such as *D. melanogaster* and *D. simulans* or *D. pseudoobscura* and *D. miranda*— shows that reduplicated sections are largely unchanged. More than that: species as remote as *D. melanogaster* and *D. pseudoobscura* have the largest number of repeats concentrated in the chromosomes which on other grounds are presumed to be homologous. This suggests that the repeats, at least in the species just named, have remained rather stationary in the phylogeny. Metz and Lawrence (1938) have described very clear repeats in *Sciara ocellaris* and *S. reynoldsii*.

Little is known about repeats in forms in which no giant chromosomes are available for study. Observations on meiosis in haploid aberrants of normally diploid species reveal, however, that occasional bivalents may be formed in which different chromosomes of the same haploid set are seen paired (Emerson 1929 and Catcheside 1932 in *Oenothera*, Tometorp 1939 in barley, Sears 1939 and Krishnaswamy 1939 in wheat, Håkansson 1940 in *Godetia*, a review in Ivanov 1938). In species which have arisen through polyploidy (such as wheats; see Chapter VII) this phenomenon shows simply that the presumed "haploid" possesses two or more sets of similar chromosomes. But where no suspicion of a polyploid origin is likely to be justified, the presence of bivalents in the haploid is most reasonably interpretable as owing to the presence of repeat areas in some of the chromosomes. The importance of the repeat formation in evolution is self-evident, since, aside from polyploidy, this is the only known process which may lead to an increase of the number of genes in the germ plasm of organisms.

A mention must be made of the unequal bivalents recorded in the meiotic divisions of some forms. The normal bivalents are, of course, equal, since they consist of similar chromosome partners. The partners included in the unequal bivalents are either different in size or in the position of the centromeres, or display features suggesting that the sections containing homologous genes are located differently within the paired chromosomes. Several processes may lead to formation of unequal bivalents. It has been shown above that twisted circles of four or more chromosomes arise at meiosis in translocation heterozygotes. The attachments holding the ends of the adjacent chromosomes in such a circle are caused by the formation of chiasmata between the homologous sections of the members of the translocation complex. Chiasmata may fail, however, to be formed between some of the homologous sections. This is especially common where the translocation is unequal, that is, where a small segment of one chromosome is exchanged for a longer segment of another. Lack of chiasmata may cause the circle of chromosomes to be broken into a chain, or into bivalents the members of which are only partly homologous and therefore unequal. Some inversions include the part of the chromosome containing the centromere (Muller 1940a has proposed to term such inversions "pericentric," to distinguish them from "paracentric" inversions, which are located entirely within a single chromosome limb; a great majority of inversions in species of *Drosophila* are paracentric). If the two breaks giving rise to a pericentric inversion are not equidistant from the centromere, the position of the latter within the chromosome is visibly changed. The inversion heterozygote may in such a case show an unequal bivalent at meiosis. Extensive duplications and deficiencies may give rise to unequal bivalents as well, and where a combination of translocations with deficiencies or duplications changes the chromosome numbers, the heterozygotes may show aggregates of three or more chromosomes instead of the normal bivalents.

Seiler (1925) has discovered two races in the moth *Phragmatobia fuliginosa* differing in chromosome number. The hybrids between these races show at meiosis a trivalent consisting of two smaller chromosomes paired with a larger one. Intraspecific variations in the chromosome numbers which are almost certainly due to translocations are known in *Viola kitaibeliana* (J. Clausen 1927) and *Ranunculus acris* (Sorokin 1927). Unequal bivalents not involving differences in the chromosome numbers between the parental forms were first described in the classical papers of S. Nawashin (1912, 1927) dealing with the plant *Galtonia candicans*. Pericentric inversions and perhaps translocations seem to be responsible for the unequal bivalents rather frequently found in various grasshoppers (Robertson 1915, Carothers 1917, Helwig 1929, Klingstedt 1939, and many others). Less clear is the origin of the unequal bivalents in *Rumex* (Yamamoto 1938 and earlier papers) and in the neuropteran *Hemerobius stigma* (Klingstedt 1933). Kikkawa (1936) described two races of *Drosophila montium* which appear to differ by a pericentric inversion in the shortest chromosome pair, which, in this species, consist mainly of inert material.

MORPHOLOGY OF METAPHASE CHROMOSOMES
IN DIFFERENT SPECIES

The relative constancy of the number, size, shape, and structure of chromosomes in each species is one of the long established tenets of cytology. It is equally well known that different species may differ widely in all these characteristics. The chromosome number (haploid) varies from one, two (*Ascaris megalocephala*), and three (*Crepis capillaris*, species of *Crocus, Drosophila earlei*) to several hundreds (*Radiolaria*). The volume of the chromosomes in a nucleus ranges from a cubic micron (certain fungi) to thousands of cubic microns (*Drosophyllum lusitanicum*). The cytological literature is filled with descriptions of chromosome numbers and sometimes of chromosome morphology in species of this or that genus. The larger part of this work is concerned with the chromosomes as they appear at the metaphase plate stage of the mitotic cycle, which is technically easiest to study.

The nature and causation of the chromosomal differences are subjects which have proved rather more elusive than the straight descriptive picture of the situation. As far as chromosome numbers are concerned, there seem to be two types of differences between related species. In many plant genera and in relatively very few animals the haploid chromosome numbers of the species of a genus from a series of simple multiples of the minimum or "basic" number (e.g., 7, 14, and 21, in species of wheats). Such differences are probably due to the reduplication of the chromosome complement (polyploidy) in the phylogenetic history, as discussed in Chapter VII. In most animals and in many plant genera no trace of polyploid series is discernible. Related species may be alike both in number and in size and morphology of chromosomes; the chromosome numbers may be similar, but the chromosomes differ in size, location of the centromeres and of secondary constrictions, presence or absence of satellites, and other structural characters; the chromosome numbers may be variable without formation of a clear series of multiples (e.g.,

11, 13, 14, 15, 19, 21, 23, 25, 27, 28, 29, 30, 31, 32, 33, 34, 37, 38, 49, 51, 56, 87 in different butterflies and moths, Beljajeff 1930); or finally both the chromosome numbers and the chromosome morphology may be variable (*Crepis*, Fig. 11, *Drosophila*).

Some investigators, particularly in recent years, have displayed much interest in studies of the comparative morphology of metaphase chromosomes in related species, in the hope that when combined with the classical comparative morphological and distribu-

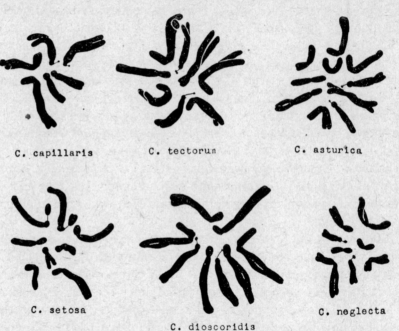

C. capillaris   C. tectorun   C. asturica

C. setosa   C. dioscoridis   C. neglecta

Fig..11. Metaphase chromosome plates in six species of *Crepis*. (After Babcock and Navashin.)

tional methods, these chromosome studies may become a powerful tool for the determination of the relative systematic closeness or remoteness of species of a genus and of genera of a family. Tracing phylogenetic relationships is to become at long last an exact procedure instead of an expression of opinions of the particular investigator. We have already seen that studies on overlapping inversions do give some hope for a rigorous method of establishing the phylogeny of certain chromosome structures, but so far as the application of metaphase chromosomes for the even wider purpose of tracing phylogenies of species and genera is concerned, much caution is necessary.

As a working hypothesis, most cytologists and geneticists hold that the chromosomal differences between species (except polyploidy) have arisen through structural changes of various kinds (translocation, inversion, deficiency, and duplication). This hypothesis has developed so gradually and has been espoused by so many authors that it appears impossible to assign credit for its origin. The instances of the control of chromosome morphology by genes (see above) show however that a cytologically visible difference in the structure of chromosomes need not necessarily be due to structural changes. This consideration may be optimistically regarded as trivial, since the rule certainly is that chromosomes retain their morphological peculiarities in the hybrid karyotype, but nevertheless it introduces an element of uncertainty into every specific instance where a comparison of chromosomes in pure species is made. Much more important is the fact that the similarity or dissimilarity of the chromosomes as seen at the metaphase plate stage is not at all necessarily proportional to the similarity of their gene arrangements.

Most of the chromosome types shown in Fig. 12 are encountered each in several species of *Drosophila*. Species possessing metaphase chromosomes that appear identical under the microscope are, however, known to be sometimes similar and sometimes sharply different in the gene arrangement (Dobzhansky and Tan 1936). The apparent identity of the metaphase chromosome configurations is therefore evidence neither of an identity nor of a dissimilarity of the internal chromosome structure. Repeated inversions may occur in a chromosome and may result in a very profound alteration in the gene arrangement, and yet the visible characteristics of this chromosome as seen at metaphase may remain unchanged, provided none of the inversions shift the locus of the spindle attachment. Conversely, a single inversion involving the centromere may alter the appearance of the metaphase chromosome quite strikingly. All the metaphase configurations known in species of *Drosophila* may be represented as results of fusion in different combinations of the five rod-shaped and one dotlike element shown in Fig. 12F, with an occasional translocation and inversion (Metz 1914). Such a representation may have some basis in fact (Sturtevant and Tan 1937), but it is now known that a large number of inversions take place in the phylogeny that are not reflected at all in the metaphase chromosome morphology. By comparing the metaphase configura-

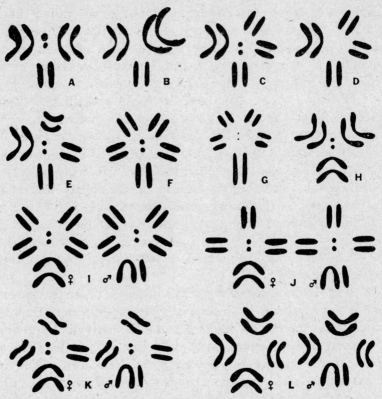

FIG. 12. Metaphase chromosome plates in several species of *Drosophila*. (From Metz.)

tions in different species of *Crepis* we cannot gauge how extensive were the structural changes in the chromosomes, and consequently cannot legitimately decide which species are and which are not similar in gene arrangement.

TRANSLOCATIONS AND INVERSIONS IN SPECIES HYBRIDS

As shown first by Federley (1913) and later corroborated by a whole phalanx of investigators, chromosomes fail to form bivalents at meiosis in many interspecific hybrids, especially in those that are sterile (see Chapter IX). This rule has, however, many exceptions. In some hybrids the chromosomes of one of the parents find their homologues among those of the other, and the formation of the bivalents proceeds more or less normally. Such species hybrids are similar to the interracial ones in that the same cytological methods for the detection of translocations and inversions are applicable to both. If an interspecific hybrid shows circles or chains of chromosomes at meiosis, it is reasonable to infer that genes located together in the same chromosome in one of the species lie in different chromosomes in the other. This condition is probably due to the occurrence of translocations in the phylogeny. Similarly, formation of chromatin bridges between the separating chromosomes at the meiotic divisions indicates the presence of inversions.

Blakeslee (1932), Bergner and Blakeslee (1932, 1935), and Bergner, Satina, and Blakeslee (1933) have studied the chromosome behavior in hybrids between species of *Datura*. Species of that genus, despite the sometimes extensive morphological differences between them, all have twelve chromosomes in the haploid, twenty-four chromosomes in the diploid. Within some of the species, races exist that probably have arisen by translocation; hybrids between such races show circles or chains of chromosomes at meiosis in addition to bivalents (see p. 113). Analogous conditions obtain also in the hybrids between species. Thus, the hybrid between the standard line of *D. stramonium* and *D. leichardtii* has two circles of four chromosomes and eight bivalents; the *D. leichardtii* × *D. meteloides* hybrid has a circle of eight, three circles of four, and two bivalents; *D. leichardtii* × *D. innoxia*, a circle of eight, two circles of four, and four bivalents; *D. inoxia* × *D. meteloides*, a circle of six, two circles of four, and five bivalent chromosomes.

Blakeslee and his collaborators have described the arrangement of the chromosome parts in species of *Datura* in terms of that observed in the standard strain of *D. stramonium*, the form best known both cytologically and genetically. Each of the twelve chromosomes of *D. stramonium* has its ends indicated by a number, so that the chromosome "formula" of this species may be written thus: 1.2, 3.4, 5.6, 7.8 . . . 19.20, 21.22, 23.24. Among the chromosomes of *D. discolor*, seven appear similar and five are different from *D. stramonium*. The chromosomes that are thus characteristic for *D. dis-*

color are 1.11, 2.17, 12.22, 15.21, and 16.18. In the *D. stramonium* × *D. discolor* hybrid seven bivalents and a circle or a chain of ten chromosomes appear. The structure of the circle is as follows:

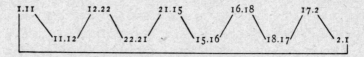

In this scheme the *D. discolor* chromosomes are shown in the upper line and those of *D. stramonium* in the lower. In *D. quercifolia,* six chromosomes are similar and six are different from *D. stramonium.* The chromosomes that differentiate *D. quercifolia* are 1.18, 2.17, 12.22, 11.21, 7.20, and 8.19. The *D. stramonium* × *D. quercifolia* hybrid has six bivalents and three circles of four chromosomes each. The structure of the circles is as follows (writing the *D. quercifolia* chromosomes in the upper and those of *D. stramonium* in the lower line):

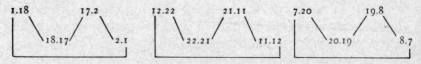

These are the chromosome configurations found in crosses between the standard line of *D. stramonium* on one hand and *D. discolor* and *D. quercifolia* on the other. But we have seen that within the species *D. stramonium* there exist also races that differ from each other in the chromosome structure. Thus, in Peru and Chile the population of *D. stramonium* has chromosomes 1.18, 2.17, 11.21, and 12.22 instead of the chromosomes 1.2, 11.12, 17.18, and 21.22 present in the standard. It may be noticed however that all the chromosomes peculiar for the population of *D. stramonium* from Peru and Chile exist also in *D. quercifolia,* and two of them (2.17 and 12.22) also in *D. discolor.* If, then, one compares the Chilean *D. stramonium* with *D. quercifolia,* they prove to differ in only two chromosomes (7.20 and 8.19 in *D. quercifolia* instead of 7.8 and 19.20 in *D. stramonium*), and give a single circle of four chromosomes and ten bivalents at meiosis. The difference between the two species, *D. stramonium* and *D. quercifolia,* seems to be no greater than the racial differences within *D. stramonium.*

Both *D. discolor* and *D. quercifolia* have the chromosome 12.22. The cross *D. discolor* × *D. quercifolia* shows however that this chromosome forms in the hybrid a bivalent consisting of two unequal halves. The inequality of the bivalent discloses the fact that although the numbered ends 12 and 22 are present in both *D. discolor* and *D. quercifolia* in the same chromosome, this chromosome is nevertheless not similarly constructed in the two species. This brings us face to face with the inadequacy of the observations on circle formation in hybrids as a method for studying chromosome structure. As pointed out above, translocations result in circle or chain formation at meiosis if they involve exchanges of large sections of chromosomes. If only small sections are exchanged, unequal bivalents may be produced, but the inequality is easily overlooked. The presence of circles including the same chromosomes in two different hybrids does not necessarily prove that the translocation in the two cases has involved exchanges of identical sections. The comparison of the chromosome structure in species of *Datura* is, as Blakeslee himself has pointed out, only the first approximation to an elucidation of the differences in the chromosome structure between species. Nevertheless, even this first approximation leaves no doubt that translocation is an active agent in the evolutionary process.

An interesting analytical study on species of *Nicotiana* has been published by Avery (1938). Three species, *N. alata, N. Langsdorfii,* and *N. bonariensis,* all have n = 9 chromosomes. The hybrid *alata* × *Langsdorfii* has at meiosis usually a complex of five chromosomes, six bivalents, and one univalent; the *alata* × *bonariensis* hybrid has one quadrivalent, two trivalents, and four bivalents; in *bonariensis* × *Langsdorfii* one complex of seven chromosomes, two trivalents, two bivalents, and a univalent are seen. If the ends of the nine chromosomes are denoted by numbers from 1 to 18, the make-up of the chromosomes of the three species is judged to be as follows:
Nicotiana alata: 1.2, 3.4, 5.6, 7.8, 9.10, 11.12, 13.14, 15.16, 17.18
N. Langsdorfii: 2.12, 3.4, 1.5.6, 7.8, 9.10, 11.5, 13.14, 15.16, 17.18
N. bonariensis: 1.18, ?.4, 5.6, 7.3, 9.10, 11.12, 13.8, 15.16, 17.2
This is, of course, only the first approximation to a description of the differences between the chromosome structures in the three species, a circumstance clearly realized by the author.

Less detailed analyses of the chromosomal differences in species of the same genus, but still amply sufficient to demonstrate the participation of translocations in the evolutionary process, are available in several plant genera. Multivalent formation has been observed in numerous hybrids between species of cereals, especially those of wheat and *Aegilops* (Kihara and Nishiyama 1930, Kihara and Lilienfeld 1932, Mather 1935, Kihara 1937, and many others), of oats (Nishiyama 1934, Ellison 1938, and others), *Phleum* (Müntzing 1935a, Nordenskiöld 1937), and various grasses. In so far as many of the species involved are presumed allopolyploids (see Chapter VII), the presence of multivalents may indicate that either the different chromosome complexes within one of the parental species or the complexes of different species are related as translocations. Multivalents are formed, however, also in hybrids between species which are apparently diploid. Here belong the hybrids between species of peas, *Pisum* (Håkansson 1935, Sansome 1938), *Allium* (Levan 1935a), *Godetia* and *Salix* (Håkansson 1931b, 1933), and many others. Circles, chains, and unequal bivalents are observed in hybrids between species which have the same chromosome numbers or numbers differing in one or two elements and which are thus free from suspicion of being related as polyploids. As examples of this phenomenon, encountered in animals as well as in plants, the hybrids between species of *Vicia* (Sveshnikova and Belekhova 1936, Sveshnikova 1936), and the moths *Orgyia* (Cretschmar 1928) and *Bombyx* (Kawaguchi 1928) may be cited. The origin of the unequal bivalents in *Ribes* (Meurman 1928) and wheat × rye hybrids (Liljefors 1936) is less clear.

Chromatin bridges between the disjoining halves of bivalents at the anaphase and telophase of the meiotic divisions in hybrids indicate, as we know, that the parents differ in having inverted sections in some of the chromosomes. Müntzing (1934) seems to have been the first to describe such chromatin bridges in an interspecific hybrid, *Crepis divaricata × C. dioscoridis*, and to recognize their significance. These two species of *Crepis* have four as the haploid number of chromosomes. At meiosis in the hybrid, from none to four bivalents appear; at the anaphase some chromatin bridges and fiberless chromosome fragments are found. The number of the latter is variable, ranging from none to five per cell, one being the average number. Similar observations were made by Müntzing (1935b) in *Nicotiana bonariensis* × *N. Langsdorfii*, by Richardson (1936) in *Lilium martagon* × *Lilium Hansonii*, by Liljefors (1936) in *Triticum turgidum* × *Secale cereale*, Emsweller and Jones (1938) in *Allium cepa* × *A. fistulosum*.

In some instances translocations may be inferred with certainty without resorting to studies on hybrid meiosis or even obtaining hybrids between the species compared. In many groups related species or genera differ in their sex-determining chromosomes: some species may have an X chromosome and no Y chromosome, others an X and a Y, and still others multiple X's or Y's in the heterogametic sex. According to White (1940a), many *Mantids* (*Orthoptera*) are XX in the female and XO (no Y) in the male, while others have four X's ($X_1X_1X_2X_2$) in the female and two X's and a Y (X_1X_2Y) in the male. In the latter, only bivalents are formed at meiosis in females, while in males a trivalent is produced in which the X's occupy the ends and the Y the middle of the chain (X_1. $Y.X_2$). The origin of the X_1X_2Y from the XO condition may be accomplished by a translocation which involves an exchange of sections between the original single X and an autosomal pair. The original autosome is retained, in the male sex only, as a chromosome without a homologue, and becomes a Y chromosome; the two chromosomes that arise through the interchange between the original X and the autosome become the two multiple X's, namely X_1 and X_2. The male meiosis is, then, that of a translocation heterozygote, and hence a chain of three chromosomes is formed; the female is a translocation homozygote, hence only bivalents appear in its meiosis (White 1940a).

We have seen that related species and even races of butterflies and moths may have different chromosome numbers of the nonpolyploid type. For example, the haploid set of one species may have one or two chromosomes more or less than that of its relative (Federley 1938, 1939). In some instances such variations of the chromosome numbers have clearly arisen by a combination of translocations with losses or duplications of centromeres (see the work of Cretschmar and Kawaguchi cited above). Federley (loc. cit.) finds that *Cerura bicuspis, C. furcula,* and *C. bifida* have 30, 29, and 49 chromosomes, respectively, in the haploid. The hybrid *furcula* × *bicuspis* shows at meiosis from 30 to 43 chromosome bodies; in the *furcula* $\times$ *bifida* from 52 to 70 bodies may be seen. Some of these bodies are obviously bivalents, others univalents and perhaps multivalents. The hybrids between *Dicranura vinula* (n $=$ 21) and its geographical race (or related species?) *D. delavoiei* (n $=$ 31) show from 21 to 37 bodies at meiosis. The simplest interpretation of these findings would seem to be that numerous translocations leading to "fragmentation" or "compounding" of chromosomes have taken place in the phylogeny of these moths. Federley prefers, however, to suppose that the number of chromosomes seen at metaphase in these species and their hybrids is simply a phenotypic characteristic determined by the genotype of the organism; in other words, chromosomes may form temporary aggregates having little to do with any changes in gene arrangements.

GENE ARRANGEMENTS IN SPECIES OF DROSOPHILA

The early studies on *Drosophila* chromosomes, based on comparisons of the mitotic metaphase plates in various species (Fig. 12), have suggested that fusion of rod-shaped chromosomes to form V-shaped ones and separation of V-shaped units into rodlike elements have taken place in the phylogeny of the genus (Metz 1914). Since, however, similar metaphase patterns occur in distantly related species and different patterns in closely related ones, fusion and fragmentation are probably not the only factors in the evolution of the chromosome apparatus. Construction of genetic chromosome maps affords a more refined method of making comparisons of the architectonics of the germ plasms of various species. Mutants arising in different species frequently produce very similar, sometimes indistinguishable, phenotypic changes. This leads to the inference that the genes involved in the production of similar mutations are homologous or even identical. Wherever hybrids between species are obtainable, this inference may be tested by observing the allelism of the respective mutants. Where hybrids cannot be obtained (as in the case in a majority of comparisons of *Drosophila* species), the judgment regarding gene homology is of necessity based on the similarity of the phenotypic effects of the genes. Admittedly, this is a serious flaw in the method, which must, consequently, be applied with greatest caution. "Mimic" mutants produced by nonallelic genes in the same species are not a rare occurrence.

Drosophila melanogaster and *D. simulans* are species with similar metaphase chromosome groups. When crossed, they produce sterile hybrids in which the allelism of the mutants can be tested. Sturtevant and Plunkett (1926) and Sturtevant (1929a) found the genetic maps of the chromosomes of the two species to be much the same, except that the right limb of the third chromosome in *D. simulans* has a single inversion compared to that of *D. melanogaster. D. melanogaster* and *D. pseudoobscura* cannot be crossed, and their metaphase chromosomes are different (Figs. 12A, and 12J, respectively). Crew and Lamy (1935), Donald (1936), and Sturtevant and Tan (1937) have compared the phenotypes of the mutants and the genetic maps known in these species. Let the chromosomes of *D. melanogaster* be designated X, IIL. IIR, IIIL. IIIR, and IV, and those of *D. pseudoobscura* XL. XR, II, III, IV, and V (IIL. IIR, IIIL. IIIR, and XL. XR refer to the respective limbs of the V-shaped chrosomomes present in these species, X is the X chromosome, and IV and V are the dotlike autosomes; the periods between the symbols of the chromosome limbs indicate that they are united into V-shaped chromosomes). The distribution of the homologous genes is as follows (the corresponding chromosome parts are in the same vertical columns):

melanogaster	X	IIL	IIR	IIIL	IIIR	IV
pseudoobscura	XL	IV	III	XR	II	V

The gene arrangements within the corresponding limbs are, however, very different indeed, from which the conclusion is drawn that paracentric inversions have been a frequent occurrence. Sturtevant and Tan (1937) and Sturtevant (1940) find these generalizations to be applicable to most comparisons of species of *Drosophila,* both where closely and where remotely related types are concerned. Some pericentric inversions have also taken place. For example, in *D. affinis* the number of chromosomes and the distribution of genes among them are the same as in *D. pseudoobscura,* and yet *D. affinis* and related species have centromeres in the large autosomes located at median and submedian positions, while in the autosomes of *D. pseudoobscura* they are strictly subterminal. The X chromosomes in *D. melanogaster* and *D. ananassae* seem to contain the same genes, and yet they are rod-shaped in the former and V-shaped in the latter species. Furthermore, the gene bobbed and some of the inert material located in *D. melanogaster* in the Y chromosome are found in *D. ananassae* to be combined with what corresponds to the dotlike autosome of the former species (Kikkawa 1937, 1938). This shows that a translocation must have taken place between the Y and the smallest autosome. The union and separation of chromosome limbs is a special form of translocation (Painter and Stone 1935).

The introduction of the technique of examining the giant chromosomes in the salivary gland cells has permitted a precise comparison of gene arrangements in the chromosomes of species hybrids. Homologous discs of giant chromosomes tend to become associated during the somatic synapsis which takes place in the salivary gland cells. Chromosome sections that carry homologous discs may be expected, at least occasionally, to pair in the hybrids. The sections thus seen paired are recorded, and by accumulating enough records it is possible to unravel the differences between the gene arrangements of the species crossed. In recent years a series of species hybrids have been examined. It is convenient to present the results of this work, starting with the cases in which the differences found were not too great.

Pätau (1935), Kerkis (1936, 1937), and especially Horton (1939) examined the chromosomes of the *Drosophila melanogaster* × *D. simulans* hybrids. The large inversion in the third chromosome which had been discovered genetically by Sturtevant (see above) was identified cytologically. In addition, twenty-four very short chromosome sections, mostly involving only a few discs each, are not identical in the two species. Among these, six sections represent minute inversions, and four sections involve undefined changes of the free ends of the chromosomes. The remainder are undefined changes which cause the respective chromosome sections to fail to pair in the hybrids; they may represent minute inversions or translocations, or qualitative changes of some kind which affect the chromosome pairing (see page 149). The A and B "races" of *D. pseudoobscura* may be regarded as closely related but distinct species. As we have seen (p. 120), the hybrids between them show at least two, and usually four, major inversions in three different chromosomes. No minute independent changes appear to be present.

Two very closely related species, *Drosophila virilis* and *D. ameri-*

cana, have been distinguished by Spencer (1940a, 1940b) on the basis of slight morphological differences and genetic tests. They can be crossed with some difficulties, and the hybrids produced are partly sterile. Hughes (1939) found that even the metaphase plates of *D. virilis* and *D. americana* are strikingly different (Fig. 13). One of the autosomes of *D. virilis* has become associated with the X chromosome, and two other autosomes have joined to form a V-shaped complex in *D. americana. D. americana* male has a V-shaped X chromosome and two Y chromosomes instead of the single rod-like X and Y present in *D. virilis.* Examination of the chromosomes

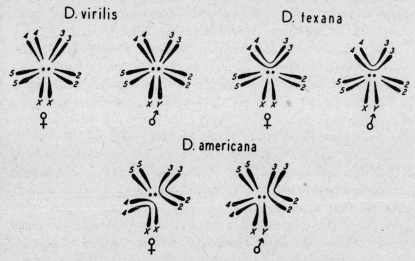

FIG. 13. Metaphase chromosome plates of *Drosophila virilis, D. texana,* and *D. americana.* (After Patterson, Stone, and Griffen.)

in the salivary glands of the hybrid larvae reveals that not less than five long inversions are present in four of the chromosomes; further-more, some chromosome sections have never been seen to pair, sug-gesting the possibility of further structural changes. The discovery of still another closely related species, *D. texana,* has been an-nounced by Patterson, Stone, and Griffen (1940). Morphologically, *D. texana* is somewhat closer to *D. americana* than to *D. virilis,* but the crosses with either relative encounter some difficulties. The meta-phase chromosomes of *D. texana* (Fig. 13) consist of one pair of V's, three pairs of rods, and a pair of dots. The V-shaped chromosomes of *D. texana* correspond neither to the X nor to the V-shaped autosomes of *D. americana:* it is a different combination of the rod-like chromosomes of *D. virilis* which gives rise to the V of *D. texana* (Fig. 13).

An analysis of the gene arrangement in *D. texana* shows this species to be in a way intermediate between *D. americana* and *D. virilis.* In the *D. americana* × *D. texana* there is a single inversion in the X and two inversions in the fourth chromosome, the fourth chromosome of *D. texana* having the same gene arrangement as that of *D. virilis.* The *D. texana* × *D. virilis* hybrids have inversions in the X and the second chromosomes. The chromosome pairing is generally disturbed in *D. virilis* × *D. americana* and *D. texana* × *D. virilis,* but not in *D. americana* × *D. texana* hybrids.

The morphological resemblance between *Drosophila pseudo-obscura* and *D. miranda* is at least as close as, and probably closer than, that between *D. melanogaster* and *D. simulans.* Their meta-phase chromosomes are identical, except that one of the autosomes of *D. pseudoobscura* is present only once in the chromosome group of the *D. miranda* male; *D. pseudoobscura* is XX and XY in the female and the male respectively, while *D. miranda* female is $X^1X^1X^2X^2$ and male X^1X^2Y (Dobzhansky 1935a). MacKnight (1939) has shown that the Y chromosome of *D. miranda* harbors some material which is almost certainly homologous to that borne in the X^2 of that species and to that in the corresponding autosomal pair of *D. pseudoobscura.* The origin of *D. miranda* must have involved a translocation of the whole or of a part of that particular autosome onto the Y chromosome, with the subsequent rearrangement of the autosomal material by repeated inversions. Dobzhansky and Tan (1936) have compared the gene arrangements in the *D. pseudoobscura* and *D. miranda* chromosomes by examining their pairing in the salivary glands of hybrid larvae. The differences between the species are so profound that the chromosomes mostly fail to pair entirely, or else form extremely complex pairing configurations, examples of which are shown in Fig. 14. Genes that in one species lie adjacent, in the other species may be far apart in the same chromosome. This indicates that inversions have taken place in the phylogenetic development of *D. pseudoobscura* and *D. miranda* from their putative common ancestor. Some genes which in one species are located in the same chromosome are borne in different chromosomes in the other. Such differences are apparently due to the occurrence of translocations. Finally, homologues of certain chromosome sections in *D. pseudoobscura* have not been detected

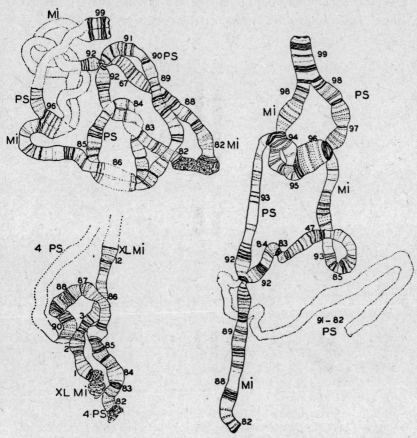

FIG. 14. Chromosome pairing in the salivary gland cells in the hybrid *Drosophila pseudoobscura* × *D. miranda*. Upper left, the fourth chromosomes; lower left, the fourth chromosome of *D. pseudoobscura* partly paired with the left limb of the X chromosome of *D. miranda;* right, the fourth chromosomes. (After Dobzhansky and Tan.)

at all in *D. miranda,* and vice versa. The nature of such sections, which are present in one species only, is a rather perplexing problem. It is conceivable that the common ancestor has had more genes than either of its surviving descendants, and that losses of genic materials have taken place in evolution. A vastly more probable explanation is however that some chromosome sections have been so thoroughly rebuilt by repeated inversions and translocations that their disc patterns in the salivary gland chromosomes no longer resemble each other, and no pairing of the homologous genes takes place. This explanation is supported by some genetic evidence. The

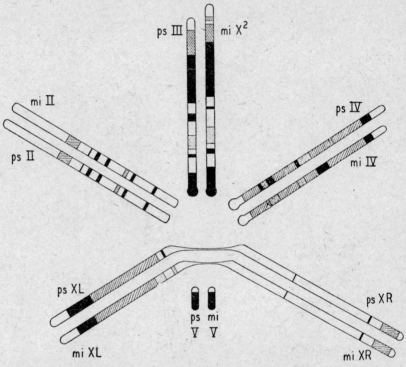

FIG. 15. A comparison of the gene arrangements in *Drosophila pseudo-obscura* and *D. miranda.* Sections having the same gene arrangements in the two species are white; inverted sections, cross-hatched; translocations, stippled; sections of which the homologues are not detectable in the other species, black.

D. pseudoobscura strains carrying various recessive mutant genes have been outcrossed to wild type *D. miranda,* and a suppression of the mutants has invariably been observed in the hybrids. It follows that *D. miranda* possesses wild-type alleles of all the mutant genes so tested.

A comparison of the chromosome structure in the two species

under consideration is shown diagrammatically in Fig. 15. If the chromosome sections that are present in one species only are temporarily disregarded, one may conclude that the chromosomal differences between *D. pseudoobscura* and *D. miranda* are due chiefly to repeated inversions. The translocations are less numerous than inversions, and wherever the former do occur they involve only relatively small blocks of genes. It is easy to visualize the derivation of the chromosome structure observed in one species from that observed in the other. The chromosomes must be broken in several places, dismantled to fragments, and then reconstructed by placing the fragments in a new linear series. Evidently, the dismemberment need not be thought of as resulting from a sort of catastrophic explosion, but rather from a gradual rebuilding by inversions and translocations. Dobzhansky and Tan have estimated that a minimum of forty-nine breakages is necessary for such a process. The sections whose homologues are not identifiable in the other species suggest however that this minimum estimate falls short of the actual number, which can be surmised to be at least twice as large.

The different chromosomes have been rebuilt to a different extent in *Drosophila pseudoobscura* and *D. miranda*. The right limbs of the X and the second chromosomes are relatively similar. On the contrary, the third and the fifth chromosomes are very thoroughly altered (Fig. 15). It is interesting that the third chromosome is also the one that is most variable in the gene arrangement within the species *D. pseudoobscura*. The overlapping inversion method of tracing the phylogeny of chromosome structures (see above) is applicable to *D. pseudoobscura* and *D. miranda*. "Race A" and "race B" of the former species differ in five inversions in four chromosomes (Tan 1935). The chromosome structure in *D. miranda* is widely distinct from either race of *D. pseudoobscura*. Yet, a careful comparison shows that the gene sequence of *D. miranda* is less different from "race A" than from "race B" of *D. pseudoobscura*. The evidence derived from a consideration of different chromosomes is consistent throughout: it takes one less inversion step to derive the *D. miranda* arrangement from "race A" than from "race B." The possibilities that may be opened by the application of the overlapping inversion method, when the chromosome structure in other species of *Drosophila* becomes better known, are difficult to gauge at present.

The greatest difference so far observed in the gene arrangement between species which produce viable, although sterile, hybrids is that found between *Drosophila azteca* and *D. athabasca*. These species are very similar externally and have identical metaphase chromosome patterns. The chromosomes in the salivary gland cells of hybrid larvae are almost entirely unpaired, and when pairing does occur it involves only short sections. Preliminary data (Bauer and Dobzhansky, unpublished) show that a very large number of inversions must have taken place in the phylogeny. Nevertheless, certain chromosomes are modified obviously less than others; this is apparent if one merely compares the disc patterns in the chromosomes of the pure species: some of the chromosomes are easily recognized as homologues, while others seem to bear no resemblance to one another. Where the hybrids are unobtainable, the only recourse is to compare the disc patterns in the salivary gland chromosomes. So compared, the chromosomes of different species frequently show no similar sections at all—this is the case, for example, in *D. melanogaster* and *D. pseudoobscura*. Occasionally, two species that are not very closely related may show some apparently similar sections not to be found in closer relatives. Thus, *D. subobscura* appears to have one of the chromosome ends not unlike that of one of the chromosomes of *D. azteca;* this particular chromosome end is, however, not identifiable in *D. pseudoobscura*, which is related to *D. subobscura* more intimately than either of these species is related to *D. azteca*. The value of such comparisons is questionable.

CONCLUSIONS

The available information on chromosomal differences between individuals, races, and species seems to fit together in a self-consistent system. The amount of chromosomal change which has taken place and is taking place in evolution is much greater than has hitherto been suspected. The extent of chromosome reconstruction is by no means necessarily proportional to the divergence in external morphology shown by the forms compared. Chromosomal differentiation is neither a precondition nor a consequence of morphological differentiation. Nevertheless, races differ usually more than individuals, related species more than races, and remote species more than related ones. More important still, the chromosomal differences between species are identical in kind, if not in degree, with those found among races and individuals. No evidence is discoverable to support Goldschmidt's (1940) view that species formation is caused by systemic chromosomal mutations which do not occur on the racial level.

Translocations and inversions are common among racial as well as among species differentials in plants. In animals, translocations and pericentric inversions are rare, while paracentric inversions are common. The rarity of these classes of changes in animals is, as we have seen, explicable on simple assumptions based on independent evidence. The fact that these "forbidden" changes nevertheless do occur occasionally even in animals is important, as we shall see in the next chapter (p. 184).

The "undefined" changes are, as their name implies, an unsolved problem. Alterations in the appearance of single discs or of small groups of discs in the salivary gland chromosomes have been described in *Drosophila pseudoobscura* × *D. miranda* (Dobzhansky and Tan 1936), *D. melanogaster* × *D. simulans* (Kerkis 1937, Horton 1939), and probably exist also in *D. virilis* × *D. americana* (Hughes 1939, Patterson, Stone, and Griffen 1940) and *D. mulleri* × *D. mojavensis* (Patterson and Crow 1940) hybrids. The discs so altered usually fail to pair with their supposed homologues in the hybrids. As we have seen, some of these undefined changes are in reality minute inversions or translocations. It is possible, however, that a phenomenon different from gene rearrangement is involved here. As pointed out by Dobzhansky and Tan and by Kerkis, gene changes may conceivably alter the cytologically visible characteristics of the chromomeres carrying the altered genes, as well as the capacity of the original and altered chromomeres to undergo normal pairing at synapsis. The importance of such gene changes from the point of view of the general gene and chromosome theory is evident. The aspect of the situation which is of more immediate concern here is, however, that no mutant within a species of *Drosophila* has been convincingly shown to have any such effects on the visible properties of its locus in the chromosome. Neither have undefined changes of this type been discovered among the naturally occurring strains or races of any species of *Drosophila*. Are such undefined changes the elusive trace of systemic mutations?

The work of Metz (1937, 1938) and of Metz and Lawrence (1938) furnishes a partial answer. The hybrids between the fly species *Sciara ocellaris* and *S. reynoldsii* show an imperfect pairing of the homologous chromosomes in the cells of the salivary glands, and yet no indication of the presence of major inversions or transloca- tions is observable. A very careful, disc by disc, comparison of the homologous chromosome sections permits the detection of minute differences between the corresponding discs. They differ in thickness or in stainability or in general conformation (entire versus dotted discs), or, in extreme cases, a disc seems to be missing entirely. While undefined differences between *Drosophila* species are on the whole infrequent, they appear to be the main method of chromosome differentiation in the two species of *Sciara* named above. The same sort of undefined changes occur, however, withing *Sciara* species as well, and are in fact the commonest kind of chromosomal differences between strains of these flies. At least some of these chromosomal differences appear to be uncorrelated with any phenotypical changes, and in *Sciara,* as in *Drosophila,* no gene mutation producing exter- nally visible effects has been shown to be accompanied by alteration of the morphology of its locus as seen in the salivary gland chromo- somes. Major inversions and translocations have as yet not been encountered in wild populations of *Sciara.* Whatever is the nature of the undefined changes, they certainly do not connote the attain- ment of the species level in evolution.

V: VARIATION IN NATURAL POPULATIONS

PREMISES

AS POINTED OUT by Darwin, any attempt to understand the mechanisms of evolution must start with an investigation of the sources of hereditary variation. Toward the accumulation of evidence bearing on this problem Darwin bent his principal efforts. He was able to satisfy himself that hereditary variations are always present, in wild as well as in domesticated species, somewhat less abundantly in the former, more abundantly, on the average, in the latter. But the mode of their origin and the cause of their appearance remained obscure to Darwin, and he was not afraid to confess his ignorance on this point. The conjecture that an increase of food supply causes an accentuation of variability in the domesticated forms was a purely provisional hypothesis, the inadequacy of which soon became apparent, prompting Darwin to fall back on the Lamarckian principle of direct adaptation.

A solution, though a partial one only, of the problem of the origin of hereditary variation has been arrived at in the present century by the application of the methods of modern genetics. It is now clear that gene mutations and chromosome changes are the principal sources of variation. Studies of these phenomena have been of necessity confined mainly to the laboratory and to organisms that are satisfactory as laboratory materials. Nevertheless, there can be no reasonable doubt that the same agencies have supplied the materials for the actual historical process of evolution. This is attested by the fact that the organic diversity existing in nature, the differences between individuals, races, and species, are experimentally resolvable into genic and chromosomal elements, which resemble in all respects the mutations and the chromosomal changes that arise in the laboratory. It may perhaps be objected that despite this resemblance, the mode of origin of laboratory and natural variations may be different. There is nothing to be said against such a criticism, except that an unnecessary multiplication of unknowns is contrary to accepted scientific procedure.

There is no contradiction between the foregoing statements and the acknowledgment which must be made of our ignorance of the exact nature of mutational and chromosomal changes. For despite the recent successes in inducing these changes by X-rays and other agents, the nature of the difference between an ancestral and a mutated gene and the mechanics of the production of such differences and of chromosomal aberrations remain obscure. In a sense we are, then, in the same position in which Darwin was: the intimate nature of the hereditary variation is still unknown. But in another respect we are in a much better position than Darwin, since at least some of the attributes of the mutation process in the wide sense of that term are no longer a mystery.

The origin of hereditary variations is, however, only a part of the mechanism of evolution. If we possessed a complete knowledge of the physiological causes producing gene mutations and chromosomal changes, as well as a knowledge of the rates with which these changes arise, there would still remain much to be learned about evolution. These variations may be compared with building materials, but the presence of an unlimited supply of materials does not in itself give assurance that a building is going to be constructed. The impact of mutation tends to increase variability. Mutations and chromosomal changes are constantly arising at a finite rate, presumably in all organisms. But in nature we do not find a single greatly variable population which becomes more and more variable as time goes on; instead, the organic world is segregated into more than a million separate species, each of which possesses its own limited supply of variability which it does not share with the others. A change of the species from one state to the other or a differentiation of a single variable population into separate ones—the origin of species in the strict sense of the word—constitutes a problem which is logically distinct from that of the origin of hereditary variation.

The origin of variation is a purely physiological, and in the last analysis physico-chemical, problem which is at the root of any theory that tries to account for the origin of species. Nevertheless, when the hereditary variation is already produced and injected into the population, it enters into the field of action of factors which are on a different level from those producing the mutations. These factors—natural and artificial selection, the manner of breeding characteristic for the particular organism, its relation to the secular environment and to other organisms coexisting in the same medium —are ultimately physiological, physical, and chemical, and yet their interactions obey rules *sui generis,* rules of the physiology of populations, not those of the physiology of individuals. The former are determined by the latter only in the same sense in which the structure of a human state may be said to depend upon the physiology of its members.

No end of misconceptions are caused by the failure to grasp the significance of this distinction. The preposterous accusation that genetics denies the importance of the environment in evolution belongs here. Genetics does assert that there is no evidence of a direct adaptation in the process of mutation, that the organism is not endowed with a providential ability to respond to the requirements of the environment by producing hereditary changes consonant with these requirements. At the individual level, the changes produced are determined by the structure of the organism itself, which is of course the result of an historical process in which the environment had played a part. But the historical process (cf. Dubinin 1931), the molding of the hereditary variation into racial, specific, generic, and other complexes, is due to action of the environment through natural selection and other channels to be discussed below.

Although population dynamics is one of the most essential parts of any evolution theory, it was until very recently largely neglected. The processes which take place in free living populations after mutations and chromosome changes have been produced and have become an integral part of the population genotype remained totally obscure. Only in recent years, a number of investigators, among whom Sewall Wright should be mentioned most prominently, have undertaken an analysis of these processes by deducing their regularities mathematically from the known properties of the Mendelian mechanism of inheritance. The importance of this work can hardly be overestimated. It has stated clearly the essential problems in the field of population dynamics, and in so doing has provided a guiding light for experimental attacks on these problems.

The experimental work itself is, however, still a task chiefly for the future.

The fundamental difference between the conception of heredity upon which Darwin had to rely and the one which is at the basis of modern views on the mechanisms of evolution can be characterized as the antithesis between the particulate and the blending theories of inheritance (Tschetwerikoff 1926, Fisher 1930). It is now known that the germ plasm consists of a finite number of discrete particles, the genes, which maintain their properties in the process of hereditary transmission. According to the first law of Mendel, the crossing of *Drosophila* flies with white and with normal red eyes results in the reappearance in the F_2 generation of flies with white and red eyes of the same shade as in their ancestors. The difference between the genes for white and for red eye color is not encroached upon in any way by hybridization; no pink or cream-colored eyes, for example, are produced. Even where the hybrid, or heterozygote, is intermediate between the parents, no contamination of the genes takes place, and the homozygotes recovered from the hybrids are like the parental races. The discovery of position effects has shown that genes are not quite as discrete and separate from each other as was formerly supposed, but this does not impinge on the thesis that the differences between genes are not swamped by hybridization.

The concept of blending inheritance, which was held universally in Darwin's time, was based on the assumption that the germ plasms of the parents undergo a sort of amalgamation in the hybrid. The difference between the ancestral germ plasms was supposed to be either lost entirely or at least impaired by passage through the hybrid organism. As an analogy, the theory of blending inheritance may be said to assume that germ plasms can mix as a water-soluble dye mixes with water. Interbreeding of the genotypically distinct forms causes, then, an eventually uniform distribution of the dye in the germ plasm of the resulting hybrid population. The particulate inheritance theory assumes, by contrast, that genes are more like blocks of solid material; these blocks are placed side by side in the hybrid, but they separate uncontaminated in the processes of germ cell formation.

The corollaries of the two theories are strikingly different. If the germ plasms can combine as a dye commingles with water, then the amount of variation present in a sexually reproducing random breeding population must be halved in every generation. Given a population which exhibits a large variability at the start, we are bound to observe a progressive, rapid, and irretrievable decay of the variability, until a complete homogeneity is reached. The only escape from this conclusion is to suppose that the variability is constantly being developed *de novo,* at a rate which is at least equal to the rate of its loss due to crossing. This is exactly the conclusion to which Darwin and his immediate followers were inexorably driven by their initial assumption of blending inheritance. In modern language this would mean that new mutations must occur with a prodigious frequency, far in excess of anything ever observed in any experiment.

No such difficulty is encountered if the germ plasm is particulate, for in this case the variability is maintained on an approximately constant level despite the interbreeding, although it will be shown below that a relatively slow decay of the variability is expected even with a particulate inheritance. Very much lower mutation rates will suffice to increase the variability and to furnish the materials for evolution, since the maintenance of the variability requires little fresh supply of mutational changes. This deduction is applicable both to genic variation and to that in the chromosome structure. Only in the realm of cytoplasmic inheritance a situation approaching blending may obtain, although too little is known about it to make any conclusion secure. With the obsolescence of the blending inheritance theory, one of the greatest impediments to the progress of evolutionary thought was removed.

A distinction must obviously be drawn between the assumption of the blending of hereditary factors and the assumption that discrete groups of forms differing in many genes will lose their discreteness if allowed to interbreed freely. Owing to the free assortment of genes (the second law of Mendel), an interbreeding of two such groups will result in a single population in which all the possible recombinations of the ancestral traits will be present in separate individuals. The amount of variation is not reduced by crossing, but the difference between the formerly discrete groups as groups is obliterated (cf. Chapter VIII).

HARDY'S FORMULA AND THE GENETIC EQUILIBRIUM

Imagine that equal numbers of homozygous individuals differing in a single gene (AA and aa) are brought together in some sort of unoccupied territory (an island, for example), and are left there to breed for an indefinite number of generations without the admission of fresh immigrants. Provided the mating is random, that is to say, individuals of the genotype AA are equally likely to mate with AA or with aa individuals, then in the next generation one-half of the population will consist of heterozygotes (Aa), and each of the two homozygotes will be represented by one-quarter of the population. The frequencies of the different genotypes in the population will be, hence, $1AA:2Aa:1aa$. If none of the three genotypes has any advantage with respect to the survival over the other two, and the mating continues to be random, the same ratio $1AA:2Aa:1aa$ will be repeated in the second and in all following generations.

Pearson (1904) and Hardy (1908) have shown that the relative frequencies of various genes in a population remain constant irrespective of the absolute values of their initial frequencies. If the AA and aa individuals are mixed in proportions q and 1-q respectively, the population in the second and all following generations will be:

$$q^2AA : 2q(1\text{-}q)Aa : (1\text{-}q)^2aa$$

This formula describes the equilibrium condition in a sexually reproducing random breeding population where the component genotypes are equivalent with respect to selection. If breeding is not random, the relative frequencies of the homozygotes and heterozygotes will be affected, but the gene frequencies $qA:(1\text{-}q)a$ will remain constant. For instance, if self-fertilization takes place, or if the carriers of each genotype exhibit a preference toward mating with their like, the relative frequencies of the homozygotes AA and aa will increase, and the frequency of the heterozygotes (Aa) will decrease. A selection favoring the survival and breeding of some genotypes over others will, on the other hand, cause alterations in the values of q and 1-q. The direction, extent, and speed with which the alterations will take place are dependent upon the intensity and the manner of action of selection. These problems have been treated mathematically by Haldane (1924–1932), Fisher (1930), and others.

Hardy's formula is important because it shows that the hereditary variability once gained by a population is automatically maintained on a constant level, instead of being eroded and finally leveled off by crossing. As mentioned already, this is a corollary to the particulate as contrasted with the blending type of inheritance. The maintenance of the genetic equilibrium is evidently a conservative and not a progressive factor. Evolution is essentially a modification of this equilibrium. We shall proceed now to show that agents that tend to modify the equilibrium actually exist in nature. A significant fact is that each of such agents is counteracted by another opposite in sign, which tends to restore the equilibrium. A living population is constantly under the stress of the opposing forces; evolution results when one group of forces is temporarily gaining the upper hand over the other.

MUTATION AND THE GENETIC EQUILIBRIUM

The value of q in Hardy's formula—for example, the frequency of a gene or a chromosome structure in a population—can be modified by mutation pressure in the wide sense of the term, that is, by gene mutations and chromosomal changes. If the change from the gene or the chromosome structure A to the state a takes place at a finite rate, the frequencies q and 1-q must change accordingly. Let the mutation in the direction $A \rightarrow a$ have a rate equal to u; the change in the frequency of A in the population will be $\Delta q = -uq$, where q is the frequency of A. If the mutation in the direction $A \rightarrow a$ is unopposed by any other factor, the population will eventually reach homozygosis for a.

Wherever the mutation is reversible, the change in the direction $A \rightarrow a$ is opposed by the change $a \rightarrow A$. With the rate of reverse mutation equal to v, the frequency of A will change as $\Delta q = -uq + v(1$-$q)$. An equilibrium will be reached obviously when the change $\Delta q = 0$. The equilibrium value of q determined by the two mutually opposed mutation rates is therefore $q = v / u + v$. Taking, for example, the rate of the mutation $A \rightarrow a$ to be equal to one in a million gametes per generation ($u = 0.000001$), and the rate of the mutation $a \rightarrow A$ equal $v = 0.0000005$, the equilibrium value for q will be 0.33, which means that 33% of the chromosomes will carry the gene A and 67% the gene a. If the mutation rates to and from a given gene are alike ($v = u$), the equilibrium values for both q and 1-q are evidently 0.5, or equal. Starting from an initially homogenous population, the mutation pressure will tend to increase the hereditary variability until the equilibrium values determined by the opposing mutation rates are reached for every gene. In an indefinitely large population this level of variability will be preserved (as shown by Hardy's formula) until some agent disturbs it.

It is important to realize that an increase of variability through mutation will take place even in case the mutational changes are unfavorable to the organism, and are thus opposed by natural selection. This is especially true when the mutational changes are recessive to the ancestral condition, which is actually the case for a majority of mutations arising in many species. If the heterozygote Aa (a being a mutant gene decreasing the viability) is as viable as the ancestral homozygote AA, the frequency of the gene a will be allowed to increase until the Aa individuals become so frequent in the population that their mating together is likely to take place, and the homozygotes aa are produced. The aa condition being unfavorable, the aa individuals will be eliminated, and this will impose a check on the further spread of the mutant gene a in the population. This reasoning is fully applicable to mutant genes the adaptive value of which is zero (that is, to lethals). It is possible to show that in very large random breeding populations the equilibrium value of a completely recessive lethal is equal to the square root of the mutation rate producing that lethal ($q = \sqrt{u}$). Thus, a lethal arises once in a million gametes, one-tenth of one percent of the chromosomes will eventually carry it. Vice versa, knowing the equilibrium value of a lethal or a semilethal in a population, one can, using the above assumptions, compute the mutation rate producing it. Haldane (1935) came to the conclusion that the gene for haemophilia arises by mutation once in fifty thousand human life cycles. Natural populations are expected to contain numerous mutant genes in their genotypes.

That this is not only a theoretical possibility but an actual process going on in nature is demonstrated by the results of the genetic analyses of wild *Drosophila* populations (Chapters III and IV). Despite their external uniformity, the free living populations of *Drosophila* carry a great mass of chromosomal variations as well as of recessive mutant genes. While the former, at least in the *Droso-phila pseudoobscura* strains studied by Sturtevant and Dobzhansky, seem to be indifferent for viability, many of the latter are lethal when homozygous. Among those mutants that are not outright lethals, a majority, at least the more striking ones, are clearly unfavorable. Their unfavorable effects are demonstrable under laboratory condi-tions, and the rarity in nature of the individuals homozygous for the mutant genes justifies the inference that they are unfavorable in the wild state as well. And yet the species is, according to the succinct metaphor of Tschetwerikoff (1926), "like a sponge," absorbing both the mutations and the chromosomal changes that arise and gradually accumulating a great store of variability, mostly concealed in hetero-zygous condition.

It is not an easy matter to evaluate the significance of the accu-mulation of germinal changes in natural populations. Such changes must necessarily accumulate in any species which (a) reproduces by cross-fertilization, (b) in which genes are subject to mutation, and (c) in which the effective populations are large enough to pre-clude a very close inbreeding which might eliminate the deleterious changes soon after their origin. Mutation rates in an organism are, however, subject to genetic modification (Demerec 1937, and others; see p. 36); genes enhancing and suppressing mutability are known. Sturtevant (1937c, 1939) and Shapiro (1938) have pointed out that, since a majority of mutants are injurious, the adaptive values of strains with high mutability tend to be lower than those of strains in which the mutability is low. Natural selection will, therefore, favor the genotypes in which the mutability is kept at a minimum. Yet, mutation is, as far as known, never suppressed entirely. Sturte-vant (1937c) surmises that the nature of the gene does not permit reduction of the mutation frequency to zero: "Mutations are acci-dents, and accidents will happen."

Looked at from another angle, the accumulation of germinal changes in the population genotypes is, in the long run, a necessity if the species is to preserve its evolutionary plasticity. The process of adaptation may be looked at as a series of conflicts between the organism and its environment. The environment is in a state of flux, and its changes, whether slow or rapid, make the genotypes of the bygone generations no longer fit for survival. The ensuing contradictions can be resolved either through extinction of the species, or through reorganization of its genotype. An ideal situation would be if the organism were to respond to the challenge of the changing environment by producing only beneficial mutations where and when needed. But nature has not been kind enough to endow its creations with such a providential ability. Mutations are changes that occur regardless of whether they are or may be potentially useful. Haldane (1937), Shapiro (1938), and the writer (in the first edition of this book) have pointed out that the preservation of a living species demands that it possess at all times a store of concealed genetical variability. This store will contain variants which under no conditions will be useful, other variants which might be useful under a set of circumstances which may never be realized in practice, and still other variants which are neutral or harmful at the time when they arise but which will prove useful later on.

Mutations which are unfavorable in a given environment may be valuable in a changed environment (see Chapter II). Since natural selection operates not with separate genes or separate mutations, but with gene patterns or genotypes, a mutation that decreases the viability when present together with certain genes may increase the viability when placed on a different genic background. If the environment were absolutely constant, one could conceive of the formation of ideal genotypes each of which would be perfectly adapted to a certain niche in this environment. In such a static world, evolution might accomplish its task and come to a standstill; doing away with the mutation process would be the ultimate improvement. The world of reality is, however, not static. A species perfectly adapted at present may be destroyed by a change in the environment if no hereditary variability is available in the hour of need. The process of evolution is generally opportunistic: natural selection favors those variants useful at a given time, regardless of their eventual value. Possessing no foresight, selection always tends to suppress mutability. But opportunism leads in the long run to retribution: species or races which become "well adapted" to the point of abolishing mutability do not respond to the challenge of a shifting environment. Evolution viewed in an historical perspective tends to perpetuate types which are, in a sense, not too well adapted (Chapter X). This long range process is a kind of selection *sub specie aeternitatis*.

SCATTERING OF THE VARIABILITY

The supply of hereditary variation is constantly augmented by the occurrence of mutations and chromosomal changes. In an ideal infinitely large population unaffected by selection and by changes in the environment, the accumulation of variability would ultimately result in every gene's being represented by several alleles, and every chromosome by several structural variants. The equilibrium frequency for each allele or variant would be determined solely by the mutation rates, according to the formula $q = v / u + v$ derived above. Ideal populations of this sort actually do not exist. In reality, natural selection tends to purge the population genotype of all the unfavorable variants. For an understanding of the dynamics of free living populations it is essential, however, not to disregard the existence of another agent besides selection, which tends to diminish the supply of hereditary variation irrespective of the adaptive value of the latter, and thus to counteract the mutation pressure. This agent is the scattering of the variability in the process of reproduction. Its significance has been almost entirely overlooked by most evolutionists.

For the sake of clarity, it is best to start the discussion of the scattering of the variability by examining the conditions that obtain in a certain ideal population. Following Dubinin and Romaschoff (1932), let us imagine a population which remains numerically stationary from generation to generation, and in which every pair of parents produce only two offspring, all of which survive to maturity and replace the parents before the next breeding season begins. A mutation from the gene A to a produces a single individual Aa. This individual must mate to a normal one, $Aa \times AA$. The offspring expected from this cross is $1Aa : 1AA$, but owing to chance, the two individuals actually produced will in 25 percent of the cases both be AA; in another 25 percent, both Aa; and in 50 percent, one AA and the other Aa. According to Hardy's formula, the frequency in the population of the newly arisen gene a is expected to remain constant. But this is not necessarily the case because in 25 percent of cases no Aa individual is present in the next generation, and hence the mutant gene a is lost. If no loss takes place in the first generation, the mutation is exposed to the risk of extinction in the next and in following generations. The same mechanism that causes the loss of some mutants produces a doubling of the frequency of others. But since the loss of a mutation is an irreversible process, the conclusion follows that some mutants, both harmful and beneficial ones, never become established in the population, and are lost to the species.

The same process of loss of the hereditary variability may be demonstrated in another way. Imagine a population in which every gene is represented only once, that is to say, every individual carries two different alleles neither of which is present in any other individual in the same population. If the breeding system is the same as in the above example (i.e., only two offspring are produced by each pair of parents), 25 percent of the variety of alleles will be lost in the very next generation, and 25 percent of the alleles will be each represented twice, hence doubled in frequency. The loss of some alleles and the increase of the frequency of others will go on in further generations as well, until the population will ultimately become homozygous for one of the alleles.

As a model of such a population, Dubinin and Romaschoff (1932) used a bowl containing 100 marbles, each marble with a different number. To illustrate the results which the process of reproduction would entail in such a population, 25 marbles taken at random were withdrawn and discarded. Another set of 25 marbles was taken out, and, in place of each of these, two new marbles (carrying the same number as the original for which they were substituted) were returned to the bowl, so that the total number of marbles (100) was restored. This operation represented one generation of breeding, and resulted in elimination of 25 "alleles," and in doubling the frequency of 25 others. Repeating the same operation several times, Dubinin and Romaschoff observed a progressive decay of the variability in the "population." Fewer and fewer different numbers remained in the bowl, although some of those which were left became represented by many marbles each. Finally, all the marbles had the same number, that is, the "population" had become homogeneous. In ten separate experiments of this sort Dubinin and Romaschoff observed the attainment of a complete "homozygosis" after from 108 to 465 "generations," the victorious allele each time having a different number.

These simple experiments illustrate the very important phenomenon of the decay of variability with time. Dr. F. B. Hanson has called my attention to the fact that this idea was first stated by Brooks (1899, p. 145). Its genetic implications were clarified by Hagedoorn and Hagedoorn (1921), and later elaborated, largely independently, by Fisher (1928, 1930, 1931), Dubinin (1931), Romaschoff (1931), Dubinin and Romaschoff (1932), and particularly by Wright (1921, 1930–1940). Hardy's formula is strictly applicable to ideal infinitely large populations, and only to gene frequencies q and $1-q$ that are not too close to zero or to unity. In reality, no living population consists of an infinitely large number of random breeding individuals, and gene frequencies may be very small and very large. The gene frequencies in finite populations vary at random. But as

TABLE 13

PROBABILITY OF EXTINCTION AND OF SURVIVAL OF A MUTATION APPEARING IN A SINGLE INDIVIDUAL (after Fisher)

GENERATION	PROBABILITY OF EXTINCTION		PROBABILITY OF SURVIVAL	
	No Advantage	1% Advantage	No Advantage	1% Advantage
1	0.3679	0.3642	0.6321	0.6358
3	0.6259	0.6197	0.3741	0.3803
7	0.7905	0.7825	0.2095	0.2175
15	0.8873	0.8783	0.1127	0.1217
31	0.9411	0.9313	0.0589	0.0687
63	0.9698	0.9591	0.0302	0.0409
127	0.9847	0.9729	0.0153	0.0271
Limit	1.0000	0.9803	0.0000	0.0197

soon as these random variations reach the values $q = 0$ or $q = 1$, a certain gene allele is lost from the population. A finite population left to its own devices must, therefore, suffer a progressive decay of its hereditary variability and sooner or later must reach a complete genetic uniformity. This, of course, disregards the occurrence of new mutations.

The models of populations devised by Dubinin and Romaschoff must be modified to conform more closely to the conditions that actually obtain in natural populations. The number of offspring produced by a pair of parents reproducing sexually is always larger than two. If the population size remains approximately constant from generation to generation, it follows that a major part of the offspring die before they reach the breeding stage themselves. The problem of the retention or loss of mutants which appear singly (and almost all mutants do appear in single individuals) in such populations has been treated mathematically by Fisher (1930) and Wright (1931a). The results are summarized by Fisher in Table 13.

If the mutational change confers no advantage on its carrier, only 153 out of 10,000 mutants avoid extinction after 127 generations of breeding. With 1 percent selective advantage, the favorable mutations will suffer much the same fate, but still 271 instead of 153 out of every 10,000 will be retained. Clearly, a majority of mutations turning up in natural populations are lost within a few generations after their origin, and this irrespective of whether they are neutral, harmful, or useful to the organism. The mutations which persist are the "lucky" remainder which may be increased in frequency instead of being lost.

Wright has made a most searching analysis of a more general aspect of the same problem. Hardy's ratio, $q^2 : 2q(1-q) : (1-q)^2$, describes only the average state of affairs in a population. If two alleles, A and a, are present in the initial population in equal numbers ($q = 1-q = 0.5$), their frequencies in the following generations will fluctuate up and down, the average, of course, tending to remain close to 0.5. Wright shows that these fluctuations may lead to most significant results. Indeed, so long as the values of q remain between 0 and 1, the fluctuations are reversible, but as soon as the latter values are reached an irreversible change has taken place: one of the two alleles is lost and the other has reached a state of fixation, that is, the population is now homozygous for it. Thus both fixation and loss of a gene in a population may occur without the participation of selection, merely because of the properties inherent in the mechanism of Mendelian inheritance.

The deviations from the constancy predicted by Hardy's formula are inversely correlated with the absolute number of breeding individuals in the population, with its "population number" denoted by the symbol N. Wright (1931a, pp. 110–111) defines the population number as follows: "The conception is that of two random samples of gametes, N sperms and N eggs, drawn from the total gametes produced by the generation in question. . . . Obviously N applies only to the breeding population and not to the total number of individuals of all ages. If the population fluctuates greatly, the effective N is much closer to the minimum number than to the maximum number. If there is a great difference between the number of mature males and females, it is closer to the smaller number than to the larger."

The greater the population size, the more closely the results of breeding will approach the constancy of the gene frequencies postulated by Hardy's formula. Conversely, the smaller the population size, the more rapid is the scattering of the variability and the eventual attainment of genetic uniformity. The great significance of the population number, N, comes from the fact that in a population of N breeding individuals, $1/2N$ genes either reach fixation or are lost in every generation. Suppose that in a population many genes are represented each by two alleles which are equivalent with respect to selection, and that the initial frequency of each allele is 50 percent ($q = 0.5$). With no mutations taking place, the frequencies of the different alleles will in the following generations fluctuate up and down from 50 percent, some becoming more and some less frequent owing to chance. Sooner or later a condition will obtain when gene frequencies from 0 percent to 100 percent will become equally numerous, and $1/4N$ of the genes will reach fixation and $1/4N$ will be lost in every generation, as indicated in Fig. 17. Wright's formula describing this process is

$$L_T = L_0 \, e^{-T/2N}$$

where L_0 and L_T are the numbers of the unfixed genes in the initial and in the T generation of breeding respectively, N is the population number, and e the base of natural logarithms.

Dubinin and Romaschoff (1932) have furnished an illustration of the significance of the population number by making their experiments with marbles in two different ways. In some experiments they used bowls containing one hundred marbles, and in others bowls containing but ten marbles. It required many more "generations" to attain a complete uniformity of the "population" in the former series of experiments than in the latter (from 108 to 465 "generations" with one hundred marbles, and from 14 to 51 "generations" with ten marbles).

THE BIOLOGICAL MEANING OF THE VALUE N

It may be useful at this point to clarify the application of the population number concept to various situations encountered in nature. It must be reiterated that the genetically effective population size, N, is not conterminous with the total number of individuals of a species or a race. The simplest situation is that of a colony isolated from the rest of the species by secular barriers, within which the population is panmictic, remains stationary in numbers from generation to generation, and in which each pair of parents produces the same number of surviving offspring. For such a colony, N is equal to the number of individuals of the generation now living which will be the actual progenitors of the following generation, or to the number of the actual parents of the now living generation. In reality, the surviving progeny of some parents is large, that of others is small, and that of still others is destroyed entirely. If N_0 is the number of parents, and K that of their gametes giving rise to the surviving offspring ($K = 2$ on the average), the effective population $N = \dfrac{4N_0 - 2}{2 + \sigma^2_k}$ (Wright 1938, 1940b). Equally important is the consideration that the gross populations of most species vary, often within an enormous range, from generation to generation. Such variations are either connected with seasonal cycles (as in insects which produce several generations per year), with climate, or with fluctuations in the abundance of parasites, enemies, or prey. Wright has shown that the effective N is much closer to the number of individuals attained at the maximum contraction, than to that attained at maximum expansion, of the population. For example, a population may increase tenfold in each of the six succeeding generations, and then return to its initial size, its minimum being N_0 and maximum $N_0 \times 10^6$. The effective size is then $N = 6.3 N_0$ (Wright 1940b).

Segregation of a species into colonies completely isolated from each other and yet perfectly panmictic within themselves is not a very common situation, although it probably does obtain in some instances. Usually there is some migration, that is, exchange of individuals between the colonies. The role of migration will be discussed later; suffice it to say that migration increases the genetically effective population size. On the other hand, the breeding structure of the population within a colony may preclude the attainment of a panmixia because of the isolation by distance. Individuals residing in any part of a territory continuously inhabited by a species have a greater chance of mating with their neighbors than with residents of remote parts of the same territory. The genetically effective population size may be very much smaller than the number of breeding individuals in a continuously inhabited area. Wright (1938, 1940b) has made a beginning of a mathematical analysis of this situation, which is biologically probably most important. In a population distributed uniformly over a territory, the parents of any given individual are drawn from a certain average area which may be smaller than the whole territory in question. It may be assumed that this average area is a circle with a diameter D, and a population of N breeding individuals. The grandparents would have come, however, from a larger territory with a greater population, which Wright shows to be $\sqrt{2}$ D and 2N respectively. For n generations the territory becomes $\sqrt{n}$ D and the population nN. The resultant function of N is a rather abstract value, but Wright shows that, if the initial N's are less than 1,000, some local differentiation of the population genotype may be expected.

Much in this field requires further theoretical elaboration. For example, Wright (1940b) discusses the special case of distribution that is nearly unidimensional, such as that of an organism inhabiting a river or a given depth contour in the sea. Here an individual's ancestors of the nth generation come from a distance $\sqrt{n}$ D with an effective population $\sqrt{n}$ N. The distance D is not necessarily equal to the limits of the activity of the individual as such: a similar concept would apply to species that are sedentary, but in which the distribution of gametes is effected by factors such as currents, wind, or insects.

Mutation pressure and the scattering of the variability are mutually opposed processes: the former tends to increase genetic diversity, and the later uniformity in populations. For the sake of clearness, we have been forced to consider the action of each of these processes separately, by studying the properties of abstract populations where one or the other process was assumed to be nonexistent. In reality mutations do occur, presumably in all organisms, although probably at different rates. The interactions of the mutation pressure with the scattering of the variability present some rather involved mathematical problems which have been treated by Wright (1931a, 1932, 1937, 1938a, b, 1940a, b).

In very large populations the scattering of the variability is evidently ineffective, and the gene frequencies are determined, in the absence of selection, by the opposing mutation rates to and from a given allele. Each allele eventually reaches its equilibrium frequency, which is maintained constant with insignificant variations. Conversely, in very small populations the gene frequencies are largely independent of the mutation rates, unless the latter are very large. This means that one of the alleles of each gene by chance displaces all others, and reaches the state of approximate fixation, practically the entire population being homozygous for it. In populations of intermediate size the greatest freedom obtains. Some alleles are lost or reach fixation at random; others fluctuate in frequency over a wide range of values, the modal value approaching that determined by the mutation rates.

This shows how important is the effective size of the breeding population of a species for its evolutionary perspectives. If population sizes in most species tend to be small on the average, the scattering of the variability and the random variations of the gene frequencies will loom important as evolutionary agents. If, on the other hand, the population sizes are usually so large that they may be regarded for practical purposes as infinite, the evolutionary role of these agents is negligible. It is no exaggeration to say that the conclusions which eventually may be reached on the dynamics of the evolutionary process will depend in no small degree on the information bearing on the problem of the population numbers. Until recently, evolution theorists assumed implicitly that effective populations in most organisms are practically infinite. Some evidence is, however, available to show this assumption to be in need of a careful revision. It seems convenient to review the pertinent data, almost all of which are of an inferential nature, under the headings of ecological, taxonomic, and genetical evidence. It is, of course, realized that such distinctions are artificial, and in the course of time are likely to break down completely.

POPULATION SIZE: ECOLOGICAL EVIDENCE

Elton (1927) has correctly emphasized that the total numbers of individuals of many species are staggeringly great. Owing to the smallness of many creatures and their habit of hiding themselves from view, the great majority of individuals of a species are usually overlooked. The human population, more than two billions, is probably equaled in many higher animals and large plants (e.g., trees), and is certainly exceeded in many lower animals and plants. Only few population estimates are, however, available. Dice (1939d) concluded that in the late summer of 1939 the 4,968 square miles of territory in the Black Hills of South Dakota were inhabited by between one million and five million mice of the species *Peromyscus maniculatus osgoodi*. The distribution area of this mouse is much wider than the territory studied. In 1939 the population of the bird *Sula bassana* was about 167,000, of which 109,000 resided in twenty-two colonies in the British Isles (Fisher and Vevers 1939). The adult population of the butterfly *Polyommatus icarus* on the small isle of Tean was about 450 to 500 (Dowdeswell, Fisher, and Ford 1940). The distribution area of some species is very small, and the total numbers of existing individuals are correspondingly limited. Thus, *Oenothera organensis* occurs only in some canyons of the Organ Range, New Mexico, and its total population is in the neighborhood of 500 (Emerson 1939).

All the individuals of a species do not necessarily constitute a single panmictic breeding unit. Formation of isolated colonies and isolation by distance may reduce the genetically effective population sizes to orders of magnitude much smaller than that of the species as a whole. Even in relic species which subsist on a very small territory the population need not be panmictic, as suggested by Wright (1939) for *Oenothera organensis*. Two factors must be taken into consideration: the limited mobility of many forms, and the homing phenomenon which causes an individual and its offspring to return to the same, often very limited, territory. The problem is not whether an individual is capable of moving from place to place, but whether such movements occur in fact. The contrast between the availability of excellent means of locomotion and the attachment to a small territory cannot be better illustrated than by the behavior of birds. Certain species of birds fly thousands of miles in the course of their yearly migrations. And yet swallows and storks return every year to the same locality, or even to the same nest, as has been proved by marking individuals with numbered bands in their nesting places and observing their return the following year. Gross (1940) has studied the behavior of herring gulls (*Larus argentatus*) nesting on Kent Island, off Nova Scotia. A total of 23,434 individuals were banded on the island, and the recovery of the banded specimens has shown that they tend to return to Kent Island for breeding. Although seasonal migrations take them as far as the Gulf of Mexico and beyond, not only the adults but also the young born on Kent Island come back to their breeding places. The behavior of many migratory species is known to be similar to that of the herring gull, although in some species the returning young settle within a smaller distance from their old nests than in other species.

Much detailed observational work has been done on another aspect of bird biology, namely their territoriality. Many migratory as well as resident species, forms that, out of the breeding season, are gregarious or single, exhibit a curious behavior pattern when the breeding season approaches. Namely, individuals subdivide the available territory among themselves, each "declares" himself the possessor of a certain area, and forcibly ejects from it intruders of the same species and sex. Nice (1937) and Erickson (1938) have published excellent accounts of the situation in the song sparrow (*Melospiza melodia*) and the wren tit (*Chamaea fasciata*), respectively, showing that in these birds the effective populations are small and the territory of a breeding unit is definitely restricted, sometimes to within a few hundred meters. Recent work has shown that many mammals also exhibit the phenomenon of territoriality in striking fashion (Burt 1940 and Blair 1940b in *Peromyscus,* Eisentraut 1934 in bats, Niethammer 1937 in rabbits and hares, Blair 1940a in voles). Noble (1934) has shown territorial behavior to occur in the lizard *Sceleropus undulatus.*

Large scale migrations of fishes have been known and exploited for a very long time. Tremendous schools of herring, aggregating 100,000 tons and more, come into shore waters for spawning, while the young lead a pelagic life in the open sea. Heincke (1898) has shown by masterful analysis that the herring species *Clupea harengus* in the North Atlantic is split up into strains which differ as to place and season of breeding, paths of migration, as well as in morphological characters. Later investigators have confirmed and extended Heincke's results for several species (reviews by Scheuring 1929–1930, Schnakenbeck 1931, and Russell 1937). In some species the effective breeding populations are likely to be small as a result of a tendency for individuals, which have lived for several years in the open sea, to return for spawning not only to the river systems but to the small tributary streams in which they were born. This phenomenon, so incredible that it was disbelieved in the face of good evidence, has been experimentally demonstrated for species of salmon of the Pacific Coast of North America. Young individuals were marked in various streams, and then observed to return as mature fish; but when young were artificially transplanted to another stream, they returned to the stream in which they had spent their early life, and not to that in which they were born.

Among the invertebrates the phenomena of territoriality and homing have been conclusively established for social insects. For example, honey bees return to their hives after their numerous honey collecting trips (cf. the experimental work of von Frisch, 1927). The absence of a fixed territory does not signify, however, that the organism is inclined toward aimless wandering. Timofeeff-Ressovsky (1939a, b) has published preliminary data on the behavior of several species of *Drosophila* secured by means of exposing numerous traps in an area subdivided in checkerboard fashion. The population density proved to be far from uniform within an area of less than a square kilometer. Releasing flies marked with certain "signal genes" in the center of this area, and recapturing them again, proved that they seldom move more than twenty-five meters from the place of release in two weeks.

The fact that even within areas relatively so uniform as the plains of North America, Russia, and northern Asia the habitats suitable for most animal and plant species are not continuous over long distances must never be lost sight of. The distribution maps showing species areas as uninterrupted stretches of territory are admittedly abstractions; in reality, distribution areas of most species are extremely complex patchworks of habitats wherein a species is frequent, wherein it is rare, and wherein it does not occur at all. In desert and mountain countries this patchwork character of the distribution of life is strikingly apparent even to a casual visitor. In recent years many acute observers have realized that segregation of species into small and partly independent colonies is a very common phenomenon. Thus, Diver (1940) finds it to be the rule not only in the snails, where it is most striking, but in nonmarine organisms in general. Smith (1939) considers colony formation to be of considerable importance to economic entomologists, especially in view of the mathematical demonstration by Nicholson (1933) and Nicholson and Bailey (1935) that in isolated colonies the host-parasite and prey-predator relationships automatically lead to large fluctuations in the population sizes of all species so related.

The tendency of the older authors to think of most living species in terms of large undivided populations was based chiefly on a misinterpretation of the fact that most organisms possess "adaptations" that engender a wide distribution of their offspring. It is, indeed, known that many insect pests and plant weeds have conquered new territories with great speed, and some apparently wild species have rapidly extended their distribution areas within a few decades. Extrapolation of such data to prove that there is no isolation between populations in colonies formed by most species is deceptive. Migrants arriving in a suitable territory unoccupied by their own species spread as fast as their reproductive potentials permit; migrants finding themselves in an area occupied to near saturation point by representatives of their own species have to contend for a place in the sun with the latter, and have in general a scanty chance to establish their progeny in the new place. The exchange of genes between colonies will, then, be very limited, unless the number of migrants per generation is large in relation to the population size in an average colony.

POPULATION SIZE: TAXONOMIC EVIDENCE

The importance of isolation for the subdivision of species into local races has been clearly realized by taxonomists for a long time; in recent years several attempts have been made to correlate this phenomenon with the limitation of the population size as a possible causative agent. Anderson (1936) found that *Iris virginica,* a common species in the eastern United States, occurs not continuously but in isolated colonies, each consisting of from one to several thousand individuals. The average number of such colonies for one hundred square miles is 120 in northern Michigan, 350 in southern Michigan, 170 in northern Illinois, 30 in southern Missouri, and 5 in Alabama and Mississippi. With the aid of statistical methods, Anderson detects small but significant differences between populations in the separate colonies. These variations are geographically rather haphazard, that is, the differences between colonies are neither proportional to the distance between them, nor do they show definite geographical clines. Differences of this sort are expected to arise from random fixation or loss of genes in colonies with limited effective population size.

Species of land snails, owing to their low mobility, are particularly apt to be subdivided into colonies the members of which seldom pass over the barriers separating one colony from the others. From the center of most of the volcanic islands in the South Seas rises a steep mountain cone, with slopes deeply crevassed by radiating valleys separated by more or less narrow ridges. The snail species inhabiting the valleys, such as *Achatinella* on Hawaii (Gulick 1905) and *Partula* on Tahiti and Moorea (Crampton 1916, 1932), show an extreme diversity of local races. Each valley, or even each part of a valley, is inhabited by a race of its own, distinct from other races in a combination of characters such as color, size, and shape of the shell, dextrality or sinistrality, and so forth. The racial characteristics vary from valley to valley with no consistent relation either to the geographical sequence or to the peculiarities of the environment. Populations of adjacent valleys may differ more widely in some characters than populations of valleys remote from each other. Different species inhabiting the same territory may vary in different directions. Thus, the shells of *Partula taeniata* in the northwestern part of the island or Moorea are smaller and stouter, and those of *Partula suturalis* are longer and more slender than in other parts of the island, and yet the two species are found on the same food plants and to all appearances are ecologically identical. Welch (1938) found that populations of *Achatinella mustellina* on the island of Oahu form significantly different colonies within the same valley, and in fact within a few meters from each other. Diver

(1939, 1940) described the same situation in several snail species in England. An average colony of *Cepaea hortensis* is estimated to consist of 79 individuals, although colonies vary numerically from ten to more than 2,000 individuals. The variation may be extremely localized. Thus, in a population continuously occupying a 45-yard strip, all subsamples for 25 yards yielded some brown-colored shells, while in the next 20 yards no browns were found.

In animals with good means of locomotion and in plants with effective mechanisms for the spreading of seeds the situation is the same in principle as in the snails, although the absolute distances which separate the colonies may be of a different order. Kramer and Mertens (1938) have examined the colonial and racial variations in the lizards inhabiting the islands of an archipelago in the Adriatic Sea. The magnitude of the difference between an island population and that of the mainland was found to be positively correlated with the length of time elapsed since the separation of the island from the mainland, as measured by depth of the intervening straits or channels. More important still, the divergence has progressed further on small islands on which the populations are numerically limited than on large islands of equal geological age. Mayr (1940) formulates similar rules to apply to racial variation in nonmarine birds of the islands in the Pacific Ocean. Dice (1939) points out that in mice the populations of even geologically young islands are apt to be racially different from those of the adjacent mainland; moreover, the individual variability of the mainland populations is greater than that of the insular ones. This is exactly what would be expected if the formation of insular races were due to restriction of population sizes.

Islandlike conditions are common on continents as well. For organisms adapted to climatic and ecological conditions found in the mountains, warm lowlands form barriers as effective as sea straits. Colonies of lowland or desert species may be rigidly isolated by mountain ranges and rivers. Mayr (1940) tabulates the proportions of endemic species and races on two oceanic islands near New Guinea and three mountain ranges isolated by lowlands of New Guinea. The percentage of endemism on the islands varies from 56 to 59 and on the mountain ranges from 27 to 60. Taxonomic papers dealing with zoological and botanical materials are replete with examples of this type. In the absence of definite ecological barriers, isolation by distance may come into play. Welch's and Diver's observations on snails have already been cited. Dice (1940a) states that populations of the mouse *Peromyscus leucopus* "living in three different woodlots in the near vicinity of Ann Arbor, Michigan, differ about as much from one another in body dimensions and in pelage color as do populations of the subspecies living hundreds of miles apart." For such strictly local and geographically irregular variations the expression "microgeographic race" has been introduced (in the first edition of this book).

The writer observed microgeographic races in the ladybird beetle *Sospita vigintiguttata*. In this species there are two clearly distinct and undoubtedly hereditary forms, one of which has black and the other yellow elytra with ten white spots on each. In the neighborhood of Kiev (Russia) several dozen colonies were observed which contained black and yellow specimens in ratios approaching equality. One colony contained, however, only blacks and another colony only yellows. This condition persisted for at least three consecutive years. The butterfly *Anthocharis cethura*, living in the foothills of the mountain ranges in southern California, has two distinct color forms among the females. The so-called typical form of the species has a yellow, and the form *deserti* a white, tip on the forewing. Mr. Charles Rudkin kindly informs me that in most localities where the species has been collected a large majority of individuals are yellow, and the whites constitute no more than 5 percent of the population. A single locality is known, however, a valley of a few square kilometers in area, in which the frequency of whites approaches 50 per cent. On either side of this exceptional valley, populations with normal frequencies of white and yellow individuals have been recorded.

Needless to say, there is probably no sharp dividing line between the microgeographic and the major geographic races; the two merge into each other, and perhaps the former might be regarded as a vestige from which the latter may develop. From perfectly irregular local variants, such as those observed in *Peromyscus*, *Sospita* and *Anthocharis*, we pass to local races showing some indications of a relation to the environment (such as those described in the fish *Zoarces viviparus* by Schmidt, 1917, 1923), and finally to races occupying more or less continuously definite geographical territories.

POPULATION SIZE: INFERENCES FROM THE GENIC VARIABILITY IN DROSOPHILA

As shown in Chapter III, natural populations of *Drosophila* and of other cross-fertilizing organisms carry a wealth of concealed genic and chromosomal variability. This variability is controlled by several factors, such as mutation and selection rates, inbreeding, and the effective population size. It follows, then, that analysis of the variability might yield an insight into the working of these factors, and permit, as well, at least a rough quantitative estimation of the magnitude of some or of all of them. Recessive autosomal lethals and chromosomal changes of the inversion type are most favorable materials for such studies. This is because autosomal lethals and extreme semilethals, provided they are completely recessive, do not affect the viability of the heterozygous carriers, while the viability of the homozygotes under natural conditions may be taken to be zero. Inversions, if they are not connected with position effects and do not permit the occurrence of certain types of crossovers leading to formation of inviable chromosomes, affect the viability of their carriers very slightly or not at all. The viability of these genetic changes is, consequently, not an unknown quantity. Experimental determination of the viability of other classes of genetic changes is a very difficult task, which becomes almost beyond reach if the viability under the conditions in which the species naturally lives is to be determined.

The genotype of an organism contains many genes capable of producing lethal alleles by mutation. In infinitely large panmictic populations the equilibrium value for any recessive autosomal lethal equals the square root of the mutation rate giving rise to this particular lethal. In populations of small effective size the gene frequencies vary, however, at random, within a range that is inversely correlated with the population size (N). In a small colony some of the lethals will be altogether absent, others may be as common as their mutation rates would permit them to be in large populations, and still others may be even more frequent. Wright (1937) showed that in a species segregated into numerous colonies with small breeding populations, each lethal will at any given time be present in a certain proportion of the colonies and absent in others. To put it in a different way, each colony will at any time contain only a fraction of the total variety of lethals which may exist in the species. Moreover, the average equilibrium frequencies of all lethals in a species as a whole will be smaller if the species is subdivided into small colonies than if it represents a very large undivided population. For a lethal which arises by mutation once in 100,000 gametes the relationships will be, according to Wright, as follows:

Population Size, N	Equilibrium Frequency, q	Percent of the Colonies Free of the Lethal
1,000,000 or more	0.0032	0
100,000	0.0030	0
10,000	0.0020	15
1,000	0.0008	87
100	0.00026	99
10	0.00008	99.9
Self-fertilization	0.00002	99.996

If a species like *Drosophila pseudoobscura* is a single breeding population, or if it is subdivided into very large breeding units, there should be no differentiation with respect to either the kind or the frequencies of the lethals present in various component populations. The frequencies of all lethals should equal the square roots of their respective mutation rates. This is, however, certainly not the case. Table 7 shows that in populations inhabiting the Death Valley region 13.54 ± 0.44 percent of the third chromosomes carry lethals or extreme semilethals. In Mexico and Guatemala, 30.00 ± 2.82 percent of the chromosomes carry such changes. The mutation rates producing the lethals are the same in the Death Valley strains on one hand and in the strains from Mexico and Guatemala on the other (see below). Therefore, the difference in the degree to which the lethals are allowed to accumulate indicates that the effective sizes of the populations are smaller in Death Valley than they are in Mexico and Guatemala. The climates of Mexico and Guatemala permit *D. pseudoobscura* to breed more or less continuously throughout the year, while in the mountains of the Death Valley region (California) the populations are periodically reduced

by the severe winters or the hot and arid summers or both (Dobzhansky 1939a). Periodic shrinkages result in a reduction of the
genetically effective size of a population (see p. 166).

In populations of *Drosophila pseudoobscura* from different localities, different sets of lethals are frequent (Dobzhansky and Wright
1941). In 1937, population samples were taken on ten mountain
ranges in the Death Valley region. Each sample consisted of flies
caught in a dozen traps placed in a line from a quarter of a mile
to half a mile long. The mountain ranges are from ten to more than
a hundred miles distant from each other, and are isolated by intervening arid deserts where the fly is very rare or absent. Third
chromosome lethals were detected in every sample. The strains containing the lethals were then intercrossed to determine how frequently these lethals are allelic. Some of the lethals were found
twice, and even four times, within the sample from a single locality,
and not found at all in samples from other localities. This may have
been due to the fact that the samples were small. The size of the
samples does not, however, affect the validity of the following observation: lethals from the same locality are allelic more frequently
than those from different localities. Among 772 intercrosses in which
both lethals were derived from the same population, 24 intercrosses,
or 3.11 ± 0.42 percent, contained allelic lethals. By contrast, only
0.407 ± 0.061 percent (20 among 4,913) of the intercrosses in
which the lethals came from different localities contained alleles.

These results were confirmed and extended in another study (unpublished), in which population samples were taken repeatedly,
at about monthly intervals during the breeding season, at nine
stations on Mount San Jacinto, California. Each "station" is in
this case a territory of at most a hundred yards square, in which
fifteen traps are exposed always in the same position. The nine
stations are in three groups or "localities." The distances between
the localities are from ten to fifteen miles, while the distances between the stations within a locality vary from a quarter of a mile
to two miles. In contrast to the work in the Death Valley region,
all the San Jacinto samples come from a territory which is nearly
continuously inhabited by the flies, and has no insuperable barriers
to migration from station to station or from locality to locality.

Nevertheless, the chances of allelism of the third chromosome lethals were found to be as follows (in percent):

Within a station:
    Collected simultaneously   2.081 ± 0.347
    Collected at different times   1.961 ± 0.243
Different stations within a locality:
    Collected simultaneously   1.194 ± 0.243
    Collected at different times   0.691 ± 0.173
In different localities   0.435 ± 0.119

It is clear that different sets of lethals accumulate not only in populations residing ten to fifteen miles apart, but even in populations of stations at distances of two miles or less in a continuously inhabited territory. As a matter of fact, no significant difference in the chances of allelism was observed among lethals collected in different localities on San Jacinto and those collected on San Jacinto and in the Death Valley region (a distance of two hundred miles or more).

Usually, the cause of recurrence of the same lethal within a population is the fact that lethal-bearing chromosomes have a common descent from a single mutation; the occurrence of alleles among lethals from remote populations is almost always due to the independent rise of similar mutations. The knowledge of the chances of allelism enables one to calculate the probable number of loci in the third chromosome of *Drosophila pseudoobscura* which produce lethals by mutation. Wright (Dobzhansky and Wright 1941) has found this number to be about 289. It must be noted that this estimate involves the assumptions that the lethals are completely recessive, and that the mutation rates at all the loci are equal. If these assumptions are incorrect (as they may well be), the figure 289 is an underestimate; it happens, however, that for the purposes for which this figure is used an underestimate is preferable to an overestimate. Through experiments in the laboratory it has been found that the gross mutation rate producing lethals and semilethals in the third chromosome of *D. pseudoobscura* (that is, the sum of the mutation rates at all loci) is 0.307 ± 0.036 percent, or about 3 new lethals per 1,000 gametes per generation. The mutation rate for the strains derived from the Death Valley region is 0.297 ±

0.032, for the Mexican strains 0.359 ± 0.062, and for the Guatemalan ones 0.284 ± 0.061 percent; the differences lie well within the limit of experimental error. With 289 loci producing the lethals, the mutation rate per locus is u = 0.000,0106 (0.003,07 ÷ 289). In an infinitely large population the equilibrium frequency of each lethal is $q = \sqrt{u} = 0.003,209$. Yet only about 15 percent of the chromosomes in the Death Valley region carry lethals. The concentration per locus is q = 0.15 : 289 = 0.000,519.

Taken at its face value, the discrepancy between the observed and the computed equilibrium frequencies indicates very low effective sizes of the population studied. Unfortunately, there are sources of error which may vitiate this conclusion. It must be reiterated that the calculations are based on the assumption that the lethals are completely recessive, and hence that the viability of the heterozygous carriers is not lowered. Experiments devised to test this assumption have so far confirmed it (Dobzhansky 1939a), but it happens that a reduction of the viability of the heterozygotes so small as to be practically undetectable in the experiments would suffice to account for the observed frequencies of the lethals in natural populations. Furthermore, it is possible that in the populations sampled there had been some very local inbreeding, such as mating of the members of the same brood soon after emergence from the pupae. These undefined variables do not affect, however, the validity of the observation that lethals detected within a population are alleles more frequently than those in different localities. This fact permits certain calculations, far too complex to be outlined here, that show that the genetically effective sizes (N) of the populations of *Drosophila pseudoobscura* in the Death Valley region can hardly be higher, and may be much lower, than 2,500. Clearly, this is indicative only of the order of magnitude of value of N. Yet, it should be kept in mind that the problem of population dynamics is now in a state in which even so crude an estimate of the numerical values of the most important variables is desirable to guide further work.

Dubinin and his collaborators (1934, 1936, 1937) have published very extensive data on the genetic composition of the populations of *Drosophila melanogaster* from various localities in the Caucasus and other parts of Russia. Studies were made of mutants producing

visible morphological changes and of lethals, chromosomal variations, genes carried in heterozygous condition, and "aberrations"
representing the rare instances in which the mutant homozygotes
had been produced. The complexes of the genetic changes encountered in different populations proved to differ very appreciably.
Moreover, collections made in successive years showed that the
genetic composition of the population inhabiting a locality may
undergo significant changes from time to time. This is exactly what
is expected to occur in populations of very limited effective size,
and it will be shown below that temporal changes take place also in
D. pseudoobscura populations. *D. melanogaster* is not native to
Russia, and is probably unable to survive the rigors of winter, except for a small number of individuals which may find hiding places
in or near human dwellings. As in many originally tropical species
which had become human commensals or parasites, its populations
are bound to be occasionally reduced to a few survivors and to be
shifted from place to place by human agencies. In another com-
mensal, namely the house mouse, Philip (1938) has obtained data
suggesting that populations from adjacent localities may not represent a single breeding unit.

POPULATION SIZE: INFERENCES FROM THE CHROMOSOMAL
VARIABILITY

We have seen (p. 121, Figs. 8 and 9) that each of the gene arrangements encountered in the third chromosome of *Drosophila
pseudoobscura* is restricted to a definite part of the distribution area
of the species, although in most localities more than one, and sometimes as many as six, gene arrangements occur in the same population. Individuals hetero- and homozygous for each arrangement or
combination of arrangements occur in the populations studied with
frequencies predictable with the aid of Hardy's formula, on the
assumption that matings of the individuals carrying the various
arrangements are at random. If population samples are taken from
localities a hundred or more miles apart, the frequencies of the different arrangements are usually found to change gradually in some
geographically definite direction. An example of geographical gradients is given in Table 14, in which the localities are arranged
roughly from west to east.

If, however, population samples are taken in localities twenty or less miles apart, the variation tends to become geographically haphazard. Thus, among the ten samples from as many isolated mountain ranges in the Death Valley region (see p. 178), only three populations failed to show statistically significant differences in the frequencies of the gene arrangements in the third chromosome. The remaining seven differed from the three, as well as from each other. Samples from neighboring ranges proved, however, to be in some instances more different than samples from remote ranges (Dobzhansky and Queal 1938a). That this geographical irregularity is purely local can be shown by combining all the samples from the

TABLE 14

FREQUENCIES (IN PERCENTS) OF SOME OF THE GENE ARRANGEMENTS IN THE THIRD CHROMOSOME OF *Drosophila pseudoobscura* ENCOUNTERED IN POPULATIONS INHABITING THE SOUTHWESTERN UNITED STATES

LOCALITY OR REGION	GENE ARRANGEMENTS				CHROMOSOMES EXAMINED
	Standard	Arrow-head	Chiri-cahua	Pikes Peak	
Santa Barbara, California	46.2	20.5	17.1	—	346
San Jacinto Mts., California	39.0	26.2	31.0	—	8,921
Western Death Valley region	30.9	51.6	15.8	—	2,834
Eastern Death Valley region	17.4	71.1	11.5	—	1,194
Prescott, Arizona	11.0	79.0	9.0	1.0	100
Flagstaff, Arizona	1.0	97.0	1.0	1.0	100
Mesa Verde, Colorado	—	100.0	—	—	100
Raton Pass, New Mexico	—	80.0	0.9	18.2	110
Trans-Pecos region, Texas	1.4	35.9	3.5	53.5	142
North central Texas	—	21.5	—	70.2	1,315
South central Texas	0.2	11.7	—	70.3	418

western half of the region and comparing the figures so obtained with the corresponding combination of all the samples from the eastern half. It may be seen in Table 14 that the differences between such combined samples are of the kind that could be expected from the knowledge of the major geographical clines.

Koller (1939a) found that population samples from localities five to ten miles apart on one of the mountain ranges in the Death Valley region differ to about the same extent as do samples from different ranges. Moreover, he found that the sample taken in a certain locality in 1938 differed in composition from that taken in the same locality by Dobzhansky in 1937. An indication of the inconstancy of the genetic composition of the population of *Droso-*

phila pseudoobscura in a given locality in successive years was observed also by Dobzhansky and Sturtevant (1938). The phenomenon of the temporal changes in the population genotype is being studied by the writer (unpublished) through comparison of population samples taken at intervals of a few weeks during the breeding season at the nine stations on Mount San Jacinto (see p. 178). A specimen of the data is shown in Table 15, which illustrates the fluctuations observed in the populations at one of the nine stations.

The changes observed are not entirely haphazard, since successive samples tend to be more similar in composition than samples

TABLE 15

FREQUENCIES (IN PERCENT) OF THE GENE ARRANGEMENTS IN THE THIRD CHROMOSOME OF *Drosophila pseudoobscura* IN SAMPLES TAKEN AT DIFFERENT TIMES IN THE SAME TERRITORY

| DATE OF COLLECTION | GENE ARRANGEMENTS | | | | CHROMO-SOMES EXAMINED |
	Standard	Arrow-head	Chiri-cahua	Others	
April 24, 1939	48.7	33.3	15.4	2.6	39
May 13–14, 1939	30.8	35.8	27.5	5.8	120
June 21–22, 1939	32.8	37.1	26.7	3.5	116
August 19–20, 1939	34.7	33.3	23.6	8.3	72
September 19–20, 1939	49.0	21.0	24.0	6.0	100
October 21–22, 1939	56.0	24.6	13.6	5.7	134
March 3, 1940	49.0	16.0	29.9	6.0	100
March 28–29, 1940	39.5	24.6	30.7	5.2	114
April 21, 1940	34.9	18.6	41.9	5.7	86
May 10, 1940	31.4	31.4	35.3	2.0	102
June 1–2, 1940	29.4	29.4	39.7	1.5	68
September 14–15, 1940	34.6	25.0	37.5	2.9	104
November 2, 1940	37.5	32.5	26.3	3.7	80

more remote in time; on the other hand, the trend indicated by a series of successive observations may become reversed later on. Thus, at the station shown in Table 15 the frequency of the Standard gene arrangement was rising in 1939, falling in the spring of 1940, and, perhaps, rising again in the fall of 1940. The populations at stations other than that illustrated in Table 15 were in some cases more, and in other cases less, constant in composition. It is important to note that the populations inhabiting localities ten to fifteen miles apart on Mount San Jacinto have preserved their differences during the period of observation, although the temporal fluctuations in some of them were so great that the more permanent differences were at times close to obliteration. It is not as yet clear whether the trends of change are like or unlike at all the stations, but the accumulating material seems to show that they are different. It is hazardous to draw definite conclusions, as the collection and analysis of the data are unfinished. The character of the chromosomal variability in *Drosophila pseudoobscura*, and especially the temporal changes observed in its populations, seem best accounted for on the assumption that the genetically effective sizes of these populations are small.

Still another evidence of the role of the restriction of population size in the evolution of *Drosophila* is afforded by the occurrence of translocations and pericentric inversions among species differentials (see Chapter IV). Heterozygosis for these chromosomal changes leads to the production of some gametes with abnormal gene complements, and hence to a semisterility of the heterozygotes. In species which reproduce exclusively by cross-fertilization, newly arisen translocations and pericentric inversions can occur only as heterozygotes, that is, as individuals which carry one normal and one altered set of chromosomes. In large panmictic populations the spread and establishment of such changes will be opposed by natural selection, which inevitably tends to eliminate any semisterile types. The possibility that some of the translocations would be associated with position effects so favorable as to overbalance the handicap of the semisterility is remote. How, then, are translocations and pericentric inversions established, though rarely, in cross-fertilizing species? It must be kept in mind that, in homozygous condition, translocations and pericentric inversions are not intrinsically inferior to the ancestral types. As a matter of fact, in a population in which more than fifty percent of the chromosomes carry such inversions or translocations, the ancestral, and not the modified, gene arrangement will be the one opposed by natural selection. The difficulty which these changes encounter in becoming established in a population would be removed by any agent permitting them to attain the frequency of fifty or more percent of the total number of chromosomes. Restrictions of the effective breeding size of a population could be such an agent (Wright 1940a, b). If the population is occasionally reduced to very few individuals, it may happen by chance that the survivors are translocation or inversion carriers. When the population expands again, it may contain approximately equal numbers of chromosomes of the ancestral and the modified type. Complete elimination of the ancestral type may then take place. If the population in question has, in addition to the translocations or inversions, some favorable genetic characters, it may grow and spread until it becomes the typical form of the species.

To recapitulate: restriction of the genetically effective size of natural populations is in all probability an important agent engendering differentiation of species into local groups possessing different genotypes. It must be admitted that, except in some relic species and in *Drosophila pseudoobscura,* we do not have even approximate estimates of the magnitude of population numbers. And yet, a large and rapidly growing amount of evidence pertaining to different subdivisions of the living world and secured by different methods and by different biological disciplines, attests the existence of phenomena which can most plausibly be accounted for by genetic "drift" in populations of limited sizes. Although it would certainly be premature to conclude that evolution in all groups and at all times is conditioned by the genetic drift, it is reasonable to assume that it is frequently assisted by this factor, the importance of which has only recently become appreciated.

VI: SELECTION

ADUMBRATED in classical antiquity, the principle of natural selection was raised to the status of a scientific theory by Darwin. With consummate mastery Darwin shows natural selection to be a direct consequence of the appallingly great reproductive powers of living beings. A single individual of the fungus *Lycoperdon bovista* produces 7×10^{11} spores; *Sisymbrium sophia* and *Nicotiana tabacum*, respectively, 730,000 and 360,000 seed; salmon, 28,000,000 eggs per season; and the American oyster up to 114,-000,000 eggs in a single spawning. Even the slowest breeding forms produce more offspring than can survive if the population is to remain numerically stationary. Death and destruction of a majority of the individuals produced undoubtedly takes place. If, then, the population is composed of a mixture of hereditary types, some of which are more and others less well adapted to the environment, a greater proportion of the former than of the latter would be expected to survive. In modern language this means that, among the survivors, a greater frequency of carriers of certain genes or chromosome structures would be present than among the ancestors, and consequently the values q and (1-q) will alter from generation to generation.

During the years that have elapsed since the publication of the theory of natural selection, it has been the subject of unceasing debate. The most serious objection raised against it is that it takes for granted the existence, and does not explain the origin, of the hereditary variations with which selection can work. Those who advance this objection fail however to notice that in so doing they commit an act of supererogation: the origin of variation is a problem entirely separate from that of the action of selection. The theory of natural selection is concerned with the fate of variations already present, and the merits and demerits of the theory must be assessed accordingly. In the beginning of the present century, real progress was made when Johannsen showed that selection is effective in genetically mixed populations but inoperative in genetically uniform ones. Johannsen's work was preceded by De Vries's discovery of the origin of hereditary variations through the occurrence of mutations. Following this discovery, some writers contended that De Vries and Johannsen had disproved Darwin's theory of evolution by natural selection and had supplanted it by a theory of evolution by mutation. The polemics that ensued around this weird contention both in popular and in scientific literature seems in retrospect to have been a sort of modern confusion of tongues. It is hardly necessary to reiterate that the theory of mutation relates to a different level of the evolutionary process than that on which selection is supposed to operate, and therefore the two theories cannot be conceived as conflicting alternatives. On the other hand, the discovery of the origin of hereditary variation through mutation may account for the presence in natural populations of the materials without which selection is known to be ineffective. The greatest difficulty in Darwin's general theory of evolution, of the existence of which Darwin himself was well aware, is hereby mitigated or removed.

In its essence, the theory of natural selection is primarily an attempt to give an account of the probable mechanism of the origin of the adaptations of the organisms to their environment, and only secondarily an attempt to explain evolution at large. Some modern biologists seem to believe that the word "adaptation" has teleological connotations, and should therefore be expunged from the scientific lexicon. With this we must emphatically disagree. That adaptations exist is so evident as to be almost a truism, although this need not mean that ours is the best of all possible worlds. A biologist has no right to close his eyes to the fact that the precarious balance between a living being and its environment must be preserved by some mechanism or mechanisms if life is to endure. No coherent attempts to account for the origin of adaptations other than the theory of natural selection and the theory of the inheritance of acquired characteristics have ever been proposed. Whether or not these theories are adequate for the purpose just stated is a real issue.

Whether the theory of natural selection explains not only adaptation but evolution as well is quite another matter. The answer here would depend in part on the conclusion we may arrive at on the problem of the relation between the two phenomena. No agreement on this issue has been reached as yet. Fisher (1936), who is probably one of the most extreme among the modern selectionists, has expressed his opinion very concisely as follows: "For these two theories (Lamarckism and selectionism) evolution is progressive adaptation and consists of nothing else. The production of differences recognizable by systematists is a secondary by-product, produced incidentally in the process of becoming better adapted." And further: "For rational systems of evolution, that is for theories which make at least the most familiar facts intelligible to the reason, we must turn to those that make progressive adaptation the driving force of the process." A good contrast to this is provided by the statement of Robson and Richards (1936): "We do not believe that natural selection can be disregarded as a possible factor in evolution. Nevertheless, there is so little positive evidence in its favor . . . that we have no right to assign to it the main causative rôle in evolution."

LABORATORY EXPERIMENTS ON NATURAL SELECTION

Natural selection in the laboratory may seem to be a contradiction in terms. This is, of course, a matter of definition. Artificial selection, in contrast to the natural, involves a control by man of the reproduction of the organism through choice of individuals which are to be preserved and bred; it is immaterial whether the choice is made with a deliberate intention and a foreknowledge of the result, or merely to suit the fancy of the selector. Placing an organism in an environment in which certain biotypes may have an advantage over others does not constitute a choice by man of the producers of the succeeding generations. Natural selection, of course, continues to operate in domestic as well as in wild forms, and it is perfectly logical to assert that certain changes have taken place in the domesticated animals and plants because of natural selection. At any rate, it is legitimate to inquire whether a change in the environment, either artificially created or produced by natural causes, can induce changes in organisms through a differential survival of genetic types in the new environment.

A promising technique for laboratory studies on natural selection in *Drosophila* has been devised by L'Heritier and Teissier (1934, 1937). Twenty containers with *Drosophila* culture medium are placed in a box so constructed that one container of food can be withdrawn every day and a fresh one substituted, without permitting the flies to escape or unduly disturbing them. Known numbers of flies of desired kinds are introduced into the box; samples of the developing populations can be taken for examination when wished. L'Heritier and Teissier have shown that in a mixture of the wild type *D. melanogaster* and its dominant mutant Bar the frequency of the mutant drops rather rapidly; the same is true for the autosomal recessive mutant vestigial; the autosomal recessive ebony is reduced in frequency at first, but after some time the population tends to be stabilized at a level of about ninety percent wild type to ten percent ebony. This is apparently due to the heterozygote wild/ebony being superior, in the case of the strains used in these experiments, to either wild/wild or ebony/ebony homozygotes. If, however, a mixed population of the wild type (winged) and vestigial (very short wings, incapable of flight) is kept in a place open to wind, it is the vestigial, rather than the wild type, which increases in frequency (L'Heritier, Neefs, and Teissier 1937). Nikoro and Gussev (1938) have kept mixtures of mutants and wild type *Drosophila melanogaster* in large jars, from which 100 pupae were taken in every generation to start a new culture. The results of these experiments are on the whole similar to those of L'Heritier and Teissier, except that the observed course of selection is very irregular because of the restriction of the effective population size. Unfortunately, the technique used by Nikoro and Gussev is open to certain objections.

The phenomena of bacterial transformation have been outlined in Chapter II. Most of these transformations can be simply accounted for on the assumption that a variety of mutations arise, each with a certain frequency, in bacterial strains. In any given environment a certain biotype or biotypes are selected to become the dominant components of the culture. Loss of virulence, "degeneration," and "involution" may be regarded as processes adapting the organisms to the media in which they occur. Since mutation is usually reversible, the bacterial transformations are likewise reversible in most cases. Although some bacteriologists are prone to believe that the behavior of bacteria is incompatible with established concepts of genetics and evolution theory, there are valid reasons to think that bacteria may prove to be the best available material for exact studies on mutation and natural selection.

HISTORICAL CHANGES IN THE COMPOSITION OF POPULATIONS

Darwin and his immediate followers were willing to concede that evolution is not observed directly but inferred from a body of morphological data. It is obviously impossible to reproduce in the laboratory the evolution of, for example, the horse tribe or of the anthropoid apes. Evolution was supposed to be so slow that no changes could be noticed within a human lifetime in wild species. The relatively rapid changes brought about in domestic animals and cultivated plants by artificial selection were considered a model of the evolution in the wild state, rather than evolution as such. Since Darwin's time, several instances of historical changes in wild species have been recorded; we still have to admit that major evolutionary steps are beyond reach of direct observation, but we need not make such a concession regarding microevolutionary processes. Temporal changes in *Drosophila pseudoobscura* have been discussed in the preceding chapter. It happens, however, that these changes are, in all probability, due to the genetic drift in populations of a limited effective size, and not to selection. Instances now to be reviewed unmistakably owe their origin to natural selection.

Fumigation with hydrocyanic gas is the most efficient known method of controlling species of scale insects (*Coccidae*), attacking the citrus trees in California. The concentration of the gas sufficient to kill nearly 100 percent of individual scales had been worked out and applied at regular intervals. In 1914 it was noticed that in orchards near Corona the standard fumigation was insufficient to destroy the red scale (*Aonidiella aurantii*), although in previous years no difficulty had been encountered. This condition has not only persisted in the Corona district ever since 1914, but has spread

to several other citrus-producing areas; in other localities the standard fumigation continues to give satisfactory results (Fig. 16).

Experiments of Quayle (1938) and his collaborators showed that
the field experiences with fumigation are due to the presence
of two races of the red scale, one of which is nonresistant while the
other is relatively resistant to the hydrocyanic gas. Thus, Dickson
(1940) finds that the exposure for 40 minutes at 24° C. to the concentration of 0.188 mg. of HCN per liter of air permits the survival
of only 4.06 percent of individuals of the nonresistant, and of 45.43
percent of the resistant, race. A similar exposure to 0.351 mg. of
HCN per liter of air leaves 0.75 percent survivors in the nonresist-

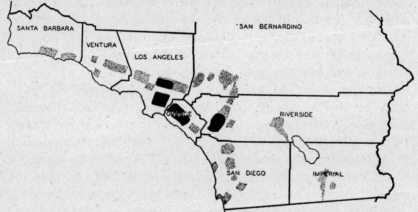

FIG. 16. The distribution of the resistant (black) and of the nonresistant
(stippled) races of the red scale (*Aonidiella aurantii*) in southern California. (After Quayle.)

ant and 22.37 percent in the resistant race. Dickson has, moreover,
made crosses of the two races. The F_1 is intermediate in resistance,
and in the F_2 a segregation takes place which shows that the two
races differ in a single sex-linked gene. The question whether the
gene for resistance in the Corona population arose by mutation or
was introduced from elsewhere is largely academic. The former of
these two possibilities is on the whole more probable; the populations of the red scale in badly infested orchards are numerically so
great that even if the mutation rate producing the gene for resistance is very low, say of the order of one per million, several mutant
individuals should be present in the citrus-growing area at any time.
However that may be, the emergence of the resistant race of the

red scale is clearly due to the differential survival of the two genotypes in fumigated orchards.

The subsequent spread of the resistant race might result either
from introduction of some resistant individuals from the vicinity
of Corona to neighboring territories, or from selection of independently arisen mutants in orchards in which the fumigation is
practiced regularly. Professor H. S. Smith very kindly informs me
that some preliminary observations indicate that the reproductive
potential of the resistant race is lower than that of the nonresistant
one in the absence of fumigation. If these observations are confirmed, it will follow, as Professor Smith quite justifiably points out,
that the equilibrium between the gene for resistance and its normal
allele is a function of the intensity of fumigation of the orchards.
The fact that the gene for resistance is semidominant should greatly
accelerate the selection process compared to what would happen to
an autosomal recessive with similar properties.

The case of the red scale is unique in that not only the physiology but also the inheritance of the resistance have been examined.
Otherwise, it is closely paralleled by other instances of the appearance of races resistant to HCN. In 1925 the standard fumigation
failed to destroy the citricola scale, *Coccus pseudomagnoliarum,* in
a small area near Riverside, California. From 1925 to 1933 the
resistant race spread very rapidly and came to occupy the entire
area in southern California where the species was recorded. Between October, 1933 and the spring of 1934, however, the species
practically disappeared, owing to an unknown cause. In 1936 it
began to reappear in a few groves; test fumigations in 1937 showed
that the resistant race is building up its population (Quayle 1938).
A cyanide resistant race of the black scale *Saissetia oleae* appeared
near Charter Oak, Los Angeles County, as far back as 1913. By
1925 it spread over a solidly planted citrus belt for a distance of
about forty miles. Attempts to control it by HCN fumigation had
to be abandoned, and control by oil sprays was introduced (Quayle
1938).

The codling moth (*Carpocapsa pomonella*) is a serious pest attacking apple and pear trees. Various sprays, especially those containing
arsenic, are used for its control. The general experience since the
time of the introduction of these sprays has been that progressively

more and more frequent treatments of the orchards are required for satisfactory control of the pest. Moreover, in different parts of the United States the requirements proved to be dissimilar; notoriously difficult to control is the codling moth in Colorado. Hough (1934), working in Virginia, obtained a Colorado strain and compared it with the native strains from Virginia. Not only has the Colorado strain proved superior to the Virginia one in its ability to enter the apples the surface of which had been sprayed with arsenic or other poison, but in "general vigor" the Colorado strain exceeds the Virginia one when bred in the Virginia environment. The hybrids between these strains are intermediate in the F_1 and in further generations, but the genetic basis of the racial difference is unclear. In the last few decades, the codling moth has undergone still another transformation: after its introduction to the Pacific Coast states in 1873 it appears to have evolved a race which attacks walnut trees as well as apples and pears. In northern California the first attack on walnuts was recorded in 1909; the damage was slight until approximately 1931, and severe thereafter. In southern California walnuts have been attacked since 1913 and seriously damaged since 1918; in Oregon the record on walnuts was secured in 1919 but no important injury is known to have developed as yet (Boyce 1935). There is an interesting difference in the behavior of the caterpillars of the apple and the walnut races, but no appreciable morphological change. Smith (1941) reviews the above instances of racial change and certain others, and points out that economic entomologists are confronted with a situation when methods of control once considered satisfactory may no longer suffice, because the pests to be controlled undergo changes themselves.

Very pronounced changes have been observed in the composition of populations of the stem rust of wheat, *Puccinia graminis tritici*.* Some species of fungi are differentiated into "biological races" adapted to different environments and to different hosts, on which they live as parasites. A variety of *Puccinia graminis* (var. *triciti*), attacks wheat, another attacks rye, oats, *Poa*, and other grasses. The wheat rust is in turn subdivided into numerous biotypes, of which more than a hundred are known, approximately sixty having

* The writer is indebted to Dr. I. W. Tervet for having called his attention to these phenomena.

been recorded in the United States. These biotypes are identified by
testing their ability to infect, and the lesions produced on, about a
dozen different wheat varieties; each wheat variety is immune to
some and easily infected by other biotypes or "forms" (as they are
called in the phytopathological literature), of the rust (Wallace
1932). A census of the frequencies of the different rust forms has
been taken every year in the United States and in Mexico for about
the last decade; the rust population has altered very appreciably
during this period (Stakman, Popham, and Cassell 1940; see that
paper for other references). Thus, form 34 was found in 0.6 per-

TABLE 16

PERCENTAGE OF ISOLATES CONTAINING CERTAIN FORMS OF *Puccinia
graminis tritici* IN DIFFERENT YEARS (after Stakman, Popham, and
Cassell)

YEAR	RACE 38		RACE 49		RACE 56	
	Northern Mexico	United States	Northern Mexico	United States	Northern Mexico	United States
1930	47	30	40	20	0	0.2
1931	35	15	52	25	0	1
1932	43	46	30	27	0	2
1933	47	33	40	37	0	4
1934	12	3	37	7	2	33
1935	22	5	22	1	12	44
1936	12	22	6	1	25	47
1937	26	9	10	7	10	56
1938	37	16	16	1	18	66
1939	28	24	3	1	14	56

cent of the samples tested in 1933, in 22 percent in 1934, and
0.6 percent in 1939; form 36 was found in 36 per cent in 1930 and
0.6 percent in 1939; form 21 in 7 percent in 1934 and not at all in
1939. Form 38 has fluctuated greatly in frequency (Table 16);
form 49 has become rare in the United States. The most striking
change has, however, taken place in the prevalence of form 56,
which was first isolated in Canada in 1927 and first detected in the
United States in two samples from Iowa in 1928.

From the published accounts it is not clear what agents have
caused these tremendous changes in the rust populations. Since the
forms of the rust differ in reaction to climate as well as in ability

to infect wheat varieties, climate fluctuations might have been one of the factors. It must, however, be noted that changes in the wheat populations are taking place as a result of the work of the breeders, who introduce new varieties more or less resistant to forms of the rust prevalent at the time and in the geographic regions where the breeding work is being done. A sort of competition between the artificial selection directed by man at the wheat plant and the natural selection in the rust is apparently being witnessed.

Gradual or explosive expansions or contractions of the geographic areas within historical times have been recorded in many species. The causes of these changes are sometimes known or suspected, but more often they are unknown (Gause 1934). The problem of competition between species falls within the province of ecology rather than that of genetics. Similar instances in which races of the same species are involved are not numerous. The two races of the white fly *Trialeurodes vaporariorum,* in one of which unfertilized eggs produce males and in the other females, may be cited as an example (Schrader 1926). The former race, apparently native to America, was introduced in Europe and spread there rather rapidly. Timofeeff-Ressovsky (1940b) has described reversible changes in the ladybird beetle *Adalia bipunctata,* which are associated with the climatic yearly cycle. This species produces at least two generations per year, hibernates as adult insect, and exhibits gregariousness in its winter quarters. Several color phases, due to a series of multiple alleles, coexist in all European and American populations; these phases may be conveniently classified into a light and a darkly pigmented group. In the vicinity of Berlin the relative frequencies of the dark individuals increase, and those of the light ones diminish, from spring to autumn. In the hibernating masses of the beetles, the mortality is so heavy that the population is decimated during the winter. By examining the hibernating individuals, Timofeeff-Ressovsky has been able to show that the proportion of survival is greater among the light than among the dark phase. It appears, then, that the dark biotypes are superior to the light ones during the breeding season, but the opposite is the case in winter. In the opinion of Ford (1937, 1940a), situations of this sort are common among polymorphic species of butterflies and other organisms.

The appearance and spread of melanic variants in several species of moths have become widely known and frequently quoted in the biological literature (see Harrison 1920, Hasebroek 1934, and Ford 1937 for references). Variants more darkly pigmented than the norm appear in the population, and in the course of several decades become more frequent than the original form, finally supplanting the latter. In a number of instances the melanic forms have been shown experimentally to differ from the paler relatives in a single or in a few genes. The apparently well-authenticated fact is that the first appearance of the melanic forms is always recorded in the vicinity of large industrial cities, and that the spread of the new variants goes hand in hand with the industrialization of the countries in question. The first records of increased melanism were secured in the industrial districts of England in the middle of the nineteenth century. Thus, the melanic form of *Amphidasys betularia* was observed originally in Manchester in 1850 and in the twentieth century has superseded the normal form. In Germany the development of "industrial melanism" was observed somewhat later, beginning with the Rhine district and the environs of Hamburg. Still later, analogous phenomena appeared in France and in other countries. The agents that bring about industrial melanism are obscure. Ford (1937, 1940b) finds evidence that melanics are superior to the light-colored types in vigor, and supposes that their spread in populations is normally prevented because they are not protectively colored. In industrial areas this disability is removed by the general darkening of the landscape. Comparative studies on the physiology of the dark and the light forms of the same species would, indeed, seem to be the most hopeful source of information on the selection mechanisms which bring about industrial melanism.

EXPERIMENTAL STUDY OF ADAPTATION IN PLANTS

Populations of most if not all species are mixtures of several biotypes which differ in their fitness for different environments. A change in the environment is a challenge to the species living in it to modify their genotypes in the direction of higher adaptive levels. Species may respond to this challenge by a sorting-out process, which results in increasing the frequencies of the component biotypes that are most suitable, and in reducing those less suitable, in the new environment. In some instances the response is rapid enough to be observed directly. Thus, the red scale has responded to fumigation with hydrocyanic gas by "developing" a cyanide-resistant race. As a counterpart to this successful response, many animal and plant species have been rendered extinct through the changes wrought by man in their habitats. These species either did not possess biotypes fit to survive in the modified environment, or else were unable to effect the transformation quickly enough.

The environment is, however, not uniform throughout the distribution areas of most species. Each habitat has a set of environmental coördinates which are, as a rule, more or less constant during short time intervals. The variation of the environment from habitat to habitat constitutes a challenge similar in principle to that arising from environmental variations in the course of time. The species responds to the challenge of diversified habitats by becoming differentiated into local races. Each local race consists of a group of biotypes having the highest adaptive value in the environment prevailing in the particular class of habitats. The term "ecotype" has been proposed for races "arising as a result of the genotypical response" of a species to a particular type of habitats (Turesson 1922). Experimental work on plant ecotypes was begun in the nineteenth century by Bonnier and Kerner von Marilaun, but it is the Swedish botanist and geneticist Turesson (1922, 1925, 1926, 1929, 1930, 1931) who must be credited with having placed it on a truly scientific basic. Outstanding contributions have also been made by the school of Turrill (a review in Turrill 1940) and Gregor (1938, 1939), and by Clausen, Keck, and Hiesey (1940). It is well known that the plant phenotype can be greatly modified by the environment, and classical botanists were inclined to regard the differences exhibited by a species in different habitats as purely environmental. Turesson showed by means of extensive experiments that if representatives of a species from different habitats are grown together in an experimental garden, they and their offspring frequently preserve their distinctive characteristics. These characteristics are hereditary. The method of reciprocal transplants is even more instructive. Representatives of the population of the habitat A are transplanted in the habitat B, and those from B are planted in A.

Comparison of the native and transplanted strains permits the observer to discriminate between the changes induced directly by the environment and those intrinsic to the strains themselves.

Californian ecotypes of *Potentilla glandulosa,* a species studied by Clausen, Keck, and Hiesey (1940), may serve as examples. One of the ecotypes occurs at low elevations in the Coast Ranges of California. This habitat has a rainless summer and an equable climate permitting the plants to grow almost throughout the year. Two other ecotypes occupy respectively the dry slopes and the meadows in the foothills of the Sierra Nevada Mountains. Here the climate is more continental, with much snow in winter and some rain in summer which is nevertheless rather hot. The subalpine and alpine ecotypes occur in the highest reaches of the Sierra Nevada, where the growing season is very short, winters are cold, and precipitation is relatively abundant. The coastal and the foothill ecotypes, when transplanted in each other's environments, do no thrive quite as well as they do in their native habitats. Nevertheless, the coastal ecotype becomes dormant during the winter in the foothills, and the foothill ecotypes remain active during most of the winter on the coast. The foothill meadow ecotype flowers about a month later on the coast than the foothill slope ecotype does, but their fruits ripen nevertheless almost simultaneously. The coastal and the foothill slope ecotypes seldom survive for a year when transplanted in the alpine zone; the foothill meadow ecotype does a little better than the others in the alpine environment. None of these ecotypes produce ripe seeds in the alpine zone, although they may flower before the advent of the killing frosts. The alpine ecotypes are dwarfish in their own environment. They remain so when planted in the coast, are dormant from mid-November to mid-February, prove to be very susceptible to diseases, and are injured by the dry summers. Yet, they grow rather tall in the foothills, where they appear to be in general more vigorous than in their own environment. We need not describe in detail the morphological differences between the ecotypes. The dwarfishness of the alpine ecotypes has been mentioned already; other differences involve pubescence, color of the flowers, stems, and seeds, and self-fertility versus self-sterility. The chromosome numbers are alike, fertile hybrids with regular chromosome conjugation are obtained, and, with respect to at least some characters, all the variations found in natural populations may be observed among the segregation products of a single cross.

It should be noted that the relations between the morphological characters distinguishing the ecotypes of *Potentilla glandulosa* and the physiological properties determining their fitness in various environments remain rather unclear, although Clausen, Keck, and Hiesey (1940) record some indications of a genetic linkage between these attributes. It seems virtually certain that geographical races in general are adapted to the environments in which they have developed and in which they live, and hence are ecotypes by Turesson's definition. Nevertheless, gaining an insight into the adaptive significance of many of the characteristics distinguishing geographical races is a highly vexatious problem. What, for example, is the adaptive value of the eye colors or of the nose shapes distinguishing the human races? In this respect, a great interest attaches to instances in which a certain constellation of heritable traits recurs in populations of a species in a definite type of habitat wherever that type of habitat is encountered in the distribution area of the species. Thus, the alpine ecotype (the subspecies *nevadensis*) of *Potentilla glandulosa*, occurs at high elevations throughout the Sierra Nevada and the Cascade Range of southern Oregon; subspecies *reflexa*, the foothill slope ecotype, the subspecies *Hanseni*, the foothill meadow ecotype, recur in their respective habitats in an altitudinal belt of the Sierra Nevada below that occupied by the alpine ecotype. According to Clausen, Keck, and Hiesey, representatives of the same ecotype from remote localities may not be identical, presumably because of a secondary differentiation into a sort of subecotypes, but they do seem to preserve certain characteristics in common.

Even more striking are examples of the occurrence of analogous ecotypes in different parts of the species distribution area in which similar ecological conditions are prevalent. Thus, the sea-cliff ecotype and the sand-dune ecotype of *Hieracium umbellatum* recur wherever the proper habitats are available; on the southern coast of Sweden these habitats alternate, and so do the ecotypes (Turesson 1922). The same phenomenon may be observed on a grander scale in alpine ecotypes. Populations of *Solidago virgaurea* from the alpine zone of Scandinavia and of the Altai Mountains have certain convergent characteristics (low growth and earliness), which distinguish them from populations of the same species residing in the adjacent foothills and lowlands. In the European Alps a subalpine ecotype of *Solidago virgaurea* is present. In other plants alpine ecotypes had been formed, however, only in Scandinavia, or only in the Alps, whereupon a given species occupies the alpine habitats in one of these regions but is barred from such habitats in the other (Turesson 1925, 1931). The ability of some species to evolve convergent ecotypes in remote but ecologically similar regions is as interesting as the failure of other species to do so. Convergent ecotypes may be formed by selection of analogous genotypic constituents: similar challenges evoke similar responses. But a challenge does not in itself insure the occurrence of the response, since a species may not have the proper genetic variants available when they are needed, even though that species is potentially able to produce such variants.

The adaptive value of some ecotypes of the dandelion (*Taraxacum officinale*) has been studied by Sukatschew (1928). Three plants were collected on the same meadow near Leningrad, and the strains, denoted as A, B, and C, respectively, were established from them; the strains proved to be morphologically recognizable. Seedlings were planted on experimental plots in two densities, namely, at a distance of three and of eighteen centimeters from each other, respectively. On some plots, representatives of a single strain, and on others of all three strains, were planted. After a lapse of two years the number of surviving individuals was counted. The percentage of individuals that had died on plots bearing a pure stand of a single strain was found as follows:

DENSITY	STRAIN A	STRAIN B	STRAIN C
Low	22.9	31.1	10.3
High	73.2	51.2	75.9

Strain C is most viable at a low and B at a high density. But in mixed stands, where the three strains grow side by side and compete with each other, the percentages of the individuals that die prove to be different, namely:

DENSITY	STRAIN A	STRAIN B	STRAIN C
Low	16.5	22.1	5.5
High	72.4	77.6	42.8

Strain C is distinctly superior to A and B at both densities employed. Besides the survival of individual plants, the numbers of flowers per plant was recorded. This has a bearing on the reproductive values of the different strains under the different conditions. At the low density in pure stands, the number of flowers was highest in strain B and lowest in C, but in mixed stands C was highest and A lowest. At the high density in pure stands, strain C had least and A and B most flowers, but in mixed stands the relation was reversed. It is clear that the flower production in a strain is not always correlated with its viability, and the relative survival value of a strain is a function of the environment in which it is placed.

In a second series of experiments, Sukatschew compared the viability of strains of different geographical origin grown under the climatic conditions of Leningrad. The two local strains, B and C, were used, and also a strain X from the extreme north (Archangel), Y from the northeast (Vologda), and Z from the south (Askania-Nova, north of Crimea). In pure stands the strains gave the following percentages of mortality:

DENSITY	B	C	X	Y	Z
Low	31.1	10.3	39.6	22.9	73.0
High	51.2	75.9	63.0	71.6	82.0

The southern strain (Z) is a failure in the new environment, but the Vologda strain did at least as well as one of the local ones (B) at the low, and the Archangel strain at the high, density. For technical reasons it was not convenient to grow all the five strains in mixed cultures, but two experiments were carried on, each with four strains in a mixture. The results are shown in Table 17.

TABLE 17

PERCENTAGE OF DEAD INDIVIDUALS IN MIXED CULTURES OF DIFFERENT STRAINS OF *Taraxacum officinale* (after Sukatschew)

DENSITY	FIRST EXPERIMENT				SECOND EXPERIMENT			
	B	C	X	Y	B	X	Y	Z
Low	66.3	37.5	66.6	50.0	4.2	12.5	8.3	41.6
High	99.5	96.3	56.0	49.2	89.0	29.3	72.8	99.0

The results obtained may seem paradoxical: the Archangel and the Vologda strains (X and Y) show in dense stands definitely greater survival values than the local strains (B and C). One may surmise that a competition between the local and the introduced strains would lead to an elimination of the former. At the lower density, however, the local strains at least hold their own in a competition with the immigrants. Such facts as these provide an excellent illustration of the correctness of the argument employed by us in discussing the survival value of mutants (Chapter II): unless the characteristics of the environment are known in detail, a judgment regarding the survival value of a given genotype is meaningless.

EXPERIMENTAL STUDIES OF ADAPTATION IN ANIMALS

An impression may be gained that the geographical differentiation of species of animals is governed by the general environment prevailing in large parts of their distribution regions, while in plants the very local environments (soil, shade or exposure to sun, etc.), recurring mosaic fashion in the species area, are relatively more important. This impression may be erroneous, because the pertinent studies in the field of botany are more extensive and detailed than in that of zoology, and because only a few workers have a firsthand knowledge of the material in both fields. If real, the difference is probably correlated with the mobility of most animals and the sedentary nature of plants. However that may be, only a few instances of convergent ecotypes having developed in ecologically similar portions of the species area are known in animals. Dice and Blossom (1937) and Dice (1939a, b) found that the pelage color of the rock pocket mouse *Perognathus intermedius* is correlated with that of the soil in its habitat. The preferred habitat of this mouse is the so-called rock hill association, which occurs in many parts of Arizona in the form of islands surrounded by sandy deserts or other types of terrain. The soil color in the rock hill association varies from light decomposed granite to a dark lava. Light and dark islands are scattered rather haphazardly over most of the area. In the eighteen colonies examined the light mice lived on light and dark mice on dark soil. In the cactus mouse (*Peromyscus eremicus*) the correlation between pelage color and that of the soil is about as close as in the pocket mouse. Dark races have been recorded from three rather remote localities in California,

Arizona, and Sonora, where the predominant soil color is dark. But in certain other localities in Arizona where outcroppings of dark lava are present only some dark individuals occur in the mice populations. Dice (1939a) advances the very reasonable conjecture that in these localities darkly colored ecotypes are in the process of development. Dice and his collaborators are inclined to believe that the parallelism between the pelage and soil colors in mice is due to selection by predators which favors a protective coloration. This is very probably justified, but in any case correlations of this sort do suggest that the variable characters of the animals in question have some adaptive value. In this connection the work of Hovanitz (1940) is of interest. He shows that the coloration of the butterfly *Oeneis chryxus* in the alpine zone of the Sierra Nevada is correlated with the predominant color of rocks in its habitat, and yet there are reasons to think that selection by predators plays no role in this case.

Evidence that geographical races of animals are adapted to the environments prevailing in their respective distribution areas is available for a number of species, but only a few examples can be quoted here. Using a very ingenious method, Timofeeff-Ressovsky (1933d, 1935a) compared the survival values of strains of *Drosophila funebris* of different geographical origin. Since geographical races of this fly are morphologically indistinguishable, different strains of *D. funebris* were compared with a standard strain of *D. melanogaster*. Equal numbers (150) of eggs of *D. melanogaster* and of a known strain of *D. funebris* were placed in a culture bottle with a definite amount of food, which was deliberately made insufficient for an optimal development of 300 larvae. Due to the crowding and the competition for food, the numbers of the adult flies which hatched were below, and frequently much below, 300. By counting the numbers of the flies of the two species which did hatch, it was possible to gauge the viability of each strain of *D. funebris* relative to that of the standard *D. melanogaster*. Table 18 shows that the viability of *D. funebris* is in general lower than that of *D. melanogaster*, the difference being more pronounced at higher temperatures (29° C. and 22° C.) than at the lower one (15° C.). This may be correlated with the fact that *D. melanogaster* is a species native to the Tropics while *D. funebris* occurs in the

Temperate Zone. A comparison of the geographical strains of *D. funebris* with each other is facilitated if their viabilities are expressed in percentages of that of some one arbitrarily chosen strain. The right half of Table 18 presents the data recalculated taking the viability of the Berlin strain of *D. funebris* to equal 100. It can

TABLE 18

THE RELATIVE VIABIITY OF THE STRAINS OF *Drosophila funebris* OF DIFFERENT GEOGRAPHICAL ORIGIN (from Timofeeff-Ressovsky)

STRAINS OF D. FUNEBRIS	VIABILITY IN % OF THAT OF DROSOPHILA MELANOGASTER			VIABILITY IN % OF THAT OF THE BERLIN STRAIN OF D. FUNEBRIS		
	$15°$	$22°$	$29°$	$15°$	$22°$	$29°$
Berlin	81	42	18	100	100	100
Sweden	88	40	21	108.6	95.2	116.6
Norway	80	41	21	98.7	97.6	116.6
Denmark	79	44	22	97.5	104.7	122.2
Scotland	84	43	20	103.7	102.4	111.1
England	78	42	21	96.3	100.0	116.6
France	80	44	25	98.7	104.7	138.8
Portugal	71	45	28	87.6	107.1	155.5
Spain	69	48	30	85.2	114.3	166.6
Italy	78	43	25	96.3	102.4	138.8
Gallipoli	75	44	26	92.6	104.7	144.4
Tripoli	64	47	31	79.0	111.9	172.2
Egypt	68	46	30	83.9	109.5	166.6
Leningrad	90	43	22	111.1	102.4	122.2
Kiev	91	44	28	112.3	104.7	155.5
Moscow	101	43	28	124.7	102.4	155.5
Saratov	92	42	30	113.6	100.0	166.6
Perm	98	41	26	121.0	97.6	144.4
Tomsk	96	42	28	118.5	100.0	155.5
Crimea	87	42	28	107.4	100.0	155.5
Caucasus I	89	43	31	109.9	102.4	172.2
Caucasus II	86	45	32	106.2	107.1	177.7
Turkestan	90	44	34	111.1	104.7	188.8
Semirechje	92	46	36	113.6	109.5	200.0

be seen that at 15° C. the viability of the strains from the Mediterranean region is lower, and that of the strains from Russia higher, than of the strains from western, central, and northern Europe. At 29° C. the strains from Russia and the Mediterranean countries are more viable than the western European ones. Western and northern Europe has a relatively mild climate throughout the year;

the climate of Russia and Siberia is more rigorous, with cold winters and hot summers; the Mediterranean region enjoys a mild winter but has a hot summer. The sensitivity of western European strains both to heat and to cold, the adaptability of the Mediterranean ones to heat but not to cold, and the hardiness of strains from Russia and Middle Asia in both extremes appear to be correlated with the exigencies of the climates in their habitats. The fecundity (the total number of eggs deposited by a female during its lifetime) of race A of *Drosophila pseudoobscura* is greater than that of race B of the same species at higher temperatures, but at lower ones race B is superior to race A (Dobzhansky 1935d). The distribution region of race B has a mild, and that of race A, a hot, summer.

A detailed analysis of the adaptive characteristics of geographical races of the gypsy moth (*Lymantria dispar*) has been made by Goldschmidt (1932c, 1933a, 1934b). One of the racial differences involves the length of the incubation period of the eggs. The embryonic development is here arrested during the coldest period of winter, but it takes a different sum of temperatures (= the incubation time) to bring out the young caterpillars to hatching in spring. The incubation time for strains coming from Europe (except the Mediterranean region) and from northern Asia (including the northern island of Japan) is very short, which fact is correlated with the long winter and the rapid onset and progress of spring. The Mediterranean strains have a much longer incubation time. Goldschmidt points out that given a mild winter as characteristic for that region, a short incubation time would bring the caterpillars out before the appearance of the foilage on the food plants. In southern and central Japan the incubation time generally increases from southwest to northeast, which Goldschmidt correlates with a peculiarity of the Japanese climate that makes for a relatively late (compared to Europe) development of the foliage with a similar sum of temperatures. The race from Manchuria has the longest incubation time of all of those studies; the adaptational significance of this remains however unclear.

The variations in length of larval development (from the hatching of the caterpillar to pupation) show a slightly different geographical regularity from that exhibited by the incubation time.

The shortest larval development is observed in strains from the northern island of Japan, the northern tip of the main island, and the northern part of the Eurasiatic continent, which may bear a relation to the short vegetation period characteristic of these countries. The Mediterranean region, Turkestan, and central Japan have a longer vegetation period, and races with a longer larval development occur there. In southern Japan the larval development is again shorter, which Goldschmidt regards as an adaptation permitting the insect to complete its larval stages before the advent of the very high summer temperatures that occur in that region. The strains from mountain localities in Japan have shorter developmental times than the strains from the adjacent subtropical coastal region.

Fox (1937, 1939) has conducted comparative physiological studies on certain marine forms living in waters of different temperature. Equal rates of beat of the respiratory organs are observed in the crustacean *Pandalus montagui* from the relatively warm waters of southern England at 16° C. and in those from the cold waters of Kristineberg, Sweden, at 6° C. The rate of the blood vessel pulsation in the annelid *Perineis cultifera* from the Mediterranean Sea at 20° C. is equal to that in the race of the same species from the English waters at 14° C. According to Moore (1939), the development rates of frog eggs at a given temperature are greater in species that occur in colder northern regions and breed early in the season than in southern species which breed when the temperatures in their habitats are warmer. Frog species which breed in cold water deposit their eggs in a compact jelly mass, while frogs that breed at higher temperatures spread their eggs in a film floating on the water surface. Moore (1940) showed that oxygen starvation arises in compact masses of eggs at higher temperatures which are not injurious to eggs in films. Results such as these ought to encourage further comparative studies on physiology of geographical races and ecotypes, a field which was almost completely neglected until recently.

REGULARITIES IN GEOGRAPHICAL VARIATION

Representatives of various species, genera, orders, and even classes inhabiting a given geographical region often undergo convergent changes, while in other regions the same groups seem to vary in directions which are again similar for all of them but different from the direction observed in the first region. Thus the denizens of each geographical area or ecological niche acquire a certain imprint, setting them apart from their close relatives inhabiting other countries, but endowing them with resemblances to their neighbors from other biological stocks. This phenomenon is a counterpart on the supraspecies level of the ecotypic differentiation within species. Zoology is far outdistanced by botany in the formulation of regularities of this kind. Structural and physiological peculiarities of desert, alpine, prairie, tundra, tropical rain forest, and other types of vegetation have been known since pre-Darwinian times. Reduction of the evaporating leaf surface, transformation of leaves into spines, development of pubescence or waxy covering on the epidermis, presence of chlorophyl in the surface layers of the bark, fleshiness of the leaves, twigs, and stems are schoolroom examples of the adaptations in desert plants. Astonishing resemblances between certain American cacti and African euphorbias are among the best illustrations of evolutionary convergence. From the standpoint of selectionism, formation by related species of analogous or convergent ecotypes in the same geographical or ecological region is of particular interest. Turesson (1925, 1930), Clausen, Keck, and Hiesey (1940), and others list fairly numerous examples of this sort. Alpine, subalpine, coastal, forest, dune, swamp, and other ecotypes can be distinguished; every class of ecotypes is like a specially equipped detachment evolved by a species to colonize a certain type of habitat.

Efforts to formulate rules of geographical and ecological variation in animals have also been made. Rensch (1929, 1936, 1938, 1939a, b) has ably summarized the pertinent evidence, which is otherwise so scattered in the descriptive zoological literature as to be practically unavailable for a nonspecialist. The following rules seem to be best established. Gloger's rule (frequently referred to in the American literature as Allen's rule) states that in mammals and birds, races inhabiting warm and humid regions have more melanin pigmentation than races of the same species in cooler and drier regions; arid desert regions are characterized by accumulation of yellow and reddish-brown phaeomelanin pigmentation. Among insects, the pigmentation increases in humid and cool and decreases in dry and hot climates, the humidity being apparently more effective than temperature (Zimmermann 1931 in wasps, Dobzhansky 1933c in ladybird beetles). For the ladybirds, eastern Asia (eastern Siberia, Japan) is the center of heavily pigmented races; to the southwest and southeast of this region, lighter and lighter races are encountered, until centers of very pale races are reached in California in the Western, and in Turkestan in the Eastern Hemisphere.

In mammals and birds, and apparently in some invertebrates as well, races living in cooler climates are larger in body size than races of the same species in the warmer climates (Bergmann's rule). In warm-blooded animals, races inhabiting cooler regions have relatively shorter tails, legs, ears, and beaks than those from warmer ones (Allen's rule). In birds, races with relatively narrower and more acuminate wings tend to occur in colder, and those with broader wings in warmer, climates (Rensch's rule). In mammals, shorter but coarser hair and a decrease in the amount of down is observed in warm countries. In birds, the inhabitants of colder countries deposit more eggs per clutch than those of warm countries. Fish of cooler waters tend to have a larger number of segments than those living in warmer waters; increase of salinity has the same effect as decrease in temperature; the forms inhabiting swiftly flowing waters tend to be larger and to have more streamlined body shapes than inhabitants of sluggish or stagnant waters; cyprinidin fishes isolated in desert springs tend to lose their pelvic fins (Hubbs 1940). The size of the shells in local races or species of molluscs is greatest in climates that show a certain optimum relation between temperature and the amount of precipitation (Rensch 1939a).

Strange as it may seem, the correlations between race formation and environment revealed by the "rules" such as those just discussed were repeatedly quoted as arguments against the natural selection theory. This amazing confusion of thought was due in the past to the almost universal acceptance among biologists of the belief in inheritance of acquired characteristics. Racial differentiation was considered a result of modification of the phenotype by the environment, perpetuated by a gradual change of the germ plasm in the direction of the phenotypic change. This interpretation was considered borne out by experiments which showed that a change analogous to that observed in a particular geographical race can also be brought about in other races of the same species by an exposure to certain environmental agents. Thus, in the classical experiments of Standfuss, exposure to heat treatment produces from the pupae of the central European races butterflies resembling the varieties known from Syria and southern Italy. On the other hand, treatment of the central European race with cold resulted in a resemblance to the form from northern Scandinavia. An exposure of a mammal to cold or heat may produce respectively an increase or a decrease of the hair length, a change quite analogous to that distinguishing the geographical races from the high and the low latitudes. Bergmann's, Allen's, and also Gloger's rules (see above) have their counterparts among the changes that can be induced in an animal by an application of appropriate environmental stimuli, namely, temperature and humidity or a combination thereof. The same is true for plants, where the phenotypic changes wrought by treatments with external agents may simulate the characteristics of races and species existing in nature.

Goldschmidt (1935, 1938) points out that theoretically any change of the phenotype caused by an alteration of the germ plasm may be reproduced as a purely phenotypic modification if a suitable experimental technique is evolved. Indeed, Goldschmidt (1935) describes special temperature treatments that induce in *Drosophila melanogaster* phenotypic variations ("phenocopies") that more or less resemble some of the well-known mutant types of that insect. Friesen (1936) secured similar results by treating the developmental stages of *Drosophila* with X-rays. It is nevertheless obvious that there exists a fundamental difference between a mutant and a phenocopy. A mutant is a genotypic change and a phenocopy is a modification solely of the phenotype. The offspring of a phenocopy is indistinguishable from the original type, unless it develops in the same environment which has induced the phenocopy to begin with; the offspring of a mutant is a mutant. In discussing this subject one must constantly keep in mind an elementary consideration all too frequently lost sight of in the writings of some biologists; what is inherited in a living being is not this or that morphological character, but a definite norm of reaction to environmental stimuli. The norm of reaction of the "normal" *Drosophila melanogaster* is such that in the usual, standard, environment the development results in the appearance of a fly with "normal" or "wild type" characteristics, but when the environment is modified in a definite fashion a phenocopy is produced. The norm of reaction in a mutant is such that certain aberrant characteristics appear in individuals that have developed in the standard environment. In other words, a mutation changes the norm of reaction, but in a phenocopy the norm of reaction remains unaltered. To suppose that geographical races were originally modifications that have subsequently been fixed by heredity is contrary to the whole sum of our knowledge, just as it would be absurd to assume that mutations are phenocopies that have become hereditary. Therefore, the regularities observed in the process of geographical race formation cannot be due to direct effects of the secular environment, albeit the results of this process can in part be imitated by some phenotypic modifications. In the light of these considerations, the parallelism between the genotypic and the phenotypic variability acquires a new and profound significance.

Adaptation, that is, a harmony between the organism and its environment, may be arrived at by two distinct methods. First, the norm of reaction of the genotype to the external stimuli may be adjusted to the effects of those environmental agents likely to be encountered under the "natural" conditions. In other words, the organism may respond to the impact of these agents by producing a phenotype that is most likely to survive in the particular environment. An ideal genotype would be capable of producing an optimal response to any environment. It appears, however, that no organism has evolved such a paragon of adaptability. A second method of becoming adapted has been resorted to, namely a genotypic specialization. A change in the genotype alters the reaction norm, and some of the alterations may enable the new genotype to produce a harmonious response where the ancestral has become a failure. Thus, the normal genotype of *Daphnia longispina* enables the organism to survive at 20° C. but not at 27° C., while the mutant found by Banta and Wood (1927) survives at 30° C. but not at 20° C. Selection deals not with the genotype as such, but with its dynamic properties, its reaction norm, which is the sole criterion of fitness in the struggle for existence.

One of the principal tenets of Lamarckism is that the response of the genotype to the environmental stimuli that are encountered in the "normal" milieu is often, perhaps even as a rule, definitely adaptive. Modern genetics may, I think, accept this as an accurate statement of the observed facts, with the important reservation that the genotype responds not by changing itself but only by begetting an altered phenotype. The adaptive value of the development of a longer pelage and a greater amount of wool in a cool climate is indeed obvious. Once this is admitted, the conclusion follows that in a cold climate natural selection must favor the genotypes which, other conditions being equal, produce a warmer pelage. In a warm climate the sign of the selective value of a genotype may be reversed. The fact that the races of mammals inhabiting cold countries usually have longer hair and more down than races of the same species from hot countries is consequently evidence for and not against the effectiveness of natural selection.

The interpretation of the other rules governing the geographical variability (some of which have been discussed above) is admittedly more difficult than is the case with the variations of the pelage. The problem involved is essentially a physiological one, but the comparative physiology of geographical races is in its infancy. As a working hypothesis, one may assume however that Bergmann's rule (large body size in the cool and small size in the warm climates) is concerned with the temperature regulation of the animal. A large body size is correlated with a relatively smaller body surface, and consequently with a more limited loss of heat. A similar explanation would appear to apply to Allen's rule as well. The protruding body parts, the extremities, tails, and ears, are especially subject to a rapid loss of heat. The increase of the body surface in just these regions is therefore unfavorable in the cold, and may prove desirable in the warm, climates. Gloger's rule for the vertebrates resembles the sun tanning reaction of the human skin, and may have an analogous significance (Rensch 1936).

PROTECTIVE AND WARNING COLORATIONS AND RESEMBLANCES

Besides the general evidence on the efficacy of natural selection, there exist in biological literature some observations of a more special kind which furnish additional testimony in favor of the selection theory. The doctrine of the protective and warning colorations and resemblances constitutes one such topic. The essentials of this doctrine are so well known that they do not need to be explained in detail. Two of the ways in which organisms are supposed to become adapted to their environment are by becoming as inconspicuous as possible in their normal surroundings, or else by acquiring a similarity to some particular object which is dangerous or distasteful to their natural enemies. By the first method the organism escapes the notice of its predators, or, in the case of the predators themselves, is able to approach the prey without being prematurely noticed by the latter. The second method leads the organism, contrariwise, to become as conspicuous as possible to advertise its presence and to warn its potential enemies of its obnoxiousness. A special kind of warning coloration and form is *mimicry*, whereby a harmless creature resembles some other which is in fact obnoxious (Batesian mimicry). The different forms protected by being dangerous or unpalatable and by having warning colorations may become even more thoroughly protected if they resemble each other, so that their enemies need learn a single sign of distastefulness instead of many (Müllerian mimicry).

The theories of protective resemblance and of mimicry were developed and widely used by the early Darwinists as illustrations of the action of natural selection and of evolution in general. The greatest effervescence of these theories was observed in the late nineteenth and the early twentieth centuries. Undoubtedly much uncritical and valueless speculation in this field has been indulged in by some writers, bringing only disrepute to the whole theory. The dangers of assuming that a given coloration is protective or mimetic are admittedly great. What to a human eye may seem to be a far-reaching similarity between an organism and some inanimate object or some other organism need not be such to the eyes of a predator against whom the protection is supposed to operate. Our own opinions of the dangers or distastefulness of a creature should not without further proof be imputed to the enemies of the latter. Some of the alleged protections and warnings have been shown to be armchair protection and museum mimicry. A heavy barrage of criticism has been laid against the whole theory by Heikertinger (1933–1936) and McAtee (1932), who seem to reject it in its entirety. Neverthe-

less, the theory has survived both criticism and the damage done
by its overenthusiastic supporters, and in fact has in recent years
staged a surprising resurgence (see Cott 1940 for an excellent review
especially of the English literature of the subject).

It must be noted that, as far as at least the concealment is concerned, the theory of protective coloration is no longer based on
mere belief that this or that animal is not easily visible in its natural
surroundings. Initiated by the at first unappreciated work of Thayer
in the second decade of this century, the techniques of camouflage
by countershading, by dazzling or disruptive patterning, and concealment of the shadow have grown up to be a full-fledged branch
of technology having important applications, among other things,
in military affairs (Cott 1940). It is now possible to evaluate crit-
ically which animals are or are not concealingly colored or shaped
in a given environment, at least to a visual apparatus resembling
man's eye. There can no longer be a reasonable doubt that many
animals are comouflaged in their natural surroundings. It is, of
course, an entirely different problem whether or not the camouflage
or the conspicuousness has developed under the influence of natural
selection, because of the protection from enemies which these properties confer on their carriers. Here one can necessarily proceed only
by inference, with experiments pointing the way. Unfortunately,
experimental work on protective coloration and mimicry has always
lagged behind the purely observational, and even farther behind the
purely speculative, endeavor. Such experimental data as are available tend, however, to support the natural selection theory. Thus,
Sumner (1935 and other works) showed that fishes whose color
contrasts with their surroundings are caught by predators more
easily than those with harmonizing colors. He used the little fish
Gambusia partuelis, which, owing to the expansion and contraction
of its pigment-bearing cells, becomes darker or lighter when placed
in tanks with respectively dark or light bottoms. Galapagos pen-
guins, a fish-eating bird, caught 70 percent of fishes which were
contrastingly colored, and only 34 percent of those which were
adaptively colored. In another experiment, with the sunfish *Apomotis
cyanellus* as the predator, 53 percent of the nonadapted and 25 percent of the adapted *Gambusia* were destroyed (for other experimental evidence, see Cott 1940).

McAtee (1932) has approached the problem from a different angle. If, for example, one insect is protected from predators by its coloration and another insect is not so protected, the first must be eaten by predators less frequently than the second. McAtee examined the contents of the stomachs of about eighty thousand birds from the United States and recorded the insects found therein. The results show that insects which are supposedly poisonous or distasteful, and which are protected by concealing or warning colorations are destroyed by birds in numbers supposedly proportional to the relative abundance of each insect species in the environment of the birds in question. It is hardly necessary to labor the point that the information on the relative abundance of different insects in nature is, to put it conservatively, inexact. To conclude, then, that the whole theory of protection is a myth, is to succumb to the old fallacy that only an absolute immunity from predators can make natural selection effective. If "protected" and "unprotected" varieties of a species are destroyed in ratios of 999:1000, a change in the composition of the species may under certain conditions take place.

ORIGIN OF DOMINANCE

Dominance of some alleles over others—one of the longest-known genetic phenomena—may be interpreted as evidence of the effectiveness of natural selection. Mutants, whether spontaneous or induced by treatments with X-rays, are as a rule recessive to the ancestral or wild type. Among the mutants recorded in *Drosophila melanogaster,* more than two hundred are recessive and only thirteen are dominant. These figures do not include the large class of the recessive lethals, since their counterpart, the dominant lethals, are difficult to detect, and consequently the relative frequencies of the two kinds cannot be accurately estimated. Of course, it must be kept in mind that dominance versus recessiveness is a matter of degree. Some of the mutant genes classed as recessives produce a slight effect in the heterozygous condition, and none of the dominants suppress the action of the wild type alleles completely. Nevertheless, the greater frequency of the recessive mutants in *Drosophila melanogaster,* as well as in most other species in which mutants have been observed, is clear enough.

With the above facts as a basis, Fisher (1928, 1930, 1931, 1932,

1935) has erected a theory of the origin of dominance through selection of modifying genes which tend to make mutant heterozygotes resemble the wild type. Fisher's arguments are, briefly, as follows. Mutants the occurrence of which is observed either in laboratory experiments or in nature have arisen repeatedly, most of them innumerable times, in the history of the species. A great majority of mutations are deleterious to the viability of their carriers. Hence, any genes that suppress the effects of mutants will be advantageous, will be favored by natural selection, and will tend to become established in the species genotype. Now, deleterious mutants are present in natural populations mostly as heterozygotes, homozygotes being relatively very rare (Chapters III and V). Selection will, therefore, deal mainly with heterozygotes. When modifiers which make mutant heterozygotes approach the wild type condition are accumulated, the dominance of the wild type over the mutant alleles will be established. In short, the dominance of the wild type over the mutant alleles is due not to the intrinsic properties of the former, but rather to the presence of a system of modifying genes which make a majority of the frequently occurring mutations recessive.

Wright (1929, 1930, 1934), Haldane (1930, 1933, 1939), Muller (1932), Plunkett (1932) and Dunn and Landauer (1934) have built very similar theories, which, although not incompatible with that of Fisher, indicate an alternative method whereby dominance might arise. These theories start from the consideration that the development of an organism involves a system of interrelated and interdependent physiological processes, the end result of which is the emergence of what we designate the normal or wild type condition. In this system the effects of most genes are integral parts. If genes act through production of enzymes or enzymelike substances, each gene must yield its normal quota of these products. It may well be that threshold reactions are frequently involved, and a doubling or even a multiplication of the effectiveness of the gene in question produces no appreciable modification of the normal course of the development, but a halving of the activity leads to a retardation or an arrest of the whole chain of reactions. Under such conditions, wild type alleles possessing a "factor of safety," that is having an activity well above the necessary minimum, will be of advantage to the organism. A mutation that curtails the activity of such a gene even to zero would then be recessive to the normal allele. Natural selection will, therefore, favor the establishment of alleles that are dominant over mutants which limit the efficiency of the respective genes.

An inconclusive polemic ensued between the proponents of the views that dominance arises through selection of modifiers or through selection of highly efficient wild type alleles. Modifying genes which produce no effect other than to shift the expression of characters in heterozygous mutants at other loci toward the wild type condition would have so small an advantage in natural populations that the selection in their favor will be very weak. If these modifying genes have other effects as well, their fate under selection will be determined regardless of their roles in mutant heterozygotes. Furthermore, if dominance modifiers arise by mutation, they are likely to be intrinsically disadvantageous, as mutant genes generally are. Although it must be admitted that natural selection, however weak, may be efficacious in the course of time and under certain circumstances, selection of wild type alleles possessing a factor of safety seems to be an easier method to secure dominance than selection of special modifiers.

According to Fisher, modifiers that act on mutant heterozygotes rather on homozygotes are selected in nature because heterozygotes are relatively common and homozygotes very rare. Yet in species which reproduce by self-fertilization (many plants) most nonlethal mutant genes are represented in natural populations by homozygotes rather than by heterozygotes. Contrary to what one might expect on Fisher's view, mutant genes in self-fertilizing species seem to be as frequently recessive to the wild type as they are in cross-fertilizing forms (Haldane 1939). In some animals, especially in hymenopterous insects, females are diploid, while males are haploid. In such forms mutant genes are hemizygous (that is, present only in single dose) in males. Yet, most of the mutants in *Habrobracon,* a hymenopteron studied by Whiting and his collaborators, are recessive to the wild type in females. The incidence of recessives appears to be alike among the sex-linked and the autosomal mutant genes in *Drosophila,* although the former are hemizygous in the male. Assuredly, these objections are not fatal to Fisher's theory. Cross-fertilization and diploidy in both sexes are phylogenetically ancestral, and self-fertilization and male haploidy phylogenetically derived, conditions. Genes that are sex linked at present might have been autosomal in the ancestors. One may suppose, therefore, that the dominance modifiers developed in the phylogeny before the advent, respectively, of self-fertilization and of haploidy in the male. Such a supposition is, however, far fetched. It is quite unlikely that the functions of genes and modifier systems remain static while radical phylogenetic transformations are enacted. On the other hand, Ford (1930) and Fisher (1932) have pointed out that in mutants with manifold effects (cf. Chapter II) the dominance is restricted mainly to that part of the sphere of action of the gene which involves viability changes. This is an argument in favor of the modifier theory of the origin of dominance.

Experimental work has established that variations in the degree of dominance may be brought about through dominance modifiers as well as through multiplicity of wild type alleles at the loci concerned. The investigations of Harland, Silow, and others on the genetics of cotton (reviewed on pp. 82–85 above) have revealed that many major mutant genes are accompanied by systems of dominance modifiers. In crosses within a species, the inheritance of mutant characters usually follows the straightforward Mendelian scheme, with a complete or nearly complete dominance in the F_1 and a $3:1$ segregation in the F_2 generation. The same mutant characters may, however, give an intermediate F_1 and a very complex F_2 segregation in species crosses. Different species may each possess systems of modifiers making certain mutant genes recessive, but these systems need not be alike in all species. The different modifier systems cancel each other, so to speak, in species hybrids. On the other hand, many genes form series of multiple alleles, so that strains of the same species as well as of different species may possess alleles exhibiting different degrees of dominance over the mutant types (see especially Silow 1939a, b). Helfer (1939) examined the behavior of the autosomal semidominant mutant Scute in *Drosophila pseudoobscura* in hybrids with wild strains of the same species and of different geographical origin. Considerable variations in the degree of dominance have been observed, and Helfer was able to show that these variations are caused by modifiers located in chromosomes other than that in which Scute itself lies. The wild type alleles of

Scute in all the strains appeared to be alike. Variations in dominance in *D. melanogaster* may be due to the presence of a variety of wild type alleles, as well as to modifying genes (a review in Goldschmidt 1938).

Dominance modifiers in poultry and in mice have been found and studied by Dunn and Landauer (1934, 1936), Fisher (1935), Dunn (1937 and unpublished data), Mather and North (1940), and others. The chief importance of these studies lies in the fact that the analysis of the modifiers themselves has been carried farther than in other similar work. Dominance modifiers may affect the expression of other genes only in heterozygotes. Different effects of the same gene may be subject to control by different modifier systems. Mice heterozygous for the gene Brachy have short tails, while the homozygotes die on account of gross disturbances in the development of the posterior part of the body. Modifiers present in certain strains of mice make the tails in heterozygous Brachy almost normal, but the same modifiers have no effect either on the time of onset or on the nature of the lethal action of the homozygous Brachy. Furthermore, the modifiers that lengthen the tails in heterozygous Brachy have the opposite effect in heterozygotes for another dominant tail reducer, Sd. Most important is, however, that detailed studies tend to show that dominance modifiers frequently have various effects of their own, aside from their influence on the expression of other genes. This amounts to saying that dominance modifiers are not a class of genes subsidiary to others, but merely genes with manifold effects which influence, among other things, the expression of certain mutants at other loci. The origin of dominance, either through modifiers or through selection of strong wild type alleles, must be considered not as something apart from the formation of generally adapted genotypes, but as a necessary corollary of the fact that development is an integrated system of physiological reactions.

SELECTION RATE AND THE GENETIC EQUILIBRIUM

The inadequacy of the experimental foundations of the theory of natural selection must be admitted, I believe, by its followers as well as by its opponents. The work to date has been concentrated mainly on proving the reality of natural selection as a process actually going on in wild populations, and a fair degree of success has been achieved in this field. The evidence presented in the foregoing paragraphs seems to demonstrate the effectiveness of selection in bringing about certain adaptational changes. The manner of action of selection has been dealt with only theoretically, by means of mathematical analysis. The results of this theoretical work (Haldane, Fisher, Wright) are however invaluable as a guide for any future experimental attack on the problem.

The main assumption inherent in the theory of natural selection is that some hereditary types of a species may have a certain advantage over others in survival and reproduction. Mathematically, the simplest case is the so-called genic selection, when the gene alleles a and A tend to be reproduced in each generation in the ratios $(1-s):1$. The selection coefficient s is a measure of the advantage or the disadvantage. Thus, if on the average there are retained only 999 gametes carrying a where 1,000 gametes carrying A are retained, the value of s equals 0.001. If the frequencies of the genes A and a in the initial population are q and $(1-q)$ respectively, in the next generation they will become $(1-s)(1-q)/1-s(1-q)$ for a, and $q/1-s(1-q)$ for A. The change in the frequency of the gene A per generation is therefore $\Delta q = sq(1-q)/1-s(1-q)$. If the selection coefficient s is small, the value $s(1-q)$ is close enough to zero to be disregarded, and the formula becomes $\Delta q = sq(1-q)$.

Zygotic selection, when the carriers of the three genotypes aa, Aa, and AA reproduce in the ratios $(1-s')$, $(1-hs')$, and 1 respectively, is probably most important in nature. Here the selection coefficient s' measures the advantage or disadvantage of one of the homozygotes, and hs' that of the heterozygotes Aa. The rate of change in the gene frequencies q and $(1-q)$ under the zygotic selection may be calculated according to the formula $\Delta q = s'q(1-q)[1-q+hs'(2q-1)]$ given by Wright (1929, 1931). A special case of zygotic selection is when A is completely dominant over a, and consequently the viability of the heterozygote Aa is equal to that of the homozygote AA; this case is important owing to the prevalence of the recessive mutant genes in wild populations (Chapter III). It is easy to see that the formula for the gene frequency change turns out to be $\Delta q = s'q(1-q)^2$.

Very interesting computations of the speed with which a change in the genetic constitution of a population may occur under the influence of selection have been made by Haldane (1932) and others. For intermediate gene frequencies the progress of selection is fairly rapid, that is to say, it takes relatively few generations to accomplish a given amount of change (Table 19). If, however, the initial gene frequency is very small or very large—approaching, respectively, zero or one hundred percent of the population—the progress of selection is appallingly slow. Table 19 shows the numbers of generations necessary to bring about a given change in the frequency of a gene having a selective advantage of one percent (s = 0.01) over its allele.

TABLE 19

NUMBER OF GENERATIONS NECESSARY FOR A GIVEN CHANGE IN THE PERCENT FREQUENCY OF A GENE HAVING A SELECTIVE ADVANTAGE OF 0.01 (after Pätau, 1939)

DOMINANT GENE		RECESSIVE GENE	
FREQUENCY	NUMBER OF GENERATIONS	FREQUENCY	NUMBER OF GENERATIONS
0.01– 0.1	230	0.01– 0.0	900,230
0.1 – 1.0	232	0.1 – 1.0	90,231
1.0 –50.0	559	1.0 – 2.0	5,070
50.0 –98.0	5,189	2.0 –50.0	5,189
98.0 –99.0	5,070	50.0 –99.0	559
99.0 –99.9	90,231	99.0 –99.9	232
99.9 –99.99	900,230	99.9 –99.99	230

It is possible to calculate that even with selection coefficients smaller than 0.001 the process will go on, that is to say, the gene frequencies may eventually increase from a very small value to nearly one hundred percent, or vice versa. Selective advantages or disadvantages for a given genetic type in the population, however small and insignificant they may seem, may be ultimately instrumental in bringing forth an evolutionary change. The number of generations, and consequently the amount of time needed for the change, may, however, be so tremendous that the efficiency of selection alone as an evolutionary agent may be open to doubt, and this even if time on a geological scale is provided.

The above calculations are, of course, based on the assumption that mutation does not occur. Combined with mutation, the process of selection may be either enhanced in speed or, vice versa, slowed down still farther. If mutation to an allele favored by selection takes place more frequently than away from that allele, the speed of the process is greatly accentuated in its initial stages. After an initial increase in frequency, the relative importance of the mutation declines, and the further increase has to proceed by selection alone (unless, of course, the mutation rate is very high). Thus, with an allele A mutating to a at a rate $1 : 1,000,000$, the change of the gene frequency from $q = 0.000,001$ to $q = 0.000,002$ is accomplished in a single generation, while a similar change requires $321,444$ generations for a recessive type with a selective advantage of 0.001.

If the predominant mutation rate is away from the allele favored by selection, the gene frequency will never reach zero or unity, and a genetic equilibrium will be established instead. The position of the equilibrium will evidently be determined by the relation between the conflicting mutation and selection rates. The calculation of the equilibrium values for various mutation rates and types of selection is possible with the aid of simple formulae given by Wright (1929, 1931a), Fisher (1930), and others. Suppose that the gene A mutates to a at a rate u per generation, and that this mutation is opposed by a genic selection of the intensity s, conferring an advantage on the allele A; the rate of change of the gene frequency q of A will be $\Delta q = -uq + sq(1-q)$. The attainment of an equilibrium means that no further change takes place, that is, $\Delta q = 0$. Solving the equation, we find the equilibrium value $q = 1 - u/s$. For a mutation opposed by a zygotic selection, the survival values of the individuals carrying the genotypes aa, Aa, and AA are $(1-s')$, $(1-hs')$, and 1, respectively. The equilibrium value proves to be $q = 1 - u/hs'$, unless h approaches zero. For an unfavorable dominant mutation, in which the viability of the heterozygote Aa equals that of the homozygote AA, the equilibrium value for the wild type gene is $q = 1 - u/s'$. Finally, for an unfavorable recessive mutation the equilibrium for the wild type gene is $q = 1 - \sqrt{u/s'}$. Taking the mutation rate u to be $0.000,01$, and the selection coefficient $s = 0.001$, the numerical values of the equilibrium points will be $q = 0.99$ and $q = 0.90$ for the normal allele of a dominant and a recessive mutant gene, respectively. In other words, the unfavorable recessive mutations will be allowed to accumulate in the populations to a much greater extent than the equally disadvantageous dominants. This is, of course, exactly what the analysis of wild populations reveals.

Evolutionary changes engendered in a population by the combined action of the mutation and selection pressures will continue to take place as long as some genes have not yet reached their equilibrium frequencies. The attainment of the equilibrium for every gene would mean cessation of evolution. In practice such a contingency is, however, very remote, since the equilibrium values themselves are constantly changing. The magnitudes as well as signs of the selection, and to a lesser extent also of the mutation rates, are determined by the environment. The environment does not remain constant, either in terms of geological periods or even from one year to the next. Selection and mutation rates, and hence the genetic equilibria, are in a state of perpetual flux. The nature of the genetic mechanism is therefore such that the composition of the species population is probably never static. A species that would remain long quiescent in the evolutionary sense is likely to be doomed to extinction. Whether the combined forces of mutation and selection are sufficient for a sustained progressive evolution is, nevertheless, not immediately clear. The extreme slowness with which the new favorable mutations that might arise in the species from time to time can acquire a hold on the species population has been pointed out already. The fluctuations of the gene frequencies caused by the variations in the equilibrium values for various genes make the process essentially reversible, since the restoration of the original environment after a temporary change brings the equilibria back to their old positions. Granted that a complete reversion is unlikely, the evolutionary effectiveness of the process is still rather low (Wright 1931a). These considerations make it especially important to examine the relations between selection and the factor discussed in the preceding chapter, namely the restriction of the population size (see Chapter X).

VII: POLYPLOIDY

CATACLYSMIC ORIGIN OF SPECIES

IT HAS BEEN pointed out in Chapter III that the sudden origin of a new species by gene mutation is an impossibility in practice. The argument employed to prove this thesis is simple enough. Races of a species, and to a still greater extent species of a genus, differ from each other in many genes, and usually also in the chromosome structure. A mutation that would catapult a new species into being must, therefore, involve simultaneous changes in many gene loci, and in addition some chromosomal reconstructions. With the known mutation rates the probability of such an event is negligible. The process of species formation is apparently a slow and gradual one, consuming time on at least a quasi-geological scale.

It is highly remarkable, therefore, that alongside this slow method of species formation there should exist in nature a quite distinct mechanism causing a rapid, sudden, cataclysmic emergence of new species. It is remarkable, furthermore, that while the slow method seems to be encountered throughout the living world and may in this sense be called the general one, the cataclysmic origin of species is confined to some, though large, groups, mostly (so far as known) in the plant kingdom. The latter method of species formation is connected with a multiplication of the chromosome complement, called polyploidy. If the term "mutation" is used in its widest sense (Chapter II), the origin of polyploidy is, of course, a mutation by definition. The difference between a "mutation" causing polyploidy and a gene mutation is clear enough, however, and the distinction between the two methods of species formation is therefore not likely to cause difficulties in practice. Moreover, one may note that species formation through gene mutation involves a gradual reconstruction of the genotype of the ancestral species to give rise to the genotypes of the derived ones. Species formation through polyploidy occurs mostly as a result of hybridization of two previously existing species (allopolyploidy). The chromosome complement is doubled in a hybrid, and the polyploid possesses all the genes which were present in both of its ancestors and no new genes. We are dealing here with a fusion of two old species to form a single derived species. Since however the ancestral species may continue to exist side by side with the polyploid, the total diversity is augmented in the process. Both methods of species formation increase the organic diversity. Goldschmidt (1940) has postulated that species in general arise through cataclysmic saltations, caused by drastic rearrangements in the chromosomal materials. These "systemic mutations" of Goldschmidt are by no means identical with polyploidy, and, as we endeavored to show above (Chapters II and III), there is no evidence whatever either of their occurrence or of their effectiveness in evolution.

How widespread polyploidy is among plants is shown by an examination of the chromosome numbers in various genera. The fact that in many genera the species have chromosome numbers that are simple multiples of a minimum or basic number was noticed very early in the history of plant cytology. Classical examples of this are wheats (*Triticum*), where species with the diploid numbers 14, 28, and 42 (the basic haploid number is 7) are known, *Chrysanthemum* with 18, 36, 54, 72, and 90 (basic number 9), *Solanum* with 24, 36, 48, 60, 72, 96, $\pm$ 108, 120, and $\pm$ 144 (basic number 12), and *Papaver* with 14, 28, 42, 70, 22, and 44 (basic numbers 7 and 11). The general statistics of the chromosome numbers among the flowering plants also reveal some interesting regularities (Table 20).

In a large sample containing 2,413 species, some numbers occur considerably more frequently than would be expected in a chance distribution. In a frequency distribution of numbers between 3 and 100, not a single peak is found at a prime number; and the most frequent prove to be the numbers with the lowest factors (8, 9, 12, 16, 18, 24, 27, 32, and 36). Moreover, the relative frequencies of certain low numbers (8, 7, 9, 10, 11, and 13) are repeated by those of their multiples (16, 14, 18, 20, 22, 26).

Winge (1917) was the first to emphasize the above regularities in the distribution of the chromosome numbers in plants. He concluded that the simplest way to account for them is to suppose that the reduplication of the chromosome complements, polyploidy, has taken place frequently in the phylogeny of some genera. Moreover, Winge put forward a suggestion that proved to be a prophetic one, namely, that the origin of a polyploid species is most likely to take place in the offspring of a hybrid between two diploid species, ,and more specifically where the chromosome pairing in the hybrid is decreased or lacking. The argument used by Winge in making this deduction is a teleological one: the "need" for a partner with which a chromosome could pair might stimulate the doubling of the whole complement which would provide such a partner for every chromosome.

TABLE 20

HAPLOID CHROMOSOME NUMBERS IN FLOWERING PLANTS (after Hernandes from Darlington, 1932)

CHROMOSOME NUMBER	NUMBER OF SPÉCIES	CHROMOSOME NUMBER	NUMBER OF SPECIES
12	391	15	27
8	332	22	25
7	236	32	25
9	170	28	24
16	153	19	22
6	134	26	20
10	126	36	19
14	125	30	11
24	80	23	8
11	70	45	8
21	64	42	6
18	58	3	5
17	48	38	5
20	47	40	5
4	42	Others	39
27	31	Totals:	
13	30	Below 12	1,242
5	27	12 and above	1,171

Nevertheless, the deduction has been borne out by the discovery of the fertile allopolyploids eight years later (Clausen and Goodspeed 1925). More recently, Müntzing (1936) has adduced some fairly convincing arguments to show that the doubling of the chromosomes in nonhybrid organisms (autopolyploidy) also must be regarded as an evolutionary factor of some consequence. The relatively greater role of the allopolyploids is, however, taken as established by most geneticists and cytologists.

Although species formation through polyploidy is restricted to certain groups of organisms, its interest can hardly be overestimated. In the particular groups where it occurs it seems to play a major role in phylogeny. Moreover, species formation through polyploidy has been studied experimentally in more detail, and is better understood than the more widespread method of the origin of species through the accumulation of mutational changes.

AUTOPOLYPLOIDS

The origin within a species of individuals possessing twice as many chromosomes as normal (autotetraploidy) is one of the oldest known chromosomal aberrations. The gigas "mutation" repeatedly observed by De Vries in his classical experiments on *Oenothera Lamarckiana* proved to have 28 instead of the normal 14 chromosomes, and hence was a tetraploid. It is interesting that this first example of the chromosome reduplication may be classed either as a case of auto- or of allopolyploidy, since *O. Lamarckiana* is now known to be a permanent structural hybrid. This serves to emphasize the fact that the distinction between auto- and allopolyploidy is a matter of degree.

Tetraploids have been obtained experimentally in a number of organisms. As early as 1914, Gregory described tetraploid strains in *Primula sinensis*. Winkler (1916) induced polyploidy in *Solanum* by grafting together the species *S. lycopersicum* (tomato) and *S. nigrum*. The adventitious shoots that arose at the grafting point were sometimes tetraploid. Jorgensen and Crane (1927), Jorgensen (1928), and Karpechenko (1935) found grafting to be not essential in this process. Some of the shoots that develop from the scar tissue in decapitated young plants are tetraploid. Certain drugs, particularly the alkaloid colchicine extracted from the autumn crocus *Colchicum autumnale*, have been known for some time to produce characteristic disturbances in cell division. If the concentrations of colchicine are not too high, the chromosome splitting takes place but the mitotic mechanism is so modified that cell fission does not occur. Blakeslee and Avery (1937) showed that treating seeds and other developmental stages of diverse plants with appropriate colchicine solutions produces patches of tetraploid tissue from which tetraploid strains may be derived. Their work has been promptly confirmed and extended by many investigators (Nebel and Ruttle 1938, Levan 1938, 1939, 1940a, Smith 1939, and many others), and the technique of colchicine treatment has been perfected to such an extent that polyploid strains may now be induced at will, furnishing a method which may prove valuable in the hands of plant breeders and geneticists. Induction of polyploidy with the aid of other chemicals, namely acenaphthene (Kostoff 1938a, Levan 1940a) and indole acetic acid or heteroauxin (Greenleaf 1938) has also been accomplished. An interesting detail is that colchicine does not, but acenaphthene does, induce polyploidy in *Colchicum* (Levan 1940a). Still another method of inducing polyploidy is heat treatment (Randolph 1932 in maize, Müntzing, Tometorp, and Mundt-Petersen 1937 in barley, Lutkov 1938 in flax, and others).

Polyploid forms arising from diploid relatives through the doubling of the chromosome number occur in nature in some plants. The whole subject has been reviewed in detail by Müntzing (1936), who lists fifty-eight examples of this phenomenon; we may confine ourselves to the consideration of only two of them. *Biscutella laevigata*, a species of *Cruciferae*, is distributed over Central Europe and Italy. Among the races into which this species is subdivided, some have 18 chromosomes and are probably diploid, while others have 36 chromosomes and are tetraploid (Manton 1934, 1937). The distribution area of the tetraploid races is a continuous one, including the Alps, Carpathians, and the mountains of Italy and of the northern part of the Balkan peninsula. The area of the diploid races is much smaller in extent than that of the tetraploids, and in addition is sharply discontinuous. The diploids are confined to the valleys of the Rhine, Elbe, Oder, upper Danube, and some of their tributaries. Although the origin of tetraploids in *Biscutella* has not been observed in experiments, it is virtually certain that they have arisen from diploid ancestors, since the change from a tetraploid to a diploid is much more rare than the opposite, and is less likely to produce a viable type. The diploids may be regarded as relics of an ancestral population of *Biscutella laevigata*, and the tetraploids as their successors. Such an interpretation agrees with the known facts of the recent geological history of Europe. The diploids are confined to regions not covered by the ice sheet during the glacial period and consequently open to habitation by plants for a long time. On the other hand, the tetraploid races occur almost exclusively in the parts of the country that were ice-covered until a geologically more recent time and must therefore be regarded as immigrants from elsewhere. Manton concludes that the diploid races represent interglacial, if not preglacial, relics.

Similar relationships are displayed by several American species of *Tradescantia* (Anderson and Woodson 1935, Anderson and Sax 1936). In each of these species, races are encountered that have twice as many chromosomes as others. Thus, *T. occidentalis* is distributed from the Rocky Mountains, over the prairie states, east to the Mississippi. Most of this area is occupied by tetraploids, but a restricted region in central and eastern Texas in inhabited by diploids. The range of *T. canaliculata* lies mostly east of that of *T. occidentalis,* but in a fairly broad strip of land west of the Mississippi the ranges of the two species overlap. The diploid form of *T. canaliculata* is, characteristically enough, confined to almost the same territory in which the diploid *T. occidentalis* is found. Anderson regards this fact as being due to more than a coincidence. The region that harbors the diploid races of both species mentioned (and of some others in addition) is geologically a very ancient territory which has been continuously open for plant habitation. It seems probable that the diploids are here also relics, and that the territory where they occur is a center from which the spread of the more successful tetraploid types has taken place; *T. occidentalis* has spread chiefly to the north and northwest, and *T. canaliculata* to the east and northeast.

The doubling of the chromosome complement increases the number of genes, but the kind of genes and their quantitative relations, the genic balance, remain unchanged. Nevertheless, polyploids are as a rule distinguishable from the diploids from which they sprang in morphological as well as in physiological characters. This is probably due to the increase of the nuclear volume, which in turn produces various alterations in the cellular physiology. Most commonly the tetraploids possess the so-called gigas complex of characters, which was first observed in the gigas mutant of *Oenothera Lamarckiana.* According to Müntzing (1936), this is expressed in the tetraploid by a thicker stem, a greater height, larger, thicker, and relatively shorter and broader leaves, a darker green pigmentation, larger flowers and seeds than in the diploid. Some of these characteristics are usually present both in the tetraploid races obtained in experiments and in the natural tetraploids, but exceptions are encountered. Some of the tetraploids are, for example, not taller than the diploids. Moreover, while some polyploid races are striking enough to have been noticed, described, and named by systematists, others differ from the diploid relatively only slightly, and have not been recognized as transgressing the limits of the ordinary individual variability. The lack of a perfect correlation between the chromosome multiplication and the external traits has been especially· emphasized by Wettstein (1924, 1928). For example, cell size in some species of mosses is positively correlated with the chromosome number over the whole range of variations studied, from the haploid to octoploid and higher. In others a maximum cell size is reached, and a further chromosome multiplication produces no new increase, or may even result in a reduction of the cell size and a dwarfism of the plants.

It seems clear enough that the doubling of the chromosome complement produces a change in the norm of reaction of the organism, and its effect is in this respect analogous to that of a gene mutation. As any other type of change in the reaction norm, that induced by polyploidy may be favorable for the organism under some and unfavorable under other environmental conditions. It is therefore not unexpected that the geographical distributions of some polyploids differ from those of the corresponding diploids. This is clear in the already discussed examples of *Biscutella* and *Tradescantia*, where the tetraploids are to all appearances more successful ecological types than the diploids, and have extended their geographical areas in geologically recent times, leaving the diploids behind as relics. According to Müntzing (1936), the geographical distribution of the diploids and tetraploids is known or suspected to be different in thirty out of thirty-eight cases in which the appropriate data are available. Much additional information on this subject is contained in the monograph of the American species of *Crepis* by Babcock and Stebbins (1938). Hagerup (1931, 1939, 1940), Tischler (1934), Flovik (1938, 1940), and others have pointed out that the proportion of polyploids in the European flora increases northward, reaching a maximum in the Arctic region (Spitzbergen). Furthermore, tetraploids produce ecotypes which are able to occupy rigorous and exacting habitats. To conclude from this that tetraploids are in general better equipped than the diploids in the struggle for life is, however, an unwarranted generalization. After all, not all diploids are extinct as yet.

An important property of autopolyploids concerns the behavior of their chromosomes at meiosis. In a diploid organism every chromosome has, as a rule, one and only one homologue. A number of bivalents equal to the haploid chromosome number is formed, and the disjunction at meiosis gives rise to gametes all of which contain haploid sets of the chromosomes. In an autopolyploid every chromosome has more than one homologue, so that opportunity presents itself for the formation of trivalents, quadrivalents, and higher associations. The disjunction at meiosis is frequently abnormal, different numbers of chromosomes going to the two poles of the division spindle. In order to breed true, an autopolyploid must produce gametes all of which have the same complements of chromosomes. Any deviation from this rule brings about an instability of the chromosome endowment in the progeny. Polyploids with odd numbers of chromosome sets (triploids, pentaploids, and so on) cannot breed true in this way. Since loss or addition of chromosomes usually reduces the viability of the offspring, the reproductive potentials of polyploids are frequently impaired. Disturbances of the chromosome mechanism inherent in autopolyploidy limit its usefulness as a evolutionary method.

Chromosome disturbances have been observed in tetraploid *Datura* by Blakeslee, Belling, and Farnham (1923), and in other experimental autopolyploids by other authors (a review in Darlington 1937b). The extent of the disturbances is, however, variable not only from species to species but from strain to strain. Thus, Jorgensen (1928) found mostly bivalents, and Lesley and Lesley (1930) bivalents as well as quadrivalents in tetraploid tomatoes. In tetraploid *Primula sinensis* quadrivalents occur, but the disjunction is fairly normal, with two chromosomes of each kind going to either pole (Darlington 1931). In some species the chromosomes form fewer chiasmata per bivalent than in other species; in the former the autopolyploids are more likely to have a regular disjunction than in the latter. According to Müntzing and Prakken

(1940) there are, however, exceptions to this rule. Mainly bivalents are formed in the polyploid grass *Phleum,* although the chiasma frequency per bivalent is high; the authors suppose that in this plant the "need" of association is satisfied by the pairing of two homologues, regardless of the presence of other homologous chromosomes in the same nucleus. However that may be, variations in chromosome numbers are common in natural autopolyploids. Thus, Manton (1934, 1937) found that only 54 out of the 67 examined plants of *Biscutella laevigata* contained the normal chromosome number, 36, while in other individuals from 34 to 37 chromosomes were found. It is important in this connection that many autopolyploids reproduce not by seeds, but asexually through formation of adventitious buds. Asexuality and apogamy are methods of reproduction frequently resorted to by organisms whose chromosomal apparatus ceases to function normally (Babcock and Stebbins 1938; see also Chapter X).

Observations of Wettstein (1937a) on the moss *Bryum caespititium* reveal an unique, and for the time being mysterious, method of "regulation" in an autopolyploid. Experimentally induced chromosome doubling in a haploid gametophyte (n=10) of this moss in which normally the sexes are separate gave rise to a diploid (n = 20) hermaphrodite strain with large cells, pronounced "gigas" characters (see above), and low fertility. Among the F_1 generation plants, there was found one individual which showed a greater tendency to develop sporogones, and consequently to be fertile, than its sibs did. This plant was maintained for many years; year after year the development of the sporogones gradually improved, until after eleven years normal spores were produced, which gave rise to a viable and fertile offspring. Hand in hand with the improvement in fertility, the cell size was decreasing. The resulting strain appears to be a new species, which received the name of *Bryum Corrensii.* It is noteworthy that a related *Bryum* species known in nature has the chromosome number n = 20, and is characterized by an hermaphroditic gametophyte.

EXPERIMENTAL ALLOPOLYPLOIDS

The intergeneric hybrids between radish (*Raphanus sativus*) and cabbage (*Brassica oleracea*) may serve as an illustration of the results obtained when the chromosome complement is reduplicated in crosses of taxonomically rather remote forms (Karpechenko 1927a, b, 1928). Both parents have the same chromosome number—eighteen diploid. The cross succeeds fairly easily; from 202 cross-pollinated flowers 123 hybrids were obtained. The F_1 hybrids have 18 chromosomes, 9 from the radish and 9 from the cabbage parent. No chromosome pairing takes place, 18 univalents are present at the metaphase of the first division, and are distributed at random to the poles. At the second division the univalents split, giving rise to cells with a varying number of chromosomes, mostly from 6 to 12. In some of the pollen mother cells, however, the first division is abortive, and nuclei are formed that include all of the 18 univalents. The second division then gives rise to two spores, and subsequently to pollen grains containing the full haploid complement of the radish as well as of the cabbage chromosomes.

The F_1 hybrids are nearly sterile; most plants produce no seeds at all, but some do produce a few (821 seeds from 90 plants). A cytological examination shows that most of the F_2 hybrids (213 out of 229) have 36 chromosomes in their somatic cells. The origin of such plants is in all probability due to the union of the exceptional gametes possessing the full chromosome complement of the F_1 hybrid. The F_2 plants contain, therefore, 18 radish and 18 cabbage chromosomes, in other words a diploid complement of the chromosomes of each parental species. Such F_2 hybrids are tetraploid. The meiotic divisions are very regular, in striking contrast with the abnormalities observed at meiosis in the F_1 hybrids. In these tetraploids, 18 bivalents are formed, disjunction is normal, and the resulting cells, with a few exceptions, contain 18 chromosomes each. It is practically certain that the 18 bivalents that appear at meiosis are due to the pairing of 9 radish chromosomes with their 9 radish homologues, and of 9 cabbage chromosomes with their 9 cabbage homologues. The pairing is consequently between similar chromosomes (autosyndesis), rather than between the chromosomes of different species (allosyndesis). With a normal disjunction, the gametes produced by a tetraploid plant are identical with the exceptional gametes of the F_1 hybrid, and carry 9 cabbage and 9 radish chromosomes.

The tetraploid plants are fully fertile. They produce numerous

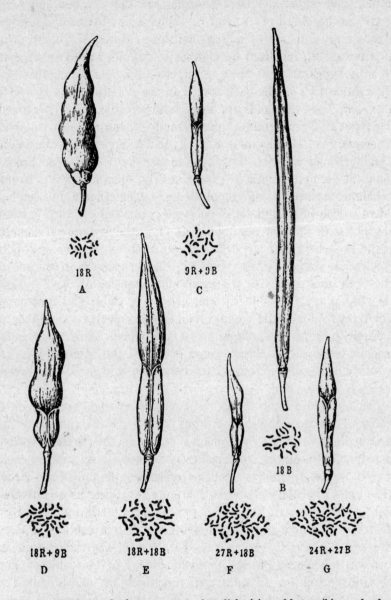

18 R

A

9R+9B

C

18 B

B

18R+9B

D

18R+18B

E

27R+18B

F

24R+27B

G

Fig. 17. Fruits and chromosomes of radish (a), cabbage (b), and of hybrids between them. (c) Diploid F_1 hybrid; (e) the tetraploid *Raphano-brassica;* (d) triploid; (f) pentaploid. (From Karpechenko.)

flowers and fruits, and from a single fruit between 900 and 1,000 seeds can be obtained. A fruit of cabbage has between 1,200 and 1,300 seeds, and that of radish about 600. Moreover, the offspring of a tetraploid, fertilized by another tetraploid, are like their parents in appearance as well as in the chromosome number. No segregation that might be expected in the offspring of a hybrid is observed. The tetraploids are hence both a fertile and a true breeding type. It is important to understand the causation of this phenomenon. The sterility of the F_1 hybrid is apparently due to the irregularity of meiosis. The random distribution of the chromosomes at the first meiotic division gives rise to gametophytes having unbalanced chromosome complements, i.e., neither a full haploid set of radish nor a full set of cabbage chromosomes. Such gametophytes are inviable or nonfunctional. Only the exceptional gametes of the F_1 hybrid that carry the full sets of the chromosomes of both species are viable. In the tetraploid, all the gametes produced are like each other, and like the exceptional gametes of the F_1. They are chromosomally balanced, and hence are viable and functional. The tetraploid is fertile because its meiosis is regular and only autosyndetic pairing of chromosomes takes place. Since there is no recombination of the chromosomes of radish and cabbage, the prerequisite of Mendelian segregation is lacking, and the hybrid breeds true.

The tetraploid hybrids represent a morphological type which is distinct both from radish and from cabbage. Some characters are intermediate, in others the influence of one of the parents predominates, and still others are peculiar to the hybrid. As chance would have it, the tetraploid has a foliage resembling the radish and a root resembling the cabbage, and is, therefore, worthless as a cultivated plant. The fruit structure (Fig. 17) is very interesting. The fruit of radish is spindle shaped, nondehiscent, that of cabbage is elongate and dehisces in two valves. The base of the radish fruit is, however, homologous to the two-valved part of the cabbage, and the cabbage fruit has an apical part resembling the radish fruit. The fruit of the F_1 hybrid (Fig. 17C) is clearly a compromise structure, resembling cabbage in the lower, and radish in the upper, part. The tetraploid resembles the F_1 diploid, but in the former (Fig. 17E) the size of the fruit is appreciably greater than in the latter.

The tetraploid hybrids possess also the gigas complex of characters discussed above in connection with the autopolyploidy. They are large luxuriant plants with large cells. Their viability is not inferior to that of the parental species. The uniformity and constancy of their characters, and the obvious differences between the tetraploid and either parental species, lead to the conclusion that we are dealing with a full-fledged new species experimentally created, to which the name *Raphanobrassica* is given to indicate the manner of its origin. The behavior of *Raphanobrassica* appears to depend in part upon the strains of the parental species used. Richardia (1937) and Howard (1938) have repeated Karpechenko's experiments with a somewhat different outcome. In the diploid radish × cabbage hybrid some bivalents and multivalents are present, and chromatin bridges may be observed at the anaphase of the meiotic division, thus showing that the parental chromosomes differ in translocations and inversions. In the tetraploid *Raphanobrassica*, meiosis is variable, some multivalents are formed, and the offspring is not quite uniform.

Raphanobrassica is by no means the only new species which has arisen through allopolyploidy in experimental cultures. Darlington (1937b) lists forty-nine allopolyploids obtained up to that time, and this number will be greatly increased by the introduction of the colchicine technique of chromosome doubling (see above). The following examples indicate the variety of conditions met with among these synthetic species. *Nicotiana digluta* (Clausen and Goodspeed 1925, Clausen 1928a), has been obtained from the hybrids between *N. tabacum* (24 chromosomes haploid) and *N. glutinosa* (12 chromosomes haploid). The F_1 hybrids are obtained with some difficulty. They possess the expected somatic number of chromosomes, 36, which at meiosis form some bivalents, but are mostly left as univalents. A majority of the F_1 plants were completely sterile, but a single plant proved to be an exception and was fertile. The offspring of this exceptional plant was externally like the F_1 but showed some gigas characteristics. The number of the chromosomes was found to be 72, which is equal to the sum of the diploid numbers of the parental species ($48 + 24 = 72$). At meiosis 36 bivalents and no univalents are formed, and the gametes produced contain 36 chromosomes, which is the sum of the haploid

numbers of *N. tabacum* and *N. glutinosa*. The F_2 plants are fertile
and breed true; they and their offspring are the new species, *N.
digluta*. The history of *N. digluta* is, then, on the whole parallel to
that of *Raphanobrassica*, with one important difference. The origin
of *Raphanobrassica* was due to the production by the F_1 hybrid of
exceptional gametes containing the entire somatic complement of
chromosomes. The union of such gametes gave rise to an allotetraploid carrying diploid sets of the chromosomes of both parents. *N.
digluta*, however, arose from a single F_1 plant which stood out
among its sibs because of its fertility. The exceptional plant had its
chromosomes doubled apparently in the somatic as well as in the
germinal tissues, and hence was already an allopolyploid. These
two methods of the origin of polyploidy, through the production of
unreduced gametes and through a somatic doubling of the chromosome number, are encountered both among the auto- and among
the allopolyploids.

Primula Kewensis (n = 18, 2n = 36) is an allotetraploid derivative from the hybrid *P. floribunda* (n = 9) × *P. verticillata* (n =
9). It has been examined by Digby (1912), Newton and Pellew
(1929), and Upcott (1939). The diploid hybrid shows a virtually
complete chromosome pairing at meiosis (mostly 9 bivalents with a
chiasma frequency somewhat lower than that in the parental species, occasionally a few univalents), but is nevertheless highly sterile. The tetraploid has mostly 18 bivalents, occasionally some quadrivalents or trivalents and univalents, and is fertile. It is, however,
not a strictly true breeding type, since it occasionally throws some
aberrant individuals whose origin is apparently due to quadrivalent
formation at meiosis. The cross *Digitalis purpurea* (n = 28) × *D.
ambigua* (n = 28) gives a semisterile F_1 generation having from 5
to 12 bivalents and from 32 to 46 univalents at meiosis. The allotetraploid *D. mertonensis* was obtained by a doubling of the chromosome complement of the F_1; it is much more fertile than its
diploid progenitor, and regularly forms 56 bivalents and no quadrivalents (Buxton and Newton 1928).

Uncommonly interesting results have been obtained by crossing
various species of *Crepis* (cf. Babcock and Navashin 1930). The
cross *C. biennis* (n = 20) × *C. setosa* (n = 4) produces a semifertile hybrid with 24 somatic chromosomes. In its meiotic division 10

bivalents and 4 univalents appear; the former disjoin normally, giving 10 chromosomes to each pole, while the latter are distributed at random. This condition must be interpreted as indicating that *C. biennis* is itself a polyploid, and contains in its haploid set two groups of 10 chromosomes, which are at least partly homologous to each other and form bivalents in the hybrid. The 4 univalents are then the chromosomes of *C. setosa*. In F_2 and further generations a variety of types appear, most of which are sterile because of disharmonious chromosome complements. However, one of these segregants proved fertile and true breeding, and received the name *Crepis artificialis* (Collins, Hollingshead and Avery 1929). A cytological examination of *C. artificialis* showed 24 somatic chromosomes that formed 12 bivalents at meiosis. The origin of this chromosome complement is interpreted as due to the presence of 10 pairs of *biennis* and of 2 pairs of *setosa* chromosomes. The four *setosa* chromosomes were identified cytologically in the chromosome group of *artificialis;* the identification was possible owing to the fact that the chromosomes of *setosa* differ in size and other characteristics from those of *biennis* and are therefore recognizable in the hybrids. *C. artificialis* is not an allopolyploid in the sense that its chromosome group is not a sum total of those of the parental species; it is rather a segregant which happens to possess a viable combination of chromosomes that gives rise to nothing but bivalents at meiosis.

The hybrids between *Crepis capillaris* ($n = 3$) and *C. tectorum* ($n = 4$) described by Hollingshead (1930b), and those between *C. rubra* ($n = 5$) and *C. foetida* ($n = 5$) studied by Poole (1931–1932) are characterized by the formation of bivalents at meiosis in the F_1 generation. The species crossed are here evidently more closely related to each other than those in the examples discussed previously, and their chromosomes still possess the pairing "affinity" for each other. Allotetraploids derived from them showed various abnormalities at meiosis. The *rubra* × *foetida* tetraploid has for example, from 0 to 5 quadrivalents and from 0 to 10 bivalents. While the F_1 hybrids were semifertile, the tetraploids not only showed no improvement in fertility compared to the F_1, but in fact manifested a deterioration.

ALLOPOLYPLOIDS IN NATURE

The experimental allopolyploids are novel types created artificially by combining various previously existing species. Some of these synthetic types can be properly regarded as new species. Indeed, they possess complexes of morphological and physiological traits not present in any known species, and, in addition, are fertile and true breeding forms similar in this respect to any "good species" found in the natural state. Last but not least, the allopolyploids are, as we shall see below, isolated from their progenitors by the barriers of incompatibility and of sterility of the hybrids. It is no exaggeration to say that the production of allopolyploids is the most powerful tool yet available to a geneticist for molding living matter into new shapes. We may turn now to a consideration of evidence that the same tool has been resorted to on a grand scale for the production of new species in nature. At least in one case, that of *Galeopsis Tetrahit*, an existing species has been experimentally resynthesized from its putative ancestors. In at least two further cases the presumptive evidence is fairly complete to make it very probable that a species found in nature had arisen from two known species. Finally, in numerous cases the origin of species through allopolyploidy may be regarded as certain, although the ancestral species can be only conjectured.

In his monographic work on the genus *Galeopsis*, Müntzing (1930, 1932, 1937b) shows that six out of the eight species investigated have the haploid number of chromosomes, 8, and the two remaining ones have $n = 16$. Among the former are the species *G. pubescens* and *G. speciosa*, and among the latter is *G. Tetrahit*. The cross *pubescens* × *speciosa* succeeds easily when *pubescens* is used as the female parent. F_1 hybrid is highly sterile; its anthers contain only 8.9 percent to 22.3 percent of visibly good pollen, and few good ovules are produced. At meiosis varying numbers of bivalents and univalents are formed. In the F_2 generation a single plant was found that proved to be triploid ($3n = 24$). Its origin is probably due to the union of a gamete containing the somatic complement of the F_1 hybrid (i.e., 8 chromosomes of *pubescens* and a like number from *speciosa*) with a gamete carrying 8 chromosomes, the proportions of the chromosomes of the two parental species in the latter gamete not being clear. This triploid plant was backcrossed to a pure *pubescens*. A single seed resulted from the backcross. It gave rise to a plant which proved to be a tetraploid ($4n = 32$). This tetraploid plant was fertile, and became the progenitor of a strain which, for reasons stated below, has been named "artificial Tetrahit." The origin of the tetraploid was due to a union of an unreduced gamete of the triploid with a normal one of *G. pubescens*.

The triploid hybrid between *G. pubescens* and *G. speciosa*, as well as its tetraploid derivatives, exhibit a striking resemblance to *G. Tetrahit*. The latter species has however taken no part in the production of the hybrids. The resemblance, which according to Müntzing reaches in some individuals an apparent identity, suggests that the true *G. Tetrahit* arose as an allotetraploid from the cross *G. pubescens* × *G. speciosa* or types similar to these species. A series of tests were imposed to prove the validity of this hypothesis.

The artificial *Tetrahit* is like the real *Galeopsis Tetrahit* in possessing 32 chromosomes in somatic cells and 16 bivalents at meiosis. The meiotic divisions are, with few exceptions, normal. The disturbance of the meiosis encountered in the F_1 hybrids between *pubescens* and *speciosa* is abated in the artificial *Tetrahit*. A cross between the artificial and the natural *Tetrahit* gives normally developed offspring which are externally similar to either parent. The fertility is complete in some individuals, while others are partially sterile; it must be taken into consideration that a partial sterility has been observed by Müntzing (1930) in some lines of the pure *G. Tetrahit* as well. The meiotic divisions are normal; 16 bivalents are formed which undergo a regular disjunction. In short, the artificial and the natural *G. Tetrahit* are similar both morphologically and in their genetic and cytological behavior.

Although the origin of the natural *Galeopsis Tetrahit* from a cross between *pubescens* and *speciosa* is very probable, it remains unknown when and where the event took place. The data of Huskins (1931) pertaining to the grass species *Spartina Townsendii* are in this respect more complete. This species was discovered in 1870 in a single locality in southern England. Soon thereafter a rapid spread of *S. Townsendii* was recorded. By 1902 its known distribution area had expanded to cover many thousands of acres along the coast of England, and in 1906 it appeared on the coast of

France. A further expansion ensued, and owing to its desirable agricultural properties, *S. Townsendii* has been introduced artificially into other parts of the world.

The origin of *Spartina Townsendii* has been a subject of discussion for some time. A comparative morphological study of various species of the genus *Spartina* has led systematists to believe that *S. Townsendii* is a hybrid between two other species, namely *S. stricta* and *S. alterniflora*. Among these, *S. stricta* is an indigenous European species known for about three hundred years; *S. alterniflora* is native in America, but it has been introduced into England and has spread somewhat, becoming common in some localities. It is suggestive in this connection that in the process of its expansion *S. Townsendii* has overrun some of the territory previously occupied by *S. stricta* and has supplanted the latter. *S. alterniflora* has suffered much the same fate where it has come in contact with *S. Townsendii*.

The chromosome number of *Spartina stricta* has been found by Huskins to be 56 (diploid). That of *S. alterniflora* is $2n = 70$. On the supposition that *S. Townsendii* is an allotetraploid derivative from the two others, it should have a chromosome number equal to the sum of the diploid numbers of its putative ancestors, $56 + 70 = 126$. The number actually found is 126, with a possible variation of ± 2 chromosomes. Meiosis in *S. Townsendii* shows mostly bivalents, but also some multivalents. The presence of the latter may account for a rather wide variation of the external characteristics observed in this species. One can assert with some confidence that *S. Townsendii* arose in the nineteenth or the eighteenth century, probably on the southern coast of England.

A somewhat different complex of evidence is presented by Anderson (1936a) to prove that *Iris versicolor* is an allopolyploid derivative of two other species, *I. virginica* and *I. setosa*. The area inhabited by *I. virginica* extends from Virginia along the coast of the Atlantic and the Gulf of Mexico; a race of the same species occupies the territory south of the Great Lakes, and the valleys of Mississippi and Ohio. The distribution region of *I. setosa* is broken up in two parts; one race inhabits the Pacific and the Bering Sea coasts of Alaska, and the other is found in Labrador, Newfoundland, and Nova Scotia. Both species are regarded as survivors from pre-glacial times. On the other hand, *I. versicolor* is likely to be a more youthful species, since it occurs in the northeastern states, and from Labrador, along the St. Lawrence and Great Lakes, to Wisconsin and Winnipeg. A major part of this area was glaciated, and the flora is conjectured to be of a more recent origin.

A cytological examination has fully corroborated the hypothesis of the origin of *Iris versicolor* from *setosa* and *virginica*. Indeed, the diploid chromosome numbers are 38 for *setosa*, 70 to 72 for *virginica*, and 38 + 70 = 108 for *versicolor*. Both *virginica* and *versicolor* show some multivalent chromosome associations at meiosis. This fact, as well as the chromosome numbers, suggest that *virginica* is itself an allotetraploid derivative of two unknown species which had chromosome numbers of the order of magnitude now present in *setosa;* its origin is hidden in antiquity. *I. versicolor* must then be an allohexaploid which has received twice as many chromosomes from the *virginica*-like as from the *setosa*-like parent. The morphological characteristics of *versicolor* may therefore be expected to approach more closely those of *virginica* than those of *setosa*.

A careful morphological comparison of all three species has shown first of all that *Iris versicolor* is closer to the Alaskan than to the Labradorean race of *I. setosa*. In fact, *versicolor* is in most characters intermediate between *virginica* and the Alaskan *setosa*, closer to the former than to the latter. Some of the traits of *versicolor* could not be found however in either species. This might be accounted for either on the supposition that *versicolor* arose from an undiscovered or extinct variety of one of its putative parents, or that its peculiar traits are a concomitant of polyploidy. A search has shown that the former possibility is more probable, because a new race, *I. setosa* variety *interior*, has been found in the Yukon valley in Alaska, and this race possesses the requisite complex of characters. It is apparently significant that the new race occupies a territory which is adjacent to, but was not covered by, the continental ice sheet.

Experimental hybridization of *Iris virginica* and *I. setosa* has been attempted, but the results are inconclusive. Owing to the difference in the flowering seasons, the crossing of the two species is difficult; some pollinations resulted in some hybrid seeds of which none germinated. This result does not, of course, preclude the possibility that sometimes hybridization may be successful.

Similar, though perhaps less complete, evidence is available on the origin of several other existing species. Thus, *Aesculus carnea* is a hybrid between *Ae. hippocastanum* and *Ae. Pavia* (Skovsted 1929); the hexaploid *Phleum pratense* is a product of crossing of the diploid *P. pratense* with the tetraploid *P. alpinum* (Gregor and Sansome 1930). According to Babcock and Stebbins (1938), American species of *Crepis* having the basic chromosome number n = 11 have descended through allopolyploidy from hybrids between Old World species having n = 4 and n = 7 respectively. Different American species have arisen from different pairs of Old World ancestors, and the authors are able to hypothesize the probable parents in several instances. In America, the development of the genus entailed the formation of further autopolyploid, as well as allopolyploid derivatives, with chromosome numbers as high as n = 44. *Artemisia Douglasiana* (n = 27) is probably derived from *A. Suksdorfii* (n = 9) and *A. ludoviciana* (n = 18); in the genus *Penstemon* several probable allopolyploids are indicated (Clausen 1933, Clausen, Keck and Hiesey 1940).

HYBRIDS BETWEEN POLYPLOID SPECIES

An allopolyploid possesses sets of chromosomes that are present separately in two or more of the species represented in its make-up. Although in allopolyploids that have arisen in the past the chromosomes have had time to undergo changes, some similarity between the chromosomes of a polyploid and those of its diploid relatives may persist and may manifest itself in pairing and bivalent formation in the hybrids. As early as 1909, Rosenberg described the chromosome behavior in a cross of *Drosera longifolia* (n = 10) and *D. rotundifolia* (n = 20). The somatic chromosome number in the hybrid is the sum of the haploid numbers of the parents, namely 30. At meiosis in the hybrid, 10 bivalents and 10 univalents are produced; the former disjoin regularly and the latter are distributed at random. In this particular case it is impossible to determine which chromosomes are giving rise to the bivalents. One may suppose that the 10 *D. longifolia* chromosomes united with 10 *D. rotundifolia* ones, and the remaining 10 *D. rotundifolia* chromosomes are left over as univalents; this assumes that the pairing is between the chromosomes of different species (allosyndesis). Or else, the 20 *D. rotundifolia* chromosomes may unite in 10 pairs, and leave the *D. longifolia* chromosomes unpaired; this would be a pairing between chromosomes of the same species (autosyndesis). If only similar chromosomes pair, autosyndesis would mean that the two sets of chromosomes of *D. rotundifolia* are more similar to each other than either of them is to *D. longifolia* chromosomes. Allosyndesis would indicate that the *D. longifolia* chromosomes resemble one set of the *D. rotundifolia* chromosomes more than they do the other, and are more alike than either of these two sets; this, in turn, might suggest the inference that *D. longifolia* is one of the ancestors of the polyploid *D. rotundifolia*.

Such an inference appears justified by analogy with the behavior of the experimental allopolyploids when crossed to their known ancestral species. The synthetic *Nicotiana digluta* (see above) has 72 chromosomes in its somatic cells, 48 of which (24 pairs) are derived from *N. tabacum*, and 24 (12 pairs) from the *N. glutinosa* ancestors. As the number 12 is basic in the genus *Nicotiana*, *N. digluta* must be regarded as an allohexaploid. A backcross of *N. digluta* to *N. tabacum* results in a hybrid carrying 60 chromosomes, i.e., a pentaploid (Clausen 1928a). The origin of these 60 chromosomes is as follows: 36 of them have been contributed by the *N. digluta* gamete, which in turn is known to contain 24 chromosomes of *N. tabacum* and 12 of *N. glutinosa;* the remaining 24 have been introduced by the *N. tabacum* gamete. The hybrid shows 24 bivalents and 12 univalents at meiosis. The bivalents are here the *N. tabacum* chromosomes, and the univalents are the remaining *N. glutinosa* ones. The cross *N. digluta* × *N. glutinosa* gives rise to a hybrid with 48 chromosomes, which forms 12 bivalents and 24 univalents at meiosis. The univalents are here the *N. tabacum* and the bivalents the *N. glutinosa* chromosomes (Clausen 1928a, 1928b).

The study of the chromosome pairing in the hybrids between polyploid species becomes a method for tracing phylogenetic relationships. The limitations of this method are however serious. The difficulty of distinguishing between auto- and allosyndesis has already been mentioned. Both of these processes are known to occur, sometimes separately and at other times in combinations. More serious still, the assumption is implicit in this method that the chromosomes that pair in a hybrid are "similar." The similarity of chromosomes is, however, a concept which is ambiguous unless defined precisely. Chromosomes may become differentiated through the occurrence of gene mutations or through changes in the gene arrangement (translocations, inversions, etc.) or both. These changes are not necessarily concomitant. Apparently equally remote species may be rather similar or may be very different in the gene arrangement (Chapter IV). Which of these changes determine the occurrence or the failure of the meiotic pairing? If chromosome pairing is a function of the similarity in the gene arrangement (cf. Chapter IX), the formation of bivalents does not exclude the possibility that the partners differ greatly in the allelic state of their genes. At best a phylogeny based on studies on the bivalent formation in the hybrids between the extant species is capable of giving only a rough approximation to the actual situation. Nevertheless, data of this kind do furnish conclusive evidence of the compound nature of polyploid species, and this alone makes them valuable.

The relationships of species of *Nicotiana* have been examined by Goodspeed and Clausen (1928), Clausen (1928b), Brieger (1928), Lammerts (1931), Webber (1930), Rybin (1927, 1929), Kostoff (1938b), and others (see these papers for further references). A group of species of this genus are diploid (n = 12), others are tetraploid (n = 24) or hexaploid. The twenty-four chromosome species are allopolyploid derived from natural crossing of twelve chromosome species. The cross *N. tabacum* × *N. sylvestris* gives a triploid hybrid (2n = 36) that forms 12 bivalents and 12 univalents at meiosis. Since the haploid *N. tabacum* (n = 24) is known to have no bivalents, the formation of the bivalents in the *N. tabacum* × *N. sylvestris* hybrid is allosyndetic. The conclusion follows that the chromosome complement of *N. tabacum* contains a set of 12 chromosomes structurally similar to those of *N. sylvestris*, and another set of twelve that are structurally different. The crosses *N. tabacum* × *N. tomentosa* and *N. tabacum* × *N. Rusbyi* gave also 12 bivalents and 12 univalents at meiosis in the F_1 hybrids. Since the cross *N. tomentosa* × *N. Rusbyi* gives 12 bivalents, these two species have structurally similar chromosomes. Hence, the complement of *N. tabacum* contains 12 chromosomes similar to either *to-*

mentosa or *Rusbyi.* The question now is this: are the chromosomes of *N. sylvestris* similar to those of *N. tomentosa* and *N. Rusbyi?* A negative answer to this question follows from the fact that the *N. tomentosa* × *N. sylvestris* and *N. Rusbyi* × *N. sylvestris* hybrids form 24 univalents and no bivalents. Hence, the haploid set of *N. tabacum* (n = 24) is composed of two dissimilar groups of chromosomes, twelve in each, which are related to the chromosomes of *N. sylvestris* and *N. tomentosa-N. Rusbyi* respectively. The inference that these species or some other species with similar chromosomes, have taken part in the production of *N. tabacum* is a probable one.

Cytogenetic investigations on species of wheat (*Triticum*) and of of the related genus *Aegilops* have furnished abundant material from which inferences regarding the phylogeny of this group can be drawn. The literature of this subject is voluminous. The work of Sax (1922), Sax and Sax (1924), Sapehin (1928), Watkins (1930, 1932), Bleier (1928, 1933), and especially that of Kihara and his school (see Kihara 1937 for references) may be mentioned. The described species of wheat fall into three groups differing in chromosome numbers:

THE EINKORN GROUP	THE EMMER GROUP	VULGARE GROUP
(n = 7, 2n = 14)	(n = 14, 2n = 28)	(n = 21, 2n = 42)
T. aegilopoides	T. dicoccoides	T. spelta
T. thaoudar	T. dicoccum	T. vulgare
T. monococcum	T. durum	T. compactum
	T. turgidum	T. sphaerococcum
	T. pyramidale	
	T. polonicum	
	T. persicum	
	T. Timopheevi	

In *Aegilops,* species with 2n = 14 and 2n = 28 are known. The basic chromosome number is evidently n = 7; the einkorn group is diploid, the emmers tetraploid, and the vulgare group (soft wheats) hexaploid. With few exceptions, the hybrids between species possessing the same number of chromosomes show only bivalents at meiosis, and are fully fertile. The hybrids between the representatives of the vulgare and emmer groups are pentaploid (21 + 14 = 35), and show at meiosis 14 bivalents and 7 univalents. The triploid hybrids (emmer $\times$ einkorn, $14 + 7 = 21$) have from 4 to 7 bivalents and from 7 to 13 univalents. The vulgare $\times$ einkorn cross ($21 + 7 = 28$) produces from none to as many as 10 bivalents, 7 being the usual number at least in certain crosses.

These relationships have been interpreted to mean that the einkorn, emmer, and vulgare groups have, respectively, one, two, and three sets of seven chromosomes which are different from each other. These sets are denoted as A, B, and D. The hybrids AAB and AABD have as a rule seven, and AABBD fourteen bivalents. The emmer group arose as an allotetraploid derivative from the hybrids between an einkorn species furnishing the genome A and some other plant that gave the genome B. Species of the vulgare group are allohexaploids, and their origin is due to a cross of an emmer (AB) with something supplying the genome D. This something is supposed to be a species of *Aegilops* which may possess D.

This hypothesis has on the whole withstood the tests imposed on it, but its schematic simplicity is largely a thing of the past. Variations in the bivalent number in some crosses have been mentioned already. In addition, Kihara and Nishiyama (1930) have described the formation of trivalents at meiosis in the hybrids *Triticum aegilopoides* $\times$ *T. dicoccum*, *T. aegilopoides* $\times$ *T. spelta,* and *T. durum* $\times$ *T. vulgare*. The presence of the trivalents may indicate that some of the chromosomes of the supposedly different genomes preserve enough similarity so that they can pair; it may also be due to some of the *T. aegilopoides* chromosomes (genome A) consisting of parts that lie in different chromosomes of the same set in *T. dicoccum* and *T. spelta*. The genomes denoted by the same letter in different species may be distinct, due to changes by translocations, inversions, etc.*

The divergent evolution of the once identical chromosome sets is nicely illustrated by the results of Lilienfeld and Kihara (1934) on *Triticum Timopheevi*, a species of the emmer group. As such, *T.*

---

* The terms "genome" and "genome analysis" unfortunately seem to have taken root in the field of wheat cyto-genetics, in spite of the fact that they are highly misleading. These terms imply that definite chromosome sets contain similar (or, respectively, different) gene complexes. Yet, the "genome analysis" has nothing to do with gene qualities. What is being studied is the chromosome pairing, which is in all likelihood determined by the gene arrangement, the gross structure of the chromosomes. To assume that the genic differentiation is proportional to the structural diversity would be gratuitous. A noncommittal expression like "set of chromosomes" would be more suitable.

Timopheevi is expected to carry the chromosome sets A and B encountered in all emmers. The crosses *T. Timopheevi* × *T. pyramidale*, *T. Timopheevi* × *T. dicoccum*, *T. Timopheevi* × *T. persicum* and *T. Timopheevi* × *T. durum* give, nevertheless, semisterile F_1 hybrids which have quadrivalents, trivalents, bivalents, and univalents in varying proportions at meiosis. In Lilienfeld and Kihara's figures the number of univalents varies from 1 to 8, and that of bivalents from 5 to 12. The cross *T. Timopheevi* × *T. aegilopoides* gives however a result similar to that obtained in the crosses between *T. aegilopoides* (an einkorn) and any other species of the emmer group. The chromosome set A is common to the einkorns and to the emmers, including *T. Timopheevi*. The difference between *T. Timopheevi* and the other emmers lies evidently in the set B. Lilienfeld and Kihara cut the Gordian knot by saying that *T. Timopheevi* possesses a special chromosome set (genome) G, not present in any other known wheat. The "formula" of *T. Timopheevi* is AG, while all other emmers are AB. From their own data it follows, however, that G is more like B than anything else; denoting this chromosome set by a separate letter does not seem to be a particularly helpful expedient. There is no assurance that *T. Timopheevi* is distinct in its origin from other emmers; the differentiation of one of its chromosome sets may have taken place before or after it has become a tetraploid species. The differentiation of the chromosome sets is a gradual process, as Kihara himself has pointed out.

A comparison of *Triticum* species with those of *Aegilops* shows especially clearly that the "similarity" and "dissimilarity" of the chromosome sets is a matter of degree (Kihara and Lilienfeld 1932, and others). In a hybrid between two races of *Ae. ventricosa*, all chromosomes pair, but two circles of four chromosomes are formed. Obviously, translocations have taken place in the phylogeny. *Ae. speltoides* × *Triticum monococcum*, a hybrid between two species each possessing 2n = 14, gives from 0 to 7 bivalents. The chromosome sets present in the two species are denoted as S and A respectively; the occasional formation of 7 bivalents shows that S and A are related, and yet they are by no means identical. The cross *Ae. Aucheri* (a species related to *Ae. speltoides*) × *T. durum* leads Kihara and Lilienfeld to believe that some of the chromosomes of the set S of *Aegilops* are more closely related to the chromosomes of the set A and others to those of the set B of *T. durum.* The tetraploid species *Ae. cylindrica* has two sets denoted C and D; the set D is somewhat related to the chromosomes that differentiate the vulgare group from the emmer group of wheats (see above). And yet, the hybrid *Ae. cylindrica* × *T. aegilopoides,* which contains the three different sets A, C, and D, has from 4 to 8 bivalents. Some of the chromosomes of these sets are obviously related.

Kihara and Lilienfeld introduce subscripts to distinguish between the supposedly similar sets of chromosomes in different species. Thus, A_{eink}, A_{em}, and A_D are the chromosomes of the A set from einkorn, emmer, and vulgare, wheats respectively. A_{eink} is clearly different from the two others, but all of them are related to the S set of the *Sitopsis* section of the genus *Aegilops.* There are four semi-homologous C sets in different *Aegilops* species, and they are also somewhat related to the sets S, T, E, F, and D found in other *Aegilops,* and to A of the *Triticum* species. Kihara and Lilienfeld have sketched a phylogenetic tree of the chromosome sets of *Aegilops* and *Triticum.* This phylogeny is merely a graphic representation of the frequencies of pairing between the chromosomes of the different sets, and it may or may not have anything to do with the phylogeny of the species that are the carriers of these chromosomes.

The evolutionary changes among wheats are of two kinds. The species formation through allopolyploidy, that is, through the emergence of new combinations of the chromosome sets dovetails with the processes of the differentiation of the chromosome sets themselves by gene mutation and by changes in the gene arrangement. The latter class of changes is perhaps less spectacular than the results of the polyploidy, but its existence can be deduced from the available data. The occurrence of allopolyploids implies as an antecedent a differentiation of the chromosomes in the ancestral species by translocation, inversion, and other means.

POLYPLOIDY IN ANIMALS AND IN DIOECIOUS PLANTS

The prevalence of polyploids among plants and their relative scarcity among animals is the most striking known difference between the evolutionary patterns in the two kingdoms. Muller

(1925) has pointed out that this difference is probably caused by
a preponderance of hermaphroditism (monoecy) among higher
plants, and of the separation of sexes (dioecy) among cytologically
examined animals. Where the sex determination is due to a hetero-
chromosome mechanism, polyploidy may result in the production
of sexually abnormal or sterile types.

The well-known data of Bridges and others demonstrate that sex
in *Drosophila* is determined by the ratio or balance between the
X chromosomes which carry the femaleness and the autosomes
which tend toward maleness. A zygote possessing equal numbers of
X chromosomes (X) and of sets of autosomes (A) develops in a
female. Diploid (2X, 2A), triploid (3X, 3A), tetraploid (4X, 4A),
and probably also haploid (1X, 1A) females are known. A ratio
$X:A = 1$ is therefore female determining. A ratio $X:A = 0.5$,
however, determines a male; a normal diploid male is 1X, 2A, and
the unpublished data of Sturtevant show that a tetraploid 2X, 4A is
also a male. Ratios intermediate between 1 and 0.5 give rise to intersexes (2X, 3A, or 3X, 4A) and zygotes of the constitution 3X,
2A and 1X, 3A develop in the so-called superfemales and supermales respectively. The Y chromosome of *Drosophila* has nothing
to do with sex determination, although a male devoid of it is sterile.

A reduplication of the chromosome complement in an organism
like *Drosophila* may give rise to tetraploid females (4X, 4A) and
tetraploid males (2X, 4A). The reduction division in tetraploid
males has not been studied, but on theoretical grounds it is believed
likely to give rise mostly to 1X, 2A spermatozoa. Such spermatozoa
uniting with the eggs of a normal diploid female (1X, 1A) would
produce intersexes (2X, 3A). A tetraploid female produces diploid
2X, 2A eggs, which on fertilization by the sperm of a normal diploid
male (1X, 1A and 1Y, 1A) give triploid females (3X, 3A) and
intersexes (2X, 3A). A triploid female crossed to a diploid male
produces triploid and diploid females, diploid males, intersexes, superfemales, and supermales. Even if tetraploid females and males
should appear at once in such quantities that they are likely to mate
with each other rather than with the normal diploids, the tetraploid
race cannot become established, for the offspring produced would
consist of tetraploid females (4X, 4A) and intersexes (3X, 4A).

An obvious corollary to the above arguments is that, where the mechanism of sex determination is like that in *Drosophila*, formation of polyploid races and species encounters difficulties in dioecious organisms. This reservation is important, because modifications of the mechanisms of sex determination and of meiosis are known in some forms which are compatible with polyploidy. Warmke and Blakeslee (1940) and Westergaard (1940) have independently demonstrated that in the dioecious plant *Melandrium album* the male-determining genes lie mainly in the Y, and the female determiners in the X chromosome; the autosomes have only a slight effect, if any, on sex. Tetraploid females (4A, 4X) and males (4A, 2X, 2Y) were obtained with the aid of colchicine and heat treatments. These males produce mostly 2A, 1X, 1Y gametes, which, uniting with 2A, 2X eggs, give rise to 4A, 3X, 1Y individuals. These individuals are, however, not intersexes as they would be in *Drosophila* but somatically normal and fertile males, although they occasionally produce some functional hermaphroditic flowers. When intercrossed, the 4A, 4X females and 4A, 3X, 1Y males give a progeny consisting of equal numbers of females and males like their parents. In so far as the autopolyploid condition permits, such individuals might constitute a true breeding, polyploid dioecious race. It may be noted that, in *Melandrium*, 3A, 2X, 1Y individuals are males, not sterile intersexes, and 2A, 2X, 1Y are self-fertile hermaphrodites, not females, as they are in *Drosophila*.

Among animals, a special kind of polyploidy is encountered in *Hymenoptera* and in certain scale insects, *Coccidae*, where it is connected with a peculiar mode of sex determination (diploid females, haploid males). Otherwise, so far as is known, polyploid races and species become established in nature only in hermaphroditic and parthenogenetic forms. This is manifestly not because the incidence of the origin of polpyloidy is low in natural populations of dioecious species. Fankhauser (1938, 1939) found 4 triploids among 100 examined larvae of the newt *Triturus viridescens*, and 13 triploids and 2 tetraploids among 134 larvae of the salamander *Eurycea bislineata*. Nevertheless, no polyploid races of these species are known in any locality. A review of the chromosome numbers in the the animal kingdom shows indications of polyploid series only in flatworms (*Rhabdocoela*), leeches (*Hirudinea*), and annelids (*Oligochaeta*), all of which are hermaphrodites (White 1940c).

Among nine parthenogenetic species of weevils (*Curculionidae*), one is diploid, five are triploid, and three are tetraploid. A single maturation division takes place in the eggs of these beetles, at which the chromosomes divide equationally, whereupon the eggs develop without fertilization. Four related bisexual species were examined, and all of them were found to be diploid, and to have normal meiosis in both sexes (Suomalainen 1940a, b). There is some reason to believe that the parthenogenetic ones may be allo-polyploid.

Species in which bisexual diploid and parthenogenetic polyploid races are known are, naturally, most interesting. A situation of this sort has been described by Vandel (1928, 1934, 1938b) in the sow bug *Trichoniscus elisabethae*. The Mediterranean countries are inhabited by a race in which females and males occur in the normal $1:1$ ratio, and in which the eggs are unable to develop without fertilization. In northern Europe occurs a parthenogenetic race consisting almost exclusively of females. Both races are found in a geographically intermediate zone. The bisexual race is diploid ($2n = 16$), and the parthenogenetic one triploid ($3n = 24$). As in the weevils mentioned above, the eggs of the parthenogenetic race undergo a single equational maturation division. Crossing parthenogenetic females to males of the bisexual race rarely succeeds because the males refuse to copulate with the triploid females. Where copulation does take place, the eggs apparently fail to be fertilized and develop parthenogenetically. The parthenogenetic race occasionally produces a few males (the sex ratio is about 100 ♀ ♀ to 1.6 ♂ ♂) which carry 24 chromosomes like their mothers. The spermatogenesis in the exceptional triploid males involves no chromosome pairing at meiosis; two equational divisions are observed, and the spermatozoa that develop contain the whole complement of 24 chromosomes. The triploid males copulate with the triploid females, and the seminal receptacles of the latter may be filled with sperm; the sperm, however, is nonfunctional and the fertilized females produce parthenogenetic eggs as usual. The reason why some triploid individuals are females and other males remains quite obscure. In the shrimp *Artemia salina*, diploid bisexual, diploid parthenogenetic, and tetraploid parthenogenetic races are known (Artom 1931, Gross 1932).

The most complex modification of the normal nuclear cycle conjoined with polyploidy is that in the moth *Solenobia triquetrella* (Seiler 1927, 1937). This species has a tetraploid ($2n = 120$) parthenogenetic race which is widespread in central Europe, and a diploid ($2n = 60$) bisexual one which is narrowly localized in a part of Germany. The chromosome behavior in the diploid race is normal. The parthenogenetic race consists of females only; the oögenesis also proceeds at first normally. The 120 chromosomes unite to form 60 bivalents. Two maturation divisions follow the normal course, and the female pronucleus with 60 chromosomes emerges from the process. It migrates to the periphery of the egg, and after some delay proceeds to cleave, of course without fertilization. Two cleavage divisions take place, resulting in the appearance of four nuclei, 60 chromosomes in each. These four nuclei form two pairs, and fuse, giving rise to two nuclei now possessing 120 chromosomes, which is the tetraploid complement. The cleavage is then resumed, and a parthenogenetic female develops.

If a male is available when the parthenogenetic female has just emerged from the pupa, a cross between the two races may take place. Moreover, the normally parthenogenetic eggs admit the spermatozoa into their cytoplasm; the penetration of several spermatozoa into a single egg (polyspermy) is frequent. The subsequent processes are rather chaotic. The female pronucleus divides twice and forms four 60-chromosome nuclei. The spermatozoa have in the meanwhile transformed into male pronuclei containing 30 chromosomes each. All four female nuclei may fuse with the sperm nuclei, giving rise to products that contain $60 + 30 = 90$ chromosomes. Or else the female nuclei may fuse in pairs, as they do in unfertilized eggs, and form 120 chromosome derivatives. Two of the female nuclei may fuse, and the remaining two may combine with the sperm nuclei, so that the organism has two kinds of cells, some bearing 120 and others 90 chromosomes. Some of the sperm nuclei can take part in the development without union with anything else, resulting in cells with only 30 chromosomes. Finally, several sperm nuclei can fuse with a single female one, which raises the chromosome number to as high as 240.

It is not surprising that the hybrids between the two races of *Solenobia* develop into strange creatures. A whole series of individuals, beginning with malelike and ending with femalelike ones, is obtained. A majority are intersexual, or show combinations of female and male parts with very frequent asymmetry. Seiler does not state whether any of them are fertile, and if so what kind of offspring they can produce. The interracial hybridization, even if it sometimes occurs in nature, is unable to give rise to a viable hybrid form that could compete with the parental races.

The phylogenetic development is customarily represented by treelike diagrams, wherein the basal trunks symbolize the ancestral forms. The branching of the trunk represents the differentiation of the ancestral species, giving rise to the variety of existing and extinct species derived from it. A more adequate image of the evolutionary process may be drawn if the trunk and the branches of the phylogenetic tree are pictured as cables consisting of numerous strings, and running on the whole parallel to each other but occasionally branching or coming to an end (Anderson 1936a). Such a representation has the advantage of taking into consideration the fact that most species and races are composites made up of numerous semi-isolated colonies that are to a certain degree independent evolutionary units.

In groups where allopolyploidy is not encountered, the cables will preserve their independence from each other. They may go parallel, or diverge, or converge somewhat, or branch further, but only in rare cases can they coalesce or intertwine where a hybridization of the separate species takes place. The emergence of an allopolyploid signifies that one or several strings have been torn away from two cables representing the two ancestral species. These strings fuse, and presently become subdivided again into a number of new ones, forming a new cable of the polyploid species. In a phylogenetic scheme this event can be represented as a simultaneous bifurcation of two cables, followed by an anastomosis of two out of the resulting four branches. Where the species formation through allopolyploidy is frequent, the phylogenetic "tree" will tend to lose its treelike appearance on account of the fusion of its branches, and will come to resemble, according to the metaphor of Epling (1939), "a gigantic and ragged *Hydrodictyon* floating in time."

VIII: ISOLATING MECHANISMS

CLASSIFICATION

THE FUNDAMENTAL importance of isolation in the evolutionary process has been recognized for a long time. Lamarck and Darwin pointed out that interbreeding of groups of hereditarily distinct individuals results in dissolution and swamping of the differences by crossing. The only way to preserve the differences between organisms is to prevent their interbreeding, to introduce isolation. Among Darwin's immediate followers the role of isolation was stressed especially by M. Wagner, in whose view it assumed the position of keystone of the whole theory of evolution. Romanes originated the oft-quoted maxim, "without isolation or the prevention of interbreeding, organic evolution is in no case possible," which if taken too literally overshoots the mark.

From the viewpoint of present knowledge it appears that these early ideas about the role of isolation confused two entirely different problems. First, the differences between individuals and groups may be due to a single gene or a single chromosome change. Such differences can never be swamped by crossing, since, in the offspring of a hybrid, segregation takes place and the ancestral traits reappear unmodified. No isolation is needed to preserve the variation due to changes in single genes, and if one consents to dignify gene mutation by applying to it the name evolution, the latter is independent of isolation. The bearing of the particulate, as opposed to the blending, theory of inheritance on the problem of the retention of hereditary variation has been discussed above (Chapter V). The second class of differences between individuals and groups is genetically more complex, owing to the coöperation of two or more genes. Races and species usually differ from each other in many genes and chromosomal alterations. Species are distinct because they carry different constellations of genes. Interbreeding of races and species results in a breakdown of these systems, although the gene differences as such are fully preserved. Hence, the maintenance of species as discrete units is contingent on their isolation. Species formation without isolation is impossible.

On the lowest level of the evolutionary process—which is concerned with the origin of hereditary variability, with changes in the basic units such as genes and chromosomes—the role of isolation is naught. But, on the next higher level the molding of the above elements into integrated systems takes place. The interactions of mutation pressure, selection, restriction of population size, and migration create not new genes but new harmonious genotypic systems adapted to different ecological niches in the environment. Unlimited interbreeding would result in a breakdown of existing systems and the emergence of a mass of recombinations. Among the recombinations some may be as harmonious as the original gene patterns; some might be in fact better than the existing ones, and thus by hydridization the organism may "discover" new evolutionary possibilities. But the chance of discovery of new adaptive geneotypes is pitted against the fact that a majority, and probably a vast majority, of the new genic patterns are discordant, unfit for any available environment, and represent a total loss to the species.

We are confronted with an apparent antinomy. Isolation prevents the breakdown of the existing gene systems, and hence precludes the formation of many worthless gene combinations that are doomed to destruction. Its role is therefore positive. But, on the other hand, isolation debars the organism from exploring greater and greater portions of the field of gene combinations, and hence decreases the chance of the discovery of new and better adaptive genotypes. Isolation is a conservative factor that slows down evolution. The antinomy is removed if one realizes that an agent useful at one stage of the evolutionary process may be harmful at another stage. If life is to endure, gene combinations whose adaptive value has been tested by natural selection must be preserved and protected from disintegration. Without isolation the ravages of natural selection might be too great. But too early an isolation of the favorable gene combinations formed in the process of race differentiation would mean too extreme a specialization of the organism to environmental conditions that may be only temporary. The end result may be extinction. Favorable conditions for a progressive evolution are created when a certain balance is struck: isolation is necessary but it must not come too early.

The mechanisms that prevent the interbreeding of groups of individuals and consequently engender isolation are remarkably diversified. It is an empirical fact that in different organisms, frequently even in fairly closely related ones, the isolation of species is accomplished by quite dissimilar means. Nor is it necessary that the interbreeding of a given pair of species be prevented by a single mechanism; on the contrary, one may observe that in many cases several mechanisms combine to make the isolation of two species more or less complete. It is an important fact, however, that any agent that hinders the interbreeding of groups of individuals produces the same genetic effect, namely, it diminishes or reduces to zero the frequency of the exchange of genes between the groups. I have proposed (Dobzhansky 1937a) the expression "isolating mechanisms" as a generic name for all such agents.

Two types of isolating mechanisms may be distinguished. First, the interbreeding of populations of the same race, or of different races or species, may be precluded by the mere fact that they live in different territories separated by geographical barriers, and hence never meet. This is geographical isolation. Second, the interbreeding of two or more populations may be prevented by a variety of intrinsic, physiological, properties of their representatives. This is reproductive or physiological isolation. The terms "reproductive" and "physiological" are used below interchangeably. Geographically separated (allopatric) populations may or may not display reproductive isolation if brought together artificially or as a result of the natural tendency of any population to expand its distribution area. Populations that are sympatric, i.e. inhabiting the same territory, can remain distinct only if reproductive isolation between them had developed.

Geographical isolation is therefore on a different plane from any kind of reproductive one. This consideration has to be qualified, because the occupation of separate areas by two species may be due not only to the fact that they have developed there, but also to the presence of physiological characteristics that make each species attached to the environment (climate, etc.) available in one but not in the other region. In this case, however, we are dealing with a kind of reproductive isolation expressed in geographical terms. The physiological isolating mechanisms may be subdivided as follows:

I. Mechanisms that prevent the production of the hybrid zygotes, or engender such disturbances in the development that no hybrids reach the reproductive stage. "Incompatibility of the parental forms" may be used as a general term for such mechanisms.
   A. The parental forms do not meet.
      a. Ecological isolation—the potential parents are confined to different habitats (ecological stations) in the same general region, and therefore seldom, or never, come together, at least during the reproductive age or season.
      b. Seasonal or temporal isolation—-the representatives of two or more species reach the adult stage each at a different season, or the breeding periods fall at different times of the year.
   B. The parental forms occur together, but hybridization is excluded, or the development of the hybrids is arrested.
      a. Sexual or psychological isolation—copulation does not occur because of the lack of mutual attraction between the individuals of different species. This lack of attraction may in turn be due to differences in scents, courtship behavior, sexual recognition signs, and the like.
      b. Mechanical isolation—copulation or crossing is difficult or impossible on account of the physical incompatibilities of the reproductive organs.
      c. The spermatozoa fail to reach the eggs or to penetrate into the eggs; in higher plants the pollen tube growth may be arrested if foreign pollen is placed on the stigma of the flower.
      d. Inviability of the hybrids—fertilization does take place, but the hybrid zygote dies at some stage of development before it becomes a sexually mature organism.
II. Hybrid sterility prevents the reproduction of hybrids that have reached the developmental stage at which the parents normally breed. Sterile hybrids produce either no functional gametes, or gametes that give rise to inviable zygotes. The classification of the phenomena of hybrid sterility will be discussed in Chapter IX.

A wealth of data on the occurrence of various isolating mechanisms in different subdivisions of the animal and plant kingdoms is scattered through biological literature. The genetic analysis of isolating mechanisms, with the possible exception of hybrid sterility, has however been left in abeyance.

ECOLOGICAL AND SEASONAL ISOLATION

Data on the habitat of a species or race, as well as information on the time of year when breeding takes place, are customarily given in the systematic and ecological literature on any one group. A perusal of such literature usually reveals some examples of related species that differ in these respects. It seems clear enough that such differences may decrease the frequency of, or preclude entirely, the interbreeding of the populations concerned. Investigations especially directed towards ascertaining to what extent the ecological and seasonal isolations are actually responsible for the maintenance of separation between species are, however, very rare. A genetic analysis of this type of difference between species or races has, to the writer's knowledge, never been made. With these qualifications in mind, we may examine a few instances in which the effectiveness of ecological or seasonal isolation suggests itself.

The experiments of Dice (1933, 1940b) show that species of the mouse *Peromyscus* are as a rule not crossable under laboratory conditions, while races (subspecies) of the same species can be crossed and produce offspring. In this connection it is interesting that some races occur in the same general geographical region, without, however, producing intermediates or losing their distinctness. Dice (1931) has made a study of two races of *P. maniculatus* whose distribution areas overlap in a part of the state of Michigan, and found that one of them lives almost exclusively in forests and the other on lake beaches. Two other races of the same species occur together in the region of Glacier National Park, Montana; but Murie (1933) reports that one of them is confined to forests and the other to prairie habitats. They occur together only at some points on the margins of their ecological provinces, but fail to interbreed even there, presumably on account of sexual isolation (Dice 1940b). The situation is somewhat different in the two species of birds, *Zonotrichia coronata* and *Z. leucophrys:* they inhabit respectively the lowlands and the higher elevations in California, but hybrids are occasionally met with at intermediate altitudes (Miller 1940).

Professor Carl Epling has reached the conclusion, which he kindly permits to be quoted here, that the two closely allied oak species *Quercus Garryana* and *Q. Douglasii* are kept separate by an ecological barrier. The former is widespread in the Coast Ranges of Oregon and California, being a member of the coastal mixed forest association which thrives in the relatively humid climatic region. The latter is a characteristic species of the drier *Quercus-Pinus* association of the Great Valley of California and of the interior valleys of the Coast Ranges; in some parts of its area *Q. Douglasii* is preclimactic to the less humid communities of the coastal forest. That these oaks are crossable is attested by a grove in Lake County, in which the hybrids are sufficiently abundant to constitute a major part of the population. Apparently a similar situation obtains in the two closely related species of pines *Pinus ponderosa* and *P. Jeffreyi*, in California: the former is widely distributed, while the latter is confined mainly to the higher elevations in the Sierra Nevada, with hybrid groves sufficiently numerous to raise serious doubts as to the validity of the species distinction. Several examples of ecological isolation between plant species of English flora, dealing chiefly with soil preferences, are quoted by Salisbury (1940).

One of the very few studies ever made deliberately to elucidate the operation of isolating mechanisms in a group of related species is that of Blair (1941) on the toads *Bufo americanus, B. fowleri, B. woodhousii*, and *B. terrestris* inhabiting Eastern and Central United States. These species are easily crossable in the laboratory, and the hybrids produced are, as far as one can tell, fully viable and fertile. The distribution areas of *B. americanus* and *B. fowleri* are rather similar, but they overlap those of the other two species only to a slight extent. In most localities where two or three species occur together individuals are encountered that are intermediate between, or have mixtures of the characters of, the species concerned. These intermediate individuals resemble the experimental hybrids, and it is legitimate to infer that they owe their origin to interspecific crosses in nature. The question of what permits the maintenance of the species as discrete entities is especially acute for the geographically coincident *B. americanus* and *B. fowleri*. In the vicinity of Bloomington, Indiana, among three populations of toads: one breeds early in the season, and is apparently pure *B. americanus;* the second breeds late, and is pure *B. fowleri;* while the third, whose breeding period overlaps the first two, includes individuals resembling the two pure species as well as the intermediates. It must be emphasized that the intermediates have in this case not only mixtures of the morphological characters but also of the mating calls of the parental species. These mating calls, that is, sounds emitted by the male toads when they congregate in their breeding places, appear to be an important stimulus in bringing the two sexes together; some observations suggest that the possessors of the different mating calls may assemble in different parts of the same body of water. Mating pairs consisting of intermediates, and of intermediates and the pure species, have, however, been observed in nature. There are, furthermore, some differences between the species in their ecological preferences. Thus, at the junction of their distribution ranges in Oklahoma, *B. fowleri* breeds mainly in streams and *B. woodhousii* mainly in prairie ponds. Where the habitats preferred by these species are geographically separate, the distribution areas do not overlap; it is mainly in the part of the country in which the environmental changes are gradual that the production of intermediates is observed. A difference between *B. americanus* and *B. fowleri* in ecological preferences is also indicated, from which Blair reasonably infers that the intercrossing of these species may in some places be of relatively recent origin, brought about in part by man's activities, such as the destruction of forests and the damming of streams.

Seasonal isolation between two closely related species of the mollusc *Sepia* has been studied by Cuénot (1933). One species breeds in the spring in the littoral zone of the Atlantic and the Mediterranean, while the other breeds in the same localities in winter and at greater depths. Dr. Edgar Anderson kindly informs me that one of the main factors isolating certain species of *Iris* is a difference in the flowering seasons; the same is true for *Hamamelis virginiana* and *H. vernalis.* Mr. C. N. Rudkin permits me to quote his observations on the time of appearance of the adults in certain related species of butterflies in southern California, which are specifically known to occur together in the same localities, although their general distribution ranges do not coincide.

{ *Euphydryas chalcedona* (Doubleday & Hewitson)--April to June
{ *Euphydryas editha wrightii* (Gunder)—March
{ *Melitaea neumoegeni* (Skinner)—late March to early April
{ *Melitaea wrightii* (Edwards)—late April to early June
{ *Argynnis macaria* (Edwards)—late April to early June
{ *Argynnis adiaste atossa* (Edwards)—late May to August
{ *Philotes sonorensis* (Felder)—February to mid-April
{ *Philotes battoides bernardino* (Barnes & McDunnough)—May

The exact flying time for each species varies according to seasonal weather conditions and altitude, but in the localities where they occur together little or no overlapping is observed. According to Professor Epling (personal communication), *Salvia Munzii* and *S. Clevelandii* are almost wholly isolated, the first named being nearly or wholly past the flowering time when the second begins flowering. No hybrids between them have been found in the wild. On the other hand, the flowering periods of *S. mellifera* and *S. apiana* overlap, and hybrids between them are commonly seen where the species occur in the same locality.

SEXUAL ISOLATION

An obvious prerequisite for a sexual union between individuals of the same or of different species is that the sexes meet and perform the series of acts that precede and enable fertilization to occur. In some forms this series of acts is relatively short and simple. In the oyster the chemical substance or substances that are released in water, together with the eggs and spermatozoa, stimulate other individuals within a certain range to spawn and to eject further masses of sex cells (Galtsoff 1930). In other animals the procedure is vastly more complex. Leiner (1934) gives the following account of the behavior patterns in the two species of fish, *Gasterosteus aculeatus* and *G. pungitius,* which build special nests in which the eggs are deposited:

G. pungitius	G. aculeatus
The nest is built hanging on water plants.	The nest is built on the bottom, in a furrow dug by the fish.
The nest is composed of soft materials.	Hard materials are used in the construction of the nest.
The nest has an entrance and an exit.	The nest has a single entrance.
No preference for light or dark building materials.	On a light bottom, dark building materials are preferred.
The nest is not changed after the eggs are deposited.	After egg deposition the nest is somewhat altered.
The male swims toward the nest in zigzags, attracting the female to follow him.	The male makes some zigzags in front of the female, and then swims straight to the nest followed by her.
The process of leading the female to the nest and the mating play coincide.	A special mating play is enacted.
The female enters the nest with little prodding by the male.	The male forces the female into the nest.

Leiner has obtained several hybrids from the cross *G. aculeatus* ♀ × *G. pungitius* ♂ with the aid of artificial insemination, and he gives some, though inconclusive, data that suggest that this cross takes place sometimes also in nature.

Regardless of whether the behavior patterns preliminary to mating are simple or complex, any incongruity in this respect between two populations may engender sexual isolation. The physiological basis of sexual isolation may, however, be as unlike as the mating reactions themselves (Huxley 1938b). Nevertheless, in higher animals where the mating reactions involve complex systems of unconditioned and conditioned reflexes, large deviations from the normal behavior can be induced in experiments. Much work in this direction has been done by the Russian school of animal husbandry (see review by Serebrovsky 1935). Stallions can be trained to mount willingly a stuffed effigy of a mare and even that of a cow, and the same is true of bulls, boars, and male sheep. Male turkeys were induced to attempt copulation with fowls. The practical application of these results is principally in the development of techniques for the collection of semen for artificial insemination. They are also interesting because they show that the bar to hybridization formed by sexual isolation can be surmounted experimentally. In general, hybrids that probably never occur in nature can sometimes be obtained in properly conducted experiments.

Specific scents play an important role in the sex life of many animals. Experiments of Standfuss, Fabre, and many others have shown that if a female moth is exposed even in very artificial surroundings, males of the same species appear and try to reach the female despite the obstacles that may be placed in their way. It is established that the males sense the presence of the females at a rather great distance; the acuteness of smell so demonstrated is remarkable. Only rarely are males of species other than that to which the female belongs attracted. When brought together artificially, males of a given species of moth as a rule pay no attention to females of species other than their own. Interspecific crosses may, however, be accomplished by placing a cage containing females of species A and males of B side by side with a cage containing females of B and males of A. The scent, and perhaps the sight, of females of their own species makes the males so excited that they copulate with females that they would not approach otherwise. In extreme cases copulation between distant species may be attempted even in the presence of partners of their own species (Standfuss 1896, Federley 1915b, 1929b, 1932).

The involved courtship antics practiced by spiders as a preliminary to copulation not only differ in different species, but the whole behavior pattern is set in motion by different stimuli (Kaston 1936). In some families, males recognize their females by sight, in others the male must both see and touch the female before he starts courting, and in still others visual stimuli play no part and the sense of touch is paramount. Kaston proved that the stimulus of touch comes from a substance present on the cuticle of females—males court parts of a female body, such as autotomized legs. This substance is ether soluble, so that a female leg washed in ether does not stimulate the male, while a glass plate on which an ether extract was allowed to evaporate does elicit the courtship response. Crushed internal organs fail to elicit such a response. The courtship behavior is often quite different in species of molluscs (see Gerhardt 1938, 1939, for references.) Diver (1940) finds that individuals of the snail *Cepaea hortensis* are sufficiently "disconcerted" by the advances of *C. nemoralis* to terminate the courtship. These two species occur in the same localities, and hybrids between them can be produced experimentally. The importance of song in the courtship in birds is well known; songs may differ not only in different species but in races of the same species (Promptoff 1930). The three orthopteran species *Nemobius fasciatus, N. socius,* and *N. tinnulus* differ in song and in preferences for definite habitats but not in geographical distribution. Fulton (1933) has crossed *N. fasciatus* with *N. tinnulus,* and shown that the song differences are determined by multiple genes.

Courtship habits differ in species of *Drosophila* (Sturtevant 1915b, 1921, and unpublished data); Sturtevant (1920–21) and Lance-

TABLE 21

FREQUENCY OF INTRASPECIFIC AND INTERSPECIFIC MATINGS IN MIXED CULTURES OF *Drosophila pseudoobscura* AND *D. miranda*

MALES	*D. pseudoobscura* FEMALES FROM STRAIN	INTRASPECIFIC		INTERSPECIFIC	
		Fertilized	Unfertilized	Fertilized	Unfertilized
D. pseudoobscura	Seattle-6 (race B)	58	5	3	60
	Seattle-4 (race B)	54	1	1	54
	La Grande-2 (race A)	67	9	9	71
	Texas (race A)	57	2	8	52
	Oaxaca-5 (race A)	41	4	7	35
D. miranda	Seattle-6 (race B)	18	17	3	34
	Seattle-4 (race B)	12	31	—	43
	La Grande-2 (race A)	14	20	4	31
	Texas (race A)	11	22	—	34
	Oaxaca-5 (race A)	22	18	4	37

field (1929) have obtained evidence that *D. melanogaster* and *D. simulans* and race A and race B of *D. pseudoobscura* exhibit a preference for mating with representatives of their own species and race in mixed cultures.

Quantitative studies on the effectiveness of sexual isolation have been made by Boche (unpublished) on race A and race B of *Drosophila pseudoobscura* and by Dobzhansky and Koller (1938) on *D. pseudoobscura* and *D. miranda.* In some experiments equal numbers of freshly hatched females of the two species to be tested were placed in a vial with males of one of the species. The males were, therefore, able to "choose" their mates. After a certain time (usually four days), all the females were dissected, and the presence or absence of sperm in their seminal receptacles was determined by microscopic examination. Table 21 illustrates the type of the results obtained. Sexual isolation between *D. pseudoobscura* and *D. miranda* is undoubtedly strong, although, since some interspecific matings do occur, it is not complete.

In another series of experiments the technique was so modified that no choice of mates was available. Females of *Drosophila miranda* were confined with an equal number of *D. pseudoobscura* males for nine days, after which the proportion of the females fertilized was determined by dissection. Table 22 gives a summary of the results. Since practically 100 percent of *D. pseudoobscura* females are fertilized if they are exposed for nine days to males of

TABLE 22

THE FREQUENCY OF FERTILIZATION (IN PERCENTS) OF *Drosophila miranda* FEMALES BY *D. pseudoobscura* MALES FROM DIFFERENT STRAINS

RACE	STRAIN	FREQUENCY	RACE	STRAIN	FREQUENCY
B	Cowichan-6	10.2 ± 2.3	A	Pavilion-5	31.3 ± 4.3
B	Quilcene-4	11.3 ± 2.7	A	Lassen-1	32.7 ± 4.6
B	Sequoia-4	17.8 ± 2.9	A	Shuswap-3	36.4 ± 3.8
B	Sequoia-8	29.4 ± 3.4	A	Estes Park-1	36.9 ± 4.2
A	Yale-7	18.3 ± 3.0	A	Sequoia-15	40.8 ± 3.7
A	Oaxaca-5	21.4 ± 3.2	A	Cuernavaca-2	46.0 ± 3.6
A	Olympic-2	23.0 ± 2.7	A	Grand Canyon-3	50.4 ± 4.7
A	La Grande-2	25.0 ± 4.1	A	Julian	52.2 ± 4.3

their own species, and since the same is true for *D. miranda,* the data in Table 22 confirm the existence of sexual isolation between these species. More important still, the intensity of isolation varies with the strain of *D. pseudoobscura* used. It can be seen at a glance that males of race B display on the average a greater aversion to mating with *D. miranda* than do the males of race A. Within a race, especially in race A, wide differences are also observed. The degree of sexual isolation seems to stand in relation to the geographical origin of the given strain. It may be noted that the distribution area of *D. miranda* is relatively small, comprising the territory around Puget Sound in the Pacific Northwest, northwestern California, and a single known locality in the Sierra Nevada. This area is wholly included in that of race B of *D. pseudoobscura*. The distribution of race A extends much further east and south than that of race B, but it barely comes in contact with that of *D. miranda*. It is important to note that the *D. miranda* females used in the experiments summarized in Table 22 came from a strain derived from flies collected on the Olympic peninsula, in the vicinity of Puget Sound. The results obtained may be generalized as follows: strains of either race of *D. pseudoobscura* coming from localities in or near the distribution area of *D. miranda* show the greatest degree of isolation (Cowichan, Quilcene, Olympic, and Yale). Strains from somewhat more remote localities (Pavilion, Shuswap, Lassen, Estes. Park) show less, and those from still more remote places (Sequoia, Julian, Grand Canyon, Cuernavaca) show least isolation. The only exception to the above geographical rule is the Oaxaca strain (from Mexico) which displays an unexpectedly high degree of isolation.

If experiments like those reported in Table 22 are made with females of *Drosophila miranda* coming from the Sierra Nevada portion of the distribution area of this species, the results obtained are somewhat different. Males of race B of *D. pseudoobscura* still show a greater aversion to mating with *D. miranda* than do males of race A, but the geographical regularity in the behavior of the different strains of race A seems to disappear. At any rate, it may be regarded as established that within either species there are variations with respect to the degree of sexual isolation displayed toward the other species. Furthermore, if males from Puget Sound strains of *D. miranda* are offered a choice of females of the same species from the same region and from the Sierra Nevada, or vice versa, there is a statistically significant, although weak, preference for mating between the flies of the same geographical origin (Dobzhansky and Koller 1938). Facts such as these are very interesting. Genetic mechanisms that determine isolation between species may be visualized as having arisen through a summation of intraspecific variations of this kind. The observed geographical regularity becomes doubly significant from this point of view. *Drosophila pseduoobscura* and *D. miranda* can be crossed, but the offspring produced are sterile. The occurrence of hybridization is evidently disadvantageous to the species, since it impairs the biotic potentials of both participants. Genetic factors increasing the sexual, or any other, isolation may therefore be favored by natural selection. The strengthening of isolation is however more immediately important for populations of *D. pseudoobscura* inhabiting territory close to *D. miranda* than for populations of more remote localities.

Systematic studies on the crossabilities of different species and subspecies in the mouse *Peromyscus* have been made by Dice (1933). Ten races of *P. maniculatus,* five of *P. leucopus,* four of *P. eremicus,* and two each of *P. truei* and *P. californicus* have been tested in many combinations. The general conclusion reached by Dice is that races of a species can be crossed and produce hybrids, while the separate species (with the exception of *P. maniculatus* × *P. polionotus*) do not cross. The cause of the nonproduction of hybrids is not exactly known, but a sexual isolation may be suspected. It does not follow, of course, that sexual isolation may occur only between separate species and not between subdivisions thereof. Spett (1931) obtained some data that suggest the existence of a rudimentary sexual isolation between mutants of *Drosophila melanogaster;* his observations are contradicted, however, by those of Sturtevant (1915b) and of Nikoro, Gussev, Pavlov, and Griasnov (1935).

MECHANICAL ISOLATION

The elaborate structure of the external genitalia and their accessories in many animals, especially among insects, has for a long time attracted the attention of morphologists and systematists. The reason for this interest has been in part a pragmatic one: closely related species that are distinguishable with great difficulty by their outward appearance can sometimes be accurately classified by the structure of their genitalia. Ormancey (1849) seems to have been the first to apply this method for distinguishing the species of a family of beetles, and soon thereafter the method was introduced in other orders of insects, and also in spiders, molluscs, fish (the forms possessing gonopodia), mammals (especially bats and rodents), and other groups. That species are frequently easily distinguishable by their genitalia is indeed a plain observational fact; on this fact much theoretical superstructure has, however, been built. The so-called "lock-and-key" theory, propounded by the great French entomologist Leon Durfour in the pre-Darwinian days and later much elaborated especially by K. Jordan (1905), asserts that the female and the male genitalia of the same species (at least in insects) are so exactly fitted to each other that even slight deviations in the structure of either make copulation physically impossible. The genitalia of each species are "a lock that can be opened by one key only," hence the different species are isolated from each other simply and safely by the noncorrespondence of their genitalia.

The experimental evidence in favor of mechanical isolation is scanty, and is confined mostly to a single order, namely *Lepidoptera*. Standfuss (1896) has described crosses between species of moths where copulation leads to injuries to the female organs that result in death. Federley (1932), who is inclined to ascribe more importance to mechanical than to sexual isolation, states that the *Chaerocampa elpenor* male may copulate with a female of *Metopsilus porcellus* (moths of the family *Sphingidae*), but is sometimes unable to withdraw its penis, making egg deposition impossible. The reciprocal cross succeeds easily. Sturtevant (1921) has observed apparently successful copulation between *Drosophila melanogaster* males and *D. pseudoobscura* females, which, however, does not lead to the production of hybrid larvae or adults. Whether fertilization of the eggs takes place is unknown. Some pairs are however unable to separate, and die in copula. What causes the different outcome of this copulation is likewise unknown. No copulation between *D. pseudoobscura* males and *D. melanogaster* females has been recorded.

Against the above facts which tend to prove the effectiveness of mechanical isolation, one may set an array of observations on crosses between species with differently built genitalia which seem to cause no injury to either participant. Copulation between rather remote species is very frequently recorded in the entomological literature, although it generally remains obscure whether any offspring is produced thereby. The production of offspring is however immaterial as far as the problem of mechanical isolation is concerned, since copulation does not necessarily insure the occurrence of fertilization and development (see below). It is significant, however, that variations in body size within a species of insects have not been shown to hinder copulation. In *Drosophila*, mutants increasing and decreasing body size are known, and they can be crossed with consequent production of normal offspring (e.g., mutations giant and dwarf in *D. melanogaster*). The variations in body size due to the abundance or scarcity of food during the larval stage are likwise no impediment to copulation.

Kerkis (1931) has made a statistical study of the variability of the external characteristics and of the genitalia in the bug *Eurygaster integriceps,* and finds the latter no less variable than the former—a conclusion contradictory to the opinions of some systematists who regard the limited variability of the genitalia as an explanation of their usefulness in classification. In fact, the explanation is to be looked for in a different direction: the complexity of the structures of the genitalia is sometimes so great that the genetic differences between the species are more likely to be manifested in these structures than in the relatively simple external ones. The conjecture is corroborated by observations that show that in those genera and families where the structure of the genitalia is simple they are less useful for classification than in groups with complicated genitalia or accessory organs. It is justifiable to conclude that, although mechanical isolation may be effective as a bar to crossing in some organisms, its significance has been exaggerated. Some systematists (e.g., Kinsey 1936) have come to the same conclusion.

The differences in the flower structure in related species of plants may prevent cross-fertilization because the flowers are pollinated by different insects. How effective this form of mechanical isolation is in nature is obscure. That different plant families are adapted for pollination by different insects is of course well known, although some insects (e.g., the honeybee) visit a surprisingly wide range of plants. Whether species of the same genus are debarred from crossing by the same method has never been adequately studied. A perusal of the Knuth-Ainsworth Davis monograph of flower pollination (1906–09) shows that the lists of insects known to visit the flowers of related plant species are in some instances different, but it remains unclear to what extent this may be accounted for by the occupation of dissimilar ecological stations by the plants involved. Perhaps only in families with very specialized flower structures (orchids, *Leguminosae,* and some others) can mechanical isolation play an important role.

FERTILIZATION IN SPECIES CROSSES

Copulation in animals with internal fertilization, or the release of the sexual products into the medium in forms with external fertilization, or the placing of the pollen on the stigma of the flower in plants is followed by chains of reactions that bring about the actual union of the gametes, or fertilization proper. These reactions may be out of balance in representatives of different species, with a consequent hindrance or a complete prevention of the formation of hybrid zygotes. In animals, the processes of hybrid fertilization have been studied, for obvious technical reasons, almost exclusively in marine forms where the fertilization can be easily observed in vitro. Moreover, a majority of the experiments concern crosses between forms so remote (e.g., different orders, classes, and even phyla), that the significance of the results from an evolutionary standpoint is limited.

Lillie (1921) has crossed two species of sea urchins, *Strongylocentrotus purpuratus* and *S. franciscanus*. Both species inhabit the shore waters in the same locality, although *S. purpuratus* occurs between the tidemarks and slightly below the low-water mark, while *S. franciscanus* rarely lives above the low-water mark and goes to greater depths than the former. There exists consequently a partial ecological isolation between the two. Eggs of each species were placed in sea water containing spermatozoa of the same or of the other species in different concentrations; the percentage of eggs that formed fertilization membranes and that cleaved was recorded. The concentrations of the *S. franciscanus* sperm that give from 73.3 percent to 100 percent of fertilization of the eggs of the same species produce from 0 percent to 1.5 percent of fertilization in *S. purpuratus* eggs. With a concentration of the sperm of *S. franciscanus* that is forty times greater than is necessary to produce a 100 percent fertilization of *S. franciscanus* eggs, only 25 percent of *S. purpuratus* eggs are fertilized. A similar, though perhaps somewhat less pronounced, disability of *S. purpuratus* sperms to fertilize the eggs of *S. franciscanus* was also detected. Moenkhaus (1910) found in the cross between the fish *Fundulus heteroclitus* and *F. majalis* up to 50 percent of polyspermic eggs which do not normally occur in intraspecific fertilizations. It may be noted that placing the eggs and spermatozoa in water of varying pH concentration sometimes permits the fertilization to take place where it would not do so otherwise.

The environment of the spermatozoa in the reproductive organs of the female of another species may be unsuitable for them and may cause their death, or at least a loss of fertilizing ability. Spermatozoa of higher animals are known to be highly sensitive to any variations in their environment, particularly to those in osmotic pressure (Serebrovsky 1935, Kato 1936, and others). The sperm can be preserved for a long time in a suitable environment for artificial insemination, but its fertilizing ability is lost very quickly otherwise. The sperm of a duck, a goose, and a cock has been injected into the genital ducts of female ducks. After 22 to 25 hours the birds were dissected, and large numbers of spermatozoa were found in the upper portions of the oviducts. But while those of the drake were alive and motile, a majority of the spermatozoa of the goose and cock were already dead (Serebrovsky 1935). Mixing the sperm of different forms may also be fatal for their viability (Godlewski 1926). Data of a similar kind are scarce for crosses between closely related species. Dr. D. D. Miller (unpublished) has, however, shown that the sperm of *Drosophila athabasca* in the seminal receptacles of *D. affinis* retains its viability for a much shorter time than in the seminal receptacles of its own species. It seems not improbable that the poor hatchability of the eggs in crosses between *D. virilis, D. americana,* and *D. texana* may be due to a similar cause (Spencer 1940a, Patterson, Stone, and Griffen 1940).

More extensive observations of the difficulties encountered in fertilization in hybrids are available for plants. Mangelsdorf and Jones (1926) and others found that in crosses between sugary and nonsugary maize (*Zea mays*) appreciable deviations from the normal segregation ratios are obtained, the numbers of sugary kernels being below the expectation. Sugary differs from nonsugary in a single gene, and the results are interpreted as indicating that if a mixture of sugary and nonsugary pollen is applied to the silks of a plant containing the normal allele of sugary, a competition between the pollen grains ensues, the rate of growth of sugary pollen tubes being presumably less than that of the normal pollen tubes. The growth rates of the two kinds of pollen tubes on sugary silks are, however, alike. Demerec (1929b) has described an even more extreme case of incompatibility between popcorn and other varieties of maize. If popcorn is used as a female parent in crosses where nonpop pollen is applied, almost no seeds are formed. Crosses in which pop is used as a male succeed without difficulty. If a popcorn plant is double pollinated (i.e., if a mixture of pop and nonpop pollen is applied), many selfed and very few hybrid seeds are obtained. When the silks of an ear of popcorn were divided in two parts and one part was pollinated with pop and the other with nonpop pollen, the resulting ears had a full complement of seeds on the selfed side and almost no seeds on the crossed side (for further examples see Brieger 1930).

An extensive series of experiments with crosses between different species of *Datura* has been described in a short preliminary communication by Buchholz, Williams, and Blakeslee (1935). They found that the speed of the pollen tube growth in the style of the same species is frequently greater than in the style of a foreign species. Species of *Datura* may differ in length of style, since there is some correlation between the speed of the pollen tube growth and the style length. The crosses in which the species with a short style is used as the female parent and that with a long style as the male parent are in general more likely to succeed than the reciprocal crosses. Moreover, the pollen tubes may burst in the style of a foreign species before they reach the ovary, the frequency of the bursting pollen tubes being characteristic for each cross. The crossability of different species is, therefore, a function of several variables: the speed of pollen tube growth, length of the style, and the frequency of bursting pollen tubes. To this must be added also the sensitivity of the process to the environmental conditions, and the viability of the embryos (see below). The failure of the pollen grains to germinate on a foreign stigma has also been observed in some crosses.

The success of crossing of species of wheat (Watkins 1932, Boyes and Thompson 1937) and of herbage grasses (Jenkin 1933) depends on several factors, one of which is the chromosome number in the parental species to be crossed. The pollen tubes grow best in the styles of plants with the same chromosome number as the male parent (that is, if the ratio of the chromosome numbers in the pollen and in the style is 1:2). In the style of a species having a higher chromosome number, the pollen tube growth is normal or reduced, while in the style with a lower chromosome number it is much reduced. The possible role of self-sterility in interspecific crosses has been discussed by Anderson (1924).

The incongruity of the allopolyploid hybrids with the parental species is an exceptionally interesting fact. It may be recalled that *Raphanobrassica* is a synthetic new species obtained by a doubling of the chromosome complement in the hybrid between radish (*Raphanus sativus*) and cabbage (*Brassica*). Karpechenko (1928) and Karpechenko and Shchavinskaia (1929) have made systematic attempts to cross *Raphanobrassica* with raddish, cabbage, and other species of cruciferous plants. The cross *Raphanobrassica* ♀ × *Raphanus* ♂ produced only eleven seeds from 382 artificially pollinated flowers, *Raphanus* ♀ × *Raphanobrassica* ♂ eleven seeds from 143 flowers, *Raphanobrassica* ♀ × *Brassica* ♂ two seeds from 551 flowers, and *Brassica* ♀ × *Raphanobrassica* ♂ no seeds from 411 flowers. No more successful were the attempts to secure offspring from such crosses by open pollinations; when the three species are planted side by side, each of them produces almost exclusively a pure progeny. The doubling of the chromosome complement within a species may also modify its crossability to the parental type as well as to other species. Thus, the diploid *Brassica oleracea* is difficult to cross to *B. carinata* and to *B. chinensis;* the tetraploid *B. oleracea* crosses to the latter species readily (Karpechenko 1937). It is not clear whether the difficulties of crossing are in these cases due to inadequate pollen tube growth or to an inviability of the hybrid zygotes. The latter has been observed in crosses of the allotetraploid derivative of *Nicotiana rustica* × *N. paniculata* to *N. rustica* (Singleton 1932).

VIABILITY OF HYBRID ZYGOTES

The occurrence of a union between the gametes of different species gives no assurance that the zygotes so formed will produce an adult hybrid organism. As a matter of fact, the life of a hybrid zygote may be cut short at any stage, from the first cleavage of the egg up to the late embryonic or post-embryonic development. The physiology of the developmental disturbances that prevent the hybrids from reaching maturity is almost entirely unknown. The theory that a lack of "affinity" or of "coöperation" between the ancestral germ plasms is not fruitful as a working hypothesis.

Hybridization between very remote forms (as echinoderms $\times$ molluscs, echinoderms $\times$ annelids) frequently results in the sperm nucleus being simply eliminated from the first cleavage spindle, or else the paternal, and sometimes also some of the maternal, chromosomes are discarded in the cytoplasm and perish. Similar, although less extreme, disturbances are observed in crosses between different families and genera of sea urchins and between families and genera of amphibians (a review in Hertwig 1936). In hybrids between different fish (Moenkhaus 1910, Newman 1914, 1915, Pinney 1918, 1922, and others) all sorts of disturbances may occur, from chromosome elimination during cleavage, and arrest of gastrulation and of organ formation, to death of the advanced embryos. The above authors emphasize that the early or late death of the embryos is not necessarily correlated with the systematic remoteness or closeness of the forms crossed. In this respect the data of Zimmermann (1936) and Strasburger (1936) are very instructive. They have investigated the races of a ladybird beetle *Epilachna chrysomelina*, which inhabits southern Europe, Africa, and western Asia. This area is subdivided into several smaller regions, each inhabited by a separate race (subspecies). The crosses between most of the races that were available for experiments gave hybrids without much difficulty. But the cross between the South African form, *E. capensis*, and *E. chrysomelina* produced no larvae on account of the profound disturbances in the embryonic development. Morphologically, *E. capensis* is not much more different from *E. chrysomelina* than the races of the latter species are from each other. On the other hand, Pictet (1936) states that the viability of the hybrids between the moths *Lasiocampa quercus* from different localities is inversely proportional to the distance between the localities. Similar results have been obtained by Pictet in another moth, *Nemeophila plantaginis*, where the hybridization of local races may result in the production of unfertilized eggs (no cytological study has, however, been made).

The death of the hybrid zygotes has been observed also in plants. In some crosses between species of *Datura*, the pollen tubes reach the ovary, fertilization takes place, but nevertheless no seeds are obtained. The hybrid *D. stramonium* $\times$ *D. metel* develops up to the eight-cell stage of the embryo, but no further. The development of the endosperm in the same hybrid proceeds aparently normally up to the seventh day after fertilization, and then stops (Satina and Blakeslee 1935). A similar situation is encountered in crosses between some species of *Nicotiana* (McCray 1933). According to Watkins (1932), the nonproduction of seeds in wheat species crosses may be due to a disharmony between the development of the embryo and that of the endosperm. On account of the double fertilization process in the higher plants, the numbers of chromosomes in the embryonic and in the endosperm tissues are normally as $2:3$. If a species with a high chromosome number is used as the pollen parent and that with a low number as the mother, the ratio of the chromosome numbers in the embryo and the endosperm is $> 2:3$, and the embryo dies. The reciprocal cross, giving rise to a ratio $< 2:3$, is less deleterious for the viability of the hybrid.

In some instances the constitutional weakness of the hybrid organism entails no great disturbances in the fundamental life processes, and the application of certain treatments enables the experimenter to bring to maturity hybrids that do not survive otherwise. A remarkable example of this phenomenon is afforded by the work of Laibach (1925) on hybrids between species of flax. In the cross *Linum perenne* $\times$ *L. alpinum*, the hybrid seeds are able to germinate with some difficulty. The seeds from the cross *L. perenne* ♀ $\times$ *L. austriacum* ♂ fail to germinate if left to their own devices. If, however, the embryos are artificially freed from the seed coat (the seed coat being here a purely maternal tissue), germination does take place, and the young seedlings may give rise to luxuriant hybrid plants that are fertile and produce normal seeds of the F_2 generation. Still greater is the suppression of the seed development in the cross *L. austriacum* ♀ $\times$ *L. perenne* ♂, and yet it can also be surmounted. The diminutive embryos are extracted from the seeds and placed in a nutrient solution containing from 10 percent to 20 percent sugar, where they continue to grow; after some days they are transferred to moist filter paper, and allowed to germinate. The seedings are then planted in soil.

In crosses between species of certain moths only males appear among the adult hybrids (*Chaerocampa elpenor* ♀ $\times$ *Metopsilus porcellus* ♂ and *Deilephila euphorbiae* ♀ × *D. galii* ♂); females are present among the caterpillars but they die in the pupal stage. The reciprocal crosses give hybrids of both sexes (Federley 1929a). Bytinski-Salz (1933) implanted the ovaries of the pupae that normally die into the pupae of the parental species. The implants developed in the new host far beyond the stage at which they would die in the body whence they came, thus proving that the inviability of a hybrid as a whole need not extend to all its tissues.

The appearance of unisexual progenies recorded in the crosses just discussed is a fairly common phenomenon in interspecific hybrids in animals; individuals of one sex die, while the viability of the other sex is affected little or not at all. Haldane (1922) has formulated a rule that, with some exceptions, holds rather well: "when in the F_1 offspring of two different animal races one sex is absent, rare, or sterile, that sex is the heterozygous sex." In mammals, *Amphibia,* and most insects, males are known to be heterozygous (XY) and females homozygous (XX) for sex, and accordingly male hybrids are defective more frequently than females. On the contrary, in birds, butterflies, and moths, females are heterozygous (XY) and males homozygous (XX); here female hybrids tend to be less viable than males.

A possible mechanism that may underlie Haldane's rule was suggested by Dobzhansky (1937b). It is known (Chapter IV) that *Drosophila pseudoobscura* and *D. miranda* differ in gene arrangement, and, what is especially important for us now, some genes that lie in one of these species in the X chromosome lie in the other in the autosomes, and vice versa. The cross *D. miranda* ♀ × *D. pseudoobscura* ♂ produces fairly viable female and abnormal male hybrids; the reciprocal cross gives rise to viable females, but the males die off. Suppose that *D. pseudoobscura* has in its X chromosome a certain group of genes *A* that lie in the autosomes of *D. miranda,* and that a group of genes *B* which in *D. miranda* lies in the X chromosome is located in the autosomes of *D. pseudoobscura;* with respect to these genes, the constitution of the females of both species and of the female hybrids is alike, namely *AABB.* Males of *D. pseudoobscura* and the male hybrids from the cross *D. miranda* ♀ × *D. pseudoobscura* ♂ are *ABB; D. miranda* males and the male offspring from the cross *D. pseudoobscura* ♀ × *D. miranda* ♂ are *AAB.* The genotypes of the pure species are evidently so adjusted by countless generations of natural selection that the constitution *ABB* in *D. pseudoobscura* and *AAB* in *D. miranda* permits the development of the "normal" males of the respective species. But the genotype of a hybrid is a compromise, an intermediate, between those of the parental species; the constitution *AABB* is normal for females of either parent and for the hybrid females as well. The constitution *ABB* is however incompatible with the genotype of *D. miranda*, and *AAB* with that of *D. pseudoobscura*. The hybrid males suffer from a disturbance of the genic balance, and consequently have an impaired viability. An explanation of this type is applicable only to hybrids between species that differ in the distribution of genes among the X chromosome and the autosomes; this is known to be the case for *D. pseudoobscura* and *D. miranda,* but, in other species crosses critical data are lacking. The explanation can be made more general if one assumes that many species have a balance of genes in the X chromosome and the autosomes peculiar to themselves and different from other species. This balance may remain undisturbed in the homozygous sex in the hybrids, but is likely to be upset in the heterozygous sex. Muller (1940a) expresses the above suggestion in more specific language by pointing out that the recessive and semidominant sex-linked genes which had become established in either parental species will be as strongly expressed in the heterozygous sex in the hybrid as in the maternal species itself, while the corresponding genes in the autosomes of the hybrid will be suppressed by their dominant alleles.

GENETIC ANALYSIS OF ISOLATING MECHANISMS

If species evolve from races, rather than as a result of cataclysmic changes exemplified by polyploidy, or through extreme catastrophic alterations such as the "systemic mutations" postulated by Goldschmidt, any type of difference observed between species must be detectable, in at least a rudimentary form, within species as well. This principle, already dealt with in Chapters III and IV, is evidently applicable to physiological isolating mechanisms which constitute species characters par excellence. As long as no proof of the origin of isolating mechanisms from building blocks present within species is adduced, that critical part of the evolution theory which deals with the emergence of species as such rests on an insecure foundation. The appalling neglect of the problem of isolating mechanisms which obtained until very recently in biology in general and in genetics in particular furnishes a partial explanation of the scepticism, not to say agnosticism, felt by some biologists regarding evolution. Fortunately, we now possess at least fragmentary information to show that genetic raw materials from which isolating mechanisms may be constructed are available in species populations. Variations in the degree of sexual isolation between *Drosophila pseudoobscura* and *D. miranda* have been discussed above; data bearing on the genetic basis of hybrid sterility will be summarized in Chapter IX. It remains now to consider some pertinent data on other forms of isolation.

The outcome of the cross *Crepis capillaris* × *C. tectorum* is variable; in some cultures all the hybrid seedlings die in the cotyledon stage, in others only half of the seedlings die, and in still others the hybrids are viable. Hollingshead (1930a) has shown that certain strains of *C. tectorum* carry a dominant gene which in the pure species produces no visible effects, and in particular has no apparent influence on the germination of the seedlings. If, however, a hybrid between *tectorum* and *capillaris* carries this gene, it does not develop beyond the cotyledon stage. The crosses in which the *tectorum* parent is homozygous for the gene in question produce accordingly no viable seedlings, while 50 percent or 100 percent of such seedlings occur in cultures in which the gene is heterozygous or absent respectively. Further experiments have shown that the same gene is lethal for the seedlings of the hybrids *C. tectorum* × *C. leontodontoides* and *C. tectorum* × *C. bursifolia,* but not in the crosses *C. tectorum* × *C. setosa* and *C. tectorum* × *C. taraxacifolia.* It is obvious that the isolation between *C. tectorum* and certain of its congeners would become complete if *C. tectorum* were homozygous for the gene which acts as a semilethal in the hybrids. No information on the frequencies of this gene in various parts of the distribution area of *C. tectorum* is available, although the data of Hollingshead indicate that some populations of this species do and others do not carry the gene in question. According to Kostoff (1936), the cross *Nicotiana rustica var. humilis* × *N. glauca* produces hybrids that die as embryos, while in the cross

N. rustica texana × *N. glauca* viable hybrids are obtained. A gene in *Triticum monococcum* which acts as a lethal in hybrids with *Aegilops umbellulata* has been described in a preliminary note by Sears (1940). Donchenko and Medvedev (1935) found that the output of hybrids from the cross *D. melanogaster* × *D. simulans* is reduced to about half if the D. *melanogaster* parent carries the gene Lobe. Whether this effect of Lobe is due to a bolstering of the sexual isolation between the species, or to a reduction of the viability of the hybrids, is unclear.

Patterson and Crow (1940) and Crow (1941) have published preliminary data on a species cross in *Drosophila* which resemble those of Hollingshead in *Crepis*. The cross *D. mulleri* ♀ × *D. aldrichi* ♂ produces sterile hybrids of both sexes; the reciprocal cross gives no offspring. If, however, males from certain strains of *D. aldrichi* are crossed to females of *D. mulleri,* the offspring consists of about 10 percent female and 90 percent male hybrids. By means of an analysis of crosses between strains of *D. aldrichi* giving different results when hybridized to *D. mulleri,* Crow has shown that in populations of the former species there occur a sex-linked gene which produces no visible effects in pure *D. aldrichi,* but which acts as a dominant semilethal in the *D. mulleri* × *D. aldrichi* female hybrids.

In Chapters II and III we have seen that the same gene may produce different effects when placed on different genotypic backgrounds. The genes in *Crepis tectorum* and in *Drosophila aldrichi,* which seem to have no phenotypic expression at all in these species, but which act as dominant lethals or semilethals in the hybrids *C. tectorum* ♂ *C. capillaris* and *D. mulleri* × *D. aldrichi* respectively, are merely extreme examples of the interdependence of genes composing a balanced genotype. Mutants which produce rather inocuous changes within a species, but which are exaggerated to pathological proportions in interspecific hybrids, are probably not rare. Instances of this kind of gene interaction were noted by Bellamy (1922), and studied in great detail by Gordon (1937, 1938), Kosswig (1929, 1937), and others in certain fish species. The dominant sex-linked gene N in *Platypoecilus maculatus* causes a black spotting due to the presence of groups of pigment cells (macromelanophores) in the integument. If a *P. maculatus* carrying the gene N is crossed to the related species (or races) *P. couchianus, P. xiphidium,* and *P. variatus,* or to the related genus (or species) *Xiphophorus helleri,* those of the F_1 hybrids which inherit N show a hypertrophy of the black pigmentation. The macromelanophores in in such hybrids may be more numerous not only than in the Nn heterozygotes, but even than in the NN homozygotes in *P. maculatus.* Backcrosses of the Nn hybrids with *Xiphophorus* to a pure (nn) *Xiphophorus* give some heterozygotes with a pathologically overdeveloped black pigmentation, which forms melanotic tumors resembling the melanosarcoma growths in mammals. The gene N is, therefore, more or less neutral with respect to the viability on the genotypic background of *P. maculatus,* but becomes virtually a lethal in the genotypes of related species. Still another gene, RSp, produces in *P. maculatus* a red and black pigmentation due to the presence of melano- and erythrophores. In hybrids with *P. variatus* and *X. helleri* the effects of RSp are greatly exaggerated.

ORIGIN OF ISOLATING MECHANISMS

It may seem premature to discuss the origin of isolating mechanisms while the knowledge of their nature and distribution is in so inchoate a state as it is at present. However, since this problem has begun to attract more and more attention in recent years, and since so much of our understanding of evolution depends upon its solution, it may not be vain to attempt formulation of working hypotheses to serve as guides in further research. The provisional nature of such hypotheses should be clearly realized.

Isolating mechanisms encountered in nature have always two aspects: the interbreeding of individuals of the species A with those of the species B is made difficult or impossible, while individuals of A as well as of B are fully able to breed *inter se.* In other words, the reproductive biology of any one species is so organized as to insure procreation of a number of offspring sufficient to maintain it on a survival level, and yet the same reproductive biology militates against the production of offspring from crosses with other species. It is not easy to visualize how such a state of affairs develops. Mutations that alter the sexual behavior, or the breeding time, or the structure of the genitalia may occur, but such mutations do not necessarily produce workable isolating mechanisms.

Genetic changes engendering isolation must not only prevent the crossbreeding between the mutant and the original type, but must simultaneously insure a normal reproduction of the mutants. Where isolation involves an inviability or a sterility of the hybrids, these effects must be confined to heterozygotes and leave the homozygotes unaffected.

It follows from the above considerations that a great difficulty is encountered in the establishment of any isolating mechanism in a single mutational step. Since mutants appear in populations at first as heterozygotes, inviable and sterile heterozygotes are eliminated, regardless of how well adapted might be the corresponding homozygotes. As far as the present writer is able to see, this consideration is fatal to Goldschmidt's (1940) theory of evolution by "systemic" mutations, since these mutations are supposed to induce at once a complete isolation of the newly emerged species from its ancestor. Even if the inviability or sterility of heterozygotes be supposed to be incomplete, these heterozygotes will be discriminated against by natural selection. Forms of isolation other than hybrid inviability and sterility fare scarcely better if they arise in a single step. For example, let us suppose that a mutant and the ancestral form reach sexual maturity at different seasons, or that the germ cells of a mutant are incompatible with those of the original type. Since the mutation rates for most genes are known to be low, the number of the mutants produced in any one generation would be so small that they could hardly find mates among masses of unchanged relatives. To some authors (e.g., Bonnier 1924, 1927) this difficulty seemed serious enough to lead to doubts whether the known genetic principles are sufficient to account for the origin of species.

The initial disadvantage which isolation-producing mutants encounter in natural populations may be partly overcome by certain modifications of the reproductive biology. Thus, in organisms with facultative self-fertilization, parthenogenesis, or asexual generation, the mutants (unless they are inviable or sterile in heterozygotes) may become multiplied and form a small colony in which cross-fertilization may then be resumed. It is indeed important that many polyploids, which are known to be at least partly isolated from their diploid ancestors by the mere doubling of the chromosomal complement, are capable of reproduction by methods other than obligatory cross-fertilization. Allopolyploids may be produced in relatively large numbers in the localities where the distribution areas of the ancestral species overlap, and yet at least many of the naturally occurring allopolyploids are known to reproduce in part by self-fertilization, by apogamy, or asexually (cf. Chapter X). However, since isolating mechanisms are universally encountered in obligatorily cross-fertilizing organisms, there must be some method of their formation compatible with that form of reproductive biology.

It seems very probable that the formation of isolating mechanisms entails mostly not single mutational steps but the building up of systems of complementary genes. Let it be assumed that the ancestral population from which two new species are to be evolved has the genetic constitution *aabb*, where *a* and *b* are single genes or groups of genes, and that this population is broken up into two parts temporarily isolated from each other by secular causes—for example by inhabiting territories separated by a geographical barrier. In one part of the population, *a* mutates to *A* and a local race *AAbb* is formed. In the other part, *b* mutates to *B*, giving rise to a race *aaBB*. Individuals of the constitutions *aabb*, *Aabb*, and *AAbb* are able to interbreed freely with each other, and hence there is no difficulty in establishing in the population the gene, or the group of genes, *A*. The same is true for the gene or genes *B*, since *aabb*, *aabB*, and *aaBB* are fully capable of interbreeding. But the cross *AAbb* × *aaBB* is difficult or impossible, because the interaction of *A* and *B* produces one of the physiological isolating mechanisms. If the carriers of the genotypes *AAbb* and *aaBB* surmount the barriers separating them, they are now able to coexist in the same territory, since interbreeding is no longer possible.

Thus, we hypothesize that in obligatorily cross-fertilizing organisms (1) the genes producing isolation are multiple and complementary, their minimum number being two; (2) that isolating genes which produce hybrid inviability or sterility are dominant and hence act in heterozygotes; (3) that the development of physiological isolation is as a rule predicated on the previous territorial separation of the populations to be isolated. This scheme may appear fanciful, but it is worth considering further since it is supported by some well-established facts and contradicted by none. In the genetically analyzed instances of hybrid inviability (see above) multiple complementary genes are invariably involved. For example, the gene discovered by Hollingshead in *Crepis tectorum* is not lethal in that species either when heterozygous or when homozygous, but acts as a dominant semilethal in the *C. tectorum* × *C. capillaris* hybrids. It follows that *C. capillaris* carries at least one gene not present in *C. tectorum* which interacts with that found in the latter species to produce a lethal genotype. In Chapter IX several cases of hybrid sterility will be shown to depend upon multiple genes or a multiplicity of chromosomal changes. Complementary genes capable of inducing isolation are encountered within species. Wiebe (1934) found two strains of barley the hybrids between which died in the seedling stage, while hybrids between either of these strains and unrelated lines of barley were fully fertile. Two complementary genes (or groups of genes) were shown to be involved. Supposing that one of these genes becomes established in the barley populations of some countries and the other gene in other countries, and that populations possessing neither gene disappear, the barley species would become split into two noninterbreeding groups.

The thesis that the development of physiological isolating mechanisms is preceded by geographical isolation finds a good deal of evidence in its support in observations on the organic variation in nature. Since Darwin, and especially since Wagner, it has been regarded as probable that the formation of geographical races is an antecedent of species formation; more recently this doctrine has been confirmed by many investigators, among whom we may name K. Jordan (1905), D. Jordan (1905), Semenov-Tian-Shansky (1910), Rensch (1929), Kinsey (1936) and Mayr (1940). Some systematists regard it as one of the greatest generalizations that has resulted from their work. The distribution regions of races of the same species as a rule do not overlap, while the areas of separate species frequently do. Now, coexistence of distinct groups of individuals in the same locality without formation of intermediates and of recombinations of characters is prima facie evidence that these groups are isolated physiologically (provided, of course, that the differences between them are due to more than one gene). The assumption that geographical isolation is a *conditio sine qua non* of species formation is, nevertheless, not a necessary one in organisms which reproduce by methods other than the obligatory cross-fertilization (see above). As far as the obligatorily cross-fertilizing forms are concerned, it is difficult to see how species can be formed without geographical isolation, but a final decision can hardly be reached at present. At any rate, it is certainly not necessary to suppose that every geographical race is always an incipient species: geographical races become species if reproductive isolating mechanisms separating them develop, but, in the opinion of the writer, geographical separation does not in itself guarantee the eventual advent of a reproductive one (cf. Goldschmidt 1940). This brings us face to face with a very difficult problem: what causes engender the development of physiological isolation between natural groups?

Evolutionists are prone to avoid this issue by assuming that if two or more populations remain separated for a long time, they accumulate more and more differences and become physiologically isolated in the process of doing so. Translated in genetical terms, this can mean one of two things: either any gene difference tends to produce a partial isolation, and, therefore, complete isolation arises when a certain number of gene differences have accumulated; or else, a certain proportion of mutations that arise in any organism have isolating effects, and, hence, when two populations become different in many genes, there will be, by chance, enough isolating ones to make such populations no longer capable of interbreeding. Unfortunately, neither of these two notions is satisfactory. Experience with gene mutations seems to show that most of them do not induce isolation. In *Drosophila melanogaster* and in other organisms strains may be obtained differing in dozens of genes, yet such strains show no indication of even beginning isolation. Of course, we have not synthesized in the laboratory strains differing in hundreds or in thousands of genes, but there is nothing to prove that such strains would be physiologically isolated.

According to Muller (1939, 1940a), isolation may arise through phylogenetic change in gene functions. Muller's premise is that, since a functional genotype is an integrated system of genes (see the discussion of the work of Harland and others on the genetics of cotton in Chapter III), evolutionary changes are not mere additions or subtractions of unrelated gene elements. The initial advantage conferred upon a species or a race by most mutations that arise and become established in the process of adaptation is slight; some mutations may, to begin with, even be neutral. But as the process of accumulation of gene differences goes on, genes which at one time might have been easily disposed of become essential constituents of the genotypic system. In other words, in the course of evolution the functions of a gene in development may undergo such changes that a gene may subtend developmental processes other than those with which it was previously concerned. Changes of gene functions in two or more races or species may be divergent, whereupon the gene systems of these groups may become so different as to be no longer compatible in the hybrids. In Muller's opinion, all kinds of isolating mechanisms may arise in the manner just indicated: "Which kind of character becomes affected earliest, and to what degree . . . will depend in part upon its general complexity (which is correlated with the number of genes affecting it), in part on the nicety or instability of the equilibria of processes necessary for its proper functioning, and in part on the accidental circumstances that determined just which incompatible mutations happened to become established first."

This very ingenious scheme is probably best adapted to explain the incompatibility, and especially the inviability, of the hybrids of remote forms. Whether this scheme is sufficient to account for the development of all isolating mechanisms is, however, doubtful. Isolating mechanisms encountered in nature appear to be *ad hoc* contrivances which prevent the exchange of genes between nascent species, rather than incongruities originating in accidental changes in the gene functions. Dobzhansky (1940) has proposed a tentative hypothesis based on the suggestion of Fisher (1930) that physiological isolating mechanisms may be a product of natural selection. This hypothesis, which may be alternative or complementary to Muller's, starts from the same premise, namely that the genotype of a species is an integrated system adapted to the ecological niche in which the species lives. Gene recombination in the offspring of species hybrids may lead to formation of individuals with discordant gene patterns, the destruction of which entails a decrease of the reproductive potentials of the species whose members interbreed. Let it be assumed that two incipient species, A and B, are in contact in a certain territory, and that mutations arise in either or in both species which make their carriers less likely to mate with the representatives of the other species. The nonmutant individuals of the species A which cross to B will produce a progeny which is, by hypothesis, inferior in viability to the pure species; the offspring of the mutant individuals will have, other things being equal, a normal viability. Since the mutants breed only or mostly within the species, their progeny will be more numerous or more vigorous than that of the nonmutants. Consequently, natural selection will favor the spread and establishment of the mutant condition. Sturtevant (1938) has pointed out one of the possible causes which may initiate such a process. Suppose that the ancestral gene arrangement in the chromosome ABCDEFGH is modified in one race to AFEDCBGH and in another race to ABGFEDCH. Structural heterozygotes carrying the ancestral and either of the modified arrangements will produce few or no inviable offspring. In a hybrid carrying the two modified arrangements crossing over may, however, be frequent in the section CDEF. The crossover products, AFEDCH and ABGFEDCBGH, contain deficiencies and duplications and, may, therefore, be inviable. Genetic factors which would prevent the interbreeding of the carriers of AFEDCBGH and ABGFEDCH will have a selective advantage.

Once an incipient physiological isolation has become initiated, natural selection will tend to strengthen it and eventually to make the isolation complete. If, for example, the hybrids between species A and B are partly sterile, it is advantageous for these species to modify their breeding seasons in such a way that as few such hybrids be produced as possible. The reproductive potential of individuals whose offspring is partly sterile is, evidently, lower than that of individuals which do not produce such offspring. Addition of a sexual isolation, or of an incompatibility of gametes, or of both, will likewise be advantageous if it makes the isolation secure. Isolating mechanisms guarding against the production of hybrids between species are, thus, interdependent, and natural selection will tend to strengthen the whole complex of these mechanisms until the possibility of gene exchange between these species disappears entirely.

The principal weakness of the view that physiological isolation develops by selection processes lies in its corollary: isolating mechanisms arise in response to the challenge of hybridization leading to formation of poorly adapted genotypes (Dobzhansky 1940). It is, therefore, not clear how physiologically isolated species could develop in noncontiguous territories, such as oceanic islands, where opportunities for hybridization are not available. How serious this difficulty really is we have no way of determining at present, since no experimental data on physiological isolation in island species are available. Systematists are, however, familiar with species that coexist at our time level in the same territory without formation of hybrids, although these species have developed presumably on separate islands (Mayr 1940). In such cases physiological isolation might have arisen because these species have repeatedly attempted to invade each other's territories; these attempts have led to the formation of isolating mechanisms, whereupon the invaders were able to establish themselves as an independent population alongside the indigenous species.

Let us consider again the situation discovered by Hollingshead in *Crepis tectorum* (see p. 278). Some individuals of this plant do, and others do not, carry a gene which is lethal in the hybrids of *C. tectorum* with certain related species. Yet, within *C. tectorum* this gene appears to have no phenotypic manifestation at all, and, hence, is assuredly not a vital part of the genotype of that species. Analogous situations are known in *Triticum monococcum* (p. 279), *Drosophila aldrichi* (p. 279), and *Drosophila macrospina* (p. 297). It seems evident that physiological isolating mechanisms could be built by natural selection from genetic variants of this type. To test this hypothesis one would like to know whether the isolating genes are encountered most frequently in those parts of the distribution areas of the respective species where a danger exists of hybridization with related species. This seems to be the case in *D. pseudoobscura*: the intensity of the sexual isolation from the northern race of *D. miranda* is greatest in the strains of *D. pseudoobscura* coming from the geographical regions in which, or close to which, that race of *D. miranda* occurs (p. 266). Data on the geographical distribution of isolating genes in other species are urgently needed.

Several instances are known in which the distribution areas of related species capable of producing fertile hybrids are in juxta-position and yet hybrids occur only along the line of the actual geographical contact, without diffusing toward the centers of the species territories. Meise (1928) has made a monographic study of the two crows *Corvus corone* and *C. cornix*. Their geographical areas are apposed along a line some three thousand kilometers in extent in Europe and Asia; intergrades of hybrid origin occur only in a zone from a dozen to one hundred kilometers wide. The following detail is very significant. During the Ice Age, *C. corone* and *C. cornix* were geographically completely separated, but their distribution regions have converged in such a manner that contacts developed earlier in some territories and later in others. The zones of intergradation are, however, narrower where the duration of the contact has been longest, and broader where the contact is more recent. This is expected if isolating mechanisms are in process of formation where these incipient species hybridize. The grackles *Quiscalus quiscala* and *Q. aeneus* present a situation similar to that in the crows just discussed (Chapman 1936, 1939). During the Ice Age the two grackles were confined respectively to Florida and to southern Texas. Later their distribution areas converged along a line extending from Louisiana to New England. Exchange of genes takes place on either side of this line, but the zone in which hybrids are found is narrowest in Louisiana where the opportunity for crossing has been available for the longest time. Fischer-Piette (1935) has described a perhaps similar case in the marine mollusc *Patella*.

IX: HYBRID STERILITY

INTRODUCTION

THE PROBLEM of hybrid sterility goes back at least to Aristotle, who in the "De generatione animalium" discussed at length the sterility of the mule. Aristotle's explanation of the sterility of mules has only an historical interest. In recent times so much work has been done, and so many valuable observations collected on sterile hybrids in various animals and plants that hybrid sterility is at present the best known among the isolating mechanisms. Nevertheless, a causal analysis is confronted with difficulties which have been only partly overcome.

Sterile hybrids are frequently vigorous somatically, but their reproductive organs, more precisely the gonads, show derangements that prevent formation of functional germ cells. This contrast is on the whole characteristic of sterile hybrids. The mule is equal, and under some conditions superior, in viability to the parental species; yet, the testes and the ovaries of mules are manifestly abnormal, so that no spermatozoa or mature eggs are formed in them. Some authors supposed that the deterioration of gonads is a sign of a general weakness of the whole organism, and believed that the gonads are the place of least resistance where such a weakness is likely to manifest itself. This conjecture is invalid; a constitutional weakness in pure species is by no means always accompanied by sterility, and many hybrids with reduced viability are fertile (e.g., the hybrids between the flax species described by Laibach, p. 275).

A dissociation between the processes taking place in the gonads of a hybrid and those in its soma has been observed in *Drosophila pseudoobscura* by Dobzhansky and Beadle (1936). The male hybrids between race A and race B of this species are sterile, their spermatogenesis being very abnormal. Testes of hybrid larvae were implanted in larvae of pure races, and vice versa. The development

of the testes was found to proceed autonomously. If a testis of a
pure race implanted into a hybrid becomes attached to the sexual
duct of the latter, the hybrid is fertile, the functional sperm coming,
of course, from the implánted testis. The spermatogenesis in the
testis of a hybrid developed in the body of a normal male shows as
great a disturbance as is customary in a hybrid. Testes of the host
are not affected by the presence of implants of a different genetic
constitution. Ephrussi and Beadle (1935) have obtained fertile
eggs from the ovaries of *Drosophila simulans* implanted in *D. melanogaster,* although the hybrids between these species are completely sterile. All such experiments are open to the criticism that
the transplantation is performed too late to change the course of
the development of the implanted gonad. Nevertheless, it is most
probable that, at least in the race A × race B hybrids in *D. pseudoobscura,* the sterility is due to processes taking place in the gonad
itself, and not to interactions between the gonads and the somatic
tissues.

In any case, the structure of the reproductive organs, and especially the chromosome behavior in the processes of gonogenesis,*
have been the principal concern of most investigators working on
the problem of hybrid sterility. The pioneer work in this field was
that of Federley (1913, 1914, 1915, 1916). He discovered that the
chromosomes of the parental species frequently fail to pair and to
form bivalents at meiosis in sterile and semisterile hybrids. The
moth species *Pygaera anachoreta, P. curtula,* and *P. pigra* have
30, 29, and 23 chromosomes, respectively (haploid); the hybrids
have the sum of the haploid chromosome numbers of the parental
species. Little or no meiotic pairing is observed in the spermatogenesis of the hybrids; most chromosomes remain univalent. In
Pygaera hybrids, the univalents split at both meiotic divisions, and
the spermatids tend to possess the somatic number of chromosomes.
Various abnormalities (fused spindles, failures of cell division)
were observed in the spermatocytes; the spermatids usually degenerate. The hybrids are semisterile.

Federley's observations have been confirmed and extended by
many investigators working on interspecific hybrids in both plants

---

* The terms "gones" and "gonogenesis" have been proposed by Lotsy to cover both
the gametes of animals and the gametophytes in plants.

and animals. The essential fact is that a failure of pairing between chromosomes of different species is observed at meiosis in most (although not in all) sterile hybrids. In detail the situation varies greatly. Some chromosomes may pair and form bivalents, others remain univalent. The proportion of bivalents and univalents varies not only in different hybrids but also in individuals and cells of the same hybrid. The bivalents disjoin normally, that is, at each division half of the bivalent passes to each pole of the spindle. The univalents split as a rule either at the first or at the second meiotic division; at the division at which no splitting takes place the univalents are distributed at random to the poles of the spindle, so that the daughter cells may come to have unequal numbers of chromosomes. The cell division mechanism itself may break down, and all sorts of degenerative phenomena appear in the cells. Few or no functional gones are produced.

The failure of the meiotic chromosome pairing is frequently the starting point of abnormalities in the gonogenesis in sterile hybrids. This fact naturally leads to the supposition that a cause and effect relationship exists between these phenomena, and hence that the sterility of a hybrid is due ultimately to the failure of chromosome pairing in meiosis. As a general theory this supposition is vitiated, however, by the occurrence of sterile hybrids in which chromosome pairing at meiosis is normal. Such hybrids have been described in *Digitalis* by Haase-Bessel (1921), in *Epilobium* by Håkansson (1934), in *Lolium perenne* × *Festuca pratensis* by Peto (1933), and in *Saxifraga* by Drygalski (1935). In *Chorthippus bicolor* × *Ch. biguttulus* chromosomes pair normally but the disjunction is highly abnormal (Klingstedt 1938). The F_1 hybrid males from the crosses of race A and race B of *Drosophila pseudoobscura* are always sterile, although the amount of chromosome pairing is highly variable (Dobzhansky 1934b). Within each race, strains are encountered that produce hybrids in which no bivalents are formed at meiosis, and other strains that produce hybrids with bivalents only and no univalents. The meiotic divisions are, however, abnormal in either case: the first division spindle elongates enormously, bends into a ring, the cell body fails to divide, the second meiotic division is absent, and the giant binucleate spermatids which are formed degenerate. The failure of chromosome pairing is here an effect rather than the cause of the general disturbances in spermatogenesis.

In other hybrids the cells of the gonads degenerate before the advent of the meiotic stages. In the hybrids between *Drosophila melanogaster* and *D. simulans,* the gonads are rudimentary, and, as shown by Kerkis (1933, 1935), spermatogenesis and oögenesis do not advance beyond spermatogonia and oögonia. Apparently similar conditions are encountered in some of the hybrids between species of gallinaceous birds (Poll 1910, 1920), and perhaps also in those between species of mammals (horse × zebra, yak × domestic cow). The malformations of flowers and anthers observed in some plant hybrids may belong to the same category (Lehmann and Schwemmle 1927, Müntzing 1930).

The degeneration of the germinal tissues leading to sterility of hybrids may set in before, during, or after the meiotic divisions, with chromosomes failing to pair, or with bivalents being formed. This great diversity of the phenomena of sterility is not in itself a decisive argument against the supposition that the failure of chromosome pairing may be a cause of the degeneration of the gametes, and consequently of the sterility. It merely suggests that more than one sterility mechanism is encountered in nature. Federley (1928) and Renner (1929) distinguish between gametic and zygotic sterility; the former consists in production of degenerate nonfunctional gametes (or gones), and the latter in production of gametes which form inviable zygotes. Müntzing (1930) prefers the terms "haplontic" and "diplontic" sterility; the former is due to the lethality of the haplophase, presumably caused by the genotypic constitution of the haplonts, and the latter to disturbances in the diploid part of the life cycle. These terms may be convenient for descriptive purposes, but such a classification hardly penetrates much below the surface of the phenomena. More basic seems to be the distinction between genic and chromosomal sterility (Dobzhansky 1933b) which is defined in the following paragraph.

GENIC AND CHROMOSOMAL STERILITY

Disturbances in chromosome pairing may be due to two classes of causes, which correspond to the two known methods of differentiation of the chromosomal materials. First, there is the mutation process which alters the structure of individual genes in the chromosomes. Second, we observe structural changes of a grosser nature, due to alterations in the relative positions of blocks of genes with respect to each other.

Meiosis, like any other physiological process, is ultimately controlled by the genotype of the organism. The normal course of meiosis involves a definite succession of events which are so delicately adjusted that a failure of any one of them, or simply a change in the normal time relationships, may cause a derangement of the whole process. Gene mutations can attack this process at any stage. Consequently, chromosome conjugation may fail despite the presence of pairs of chromosomes having similar genes arranged in identical linear series. The resulting sterility will be due not to dissimilarities in the gross structure of the chromosomes, but to the genetic constitution of the organism. This is *genic sterility*.

On the other hand, a chromosome may fail to pair and to form a bivalent with another chromosome because it has no structurally similar partner. Two chromosomes may contain identical genes, but in one of them the arrangement may be *abcde,* and in the other *caebd;* or else, two chromosomes may have some genes in common, but each of them may contain also genes not present in the other (for instance, *abcde* and *abfgh*). Sterility due to such structural dissimilarities is termed *chromosomal sterility*.

Disturbances in the sex organs of hybrids may be initiated before, as well as after, meiotic chromosome pairing has taken place and the divisions have been successfully completed; this fact proves that genic sterility does not necessarily involve any interference with the chromosomal mechanism. On the other hand, where the abnormalities in the gonogenesis of a hybrid begin with a failure of chromosome pairing, the sterility may be either chromosomal or genic. The possibility that the sterility of some hybrids may be caused by a combination of the two causes must also be considered, since the interbreeding of many species is known to be prevented not by a single isolating mechanism, but by several, which reinforce each other's action.

GENIC STERILITY WITHIN A SPECIES

Sterility of the genic type has been described in several organisms. The "asynaptic" gene studied by Beadle (1930, 1933) in *Zea mays* may serve as an illustration of the kind of changes that may be observed. Maize plants heterozygous for this gene appear normal in every respect, but homozygous plants are distinguished by abortion of most of the pollen and of a majority of the ovules. The gene is, therefore, a recessive, and inbreeding of heterozygous plants produces segregations in the ratio 3 fertile : 1 sterile plants. Cytological examination shows that the beginning of meiosis is normal, and the chromosomes pair to form ten double strands. However, no chiasmata are formed between the paired strands, members of a pair fall apart, and univalents are present at the meiotic division. The spindle elongates abnormally and aberrant chromosome complements are formed in the resulting daughter cells, most of which degenerate.

Recessive genes causing sterility of homozygotes are apparently rather common in maize (Beadle 1931, 1932a, b, c, Clark 1940, and others). The abnormalities engendered by them are diverse in kind, and become manifest at different stages of meiosis. Thus, in homozygotes for the "sticky" gene, meiosis is abnormal from the beginning, while another gene causes supernumerary cell divisions after the completion of meiosis. Some genes affect meiosis in both sexes, while others act in one sex only. Genes of this type are known also in organisms other than maize: *Drosophila melanogaster* (Gowen 1931), *D. simulans* (Sturtevant 1929b), *Crepis* (Hollingshead 1930b, Richardson 1935), oats and wheat (Huskins and Hearne 1933), *Datura* (Bergner, Cartledge, and Blakeslee 1934), and *Sorghum* (Huskins and Smith 1934). For further references see Darlington (1937b) and Levan (1940b). In *Allium amplectens* an asynaptic condition occurs in natural populations, with the individuals affected reproducing asexually (Levan 1940b). Smith (1936) found some asynaptic plants among the segregation products from the cross *Triticum monococcum* × *T. aegilopoides* var. *baidaricum*. This case is particularly interesting because the asynaptic condition proved to be due to a complementary action of two recessive genes contributed by the respective parents, so that the double recessive homozygotes (aabb) are sterile while the heterozygotes are fertile.

Mutant genes that make their carriers sterile because of malformations in the flowers (e.g., in *Antirrhinum*, Baur 1924) or in the reproductive organs or the genitalia (the mutant "rotated abdomen" in *Drosophila melanogaster*), are not rare. The recessive sex-linked mutant gene fused in *D. melanogaster* is especially interesting. Eggs that are visibly abnormal in shape and that produce no viable larvae or adults when fertilized by the spermatozoa of fused males are deposited by females homozygous for fused. The same eggs, are, however, viable if fertilized by spermatozoa not carrying fused. The eggs of females heterozygous for fused or free from it develop normally when fertilized by spermatozoa of fused males (Lynch 1919). Here, then, we are dealing with a gene whose action is somehow impressed on the cytoplasm of the egg during oögenesis (maternal effect). The fate of the egg is not sealed, however, until after fertilization, since the genes brought in by the spermatozoon can either mitigate the unfavorable maternal effects or make the resulting genetic constitution lethal. It will be shown below that similar phenomena are encountered also in interspecific hybrids.

The mechanism of action of many recessive genes inducing sterility in homozygotes has never been examined. Such genes are, however, very common: Berg (1937) and Prabhu (1939) found numerous mutants of this type in the progeny of X-ray treated *Drosophila melanogaster,* and unpublished data of the present writer indicate that many such mutants are borne in heterozygous condition in the autosomes of natural populations of *D. pseudoobscura.* The abundance of mutant genes producing sterility tempts one to suppose that such genes are the building blocks from which sterility barriers between species are made. Inasmuch as these genes are recessive and cause sterility only when homozygous, the analogy with hybrid sterility is, however, incomplete. As stated above, the term "hybrid sterility" is applicable where two forms each of which is fertile *inter se* (e.g., horse and ass) produce a hybrid that is partly or completely sterile (mule). Hybrid sterility could be produced by a single gene only provided this gene would make both homozygotes (AA and aa) fertile and the heterozygotes (Aa) sterile.* It is quite possible that such genes arise by mutation, but

---

* Alleles at the T locus in mice affect the development of the tail and a number of other characters. Two of these alleles, t^0 and t^1, produce male sterility in the compound t^0t^1. It is possible to obtain two fertile and true breeding strains involving balanced lethals, Tt^0 and Tt^1. When crossed, these strains produce offspring one-third of which is t^0t^1 and consequently male sterile (Dunn, 1937). A situation of this sort could become an isolating mechanism, but its establishment in nature would be difficult.

their detection is obviously difficult. Of course, genetic situations are thinkable which might mold the originally recessive sterility genes into workable isolating mechanisms. Klingstedt (1939) supposes that sterility genes which are recessive within a species might become dominant, or at least semidominant, in an interspecific hybrid. If, then, individuals of the two parental species crossed are each heterozygous for several recessive sterility genes, the hybrid may prove to be sterile. A wide applicability of Klingstedt's hypothesis may be doubted, since the hybrid sterility so produced would

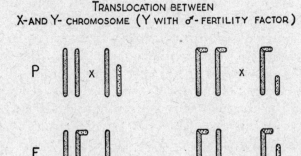

Translocation between
X- and Y- chromosome (Y with ♂- fertility factor)

Fig. 18. Two strains of *Drosophila melanogaster* that produce sterile male hybrids when crossed. X chromosome, stippled; Y chromosome, dotted. Upper left, normal female; upper right, male from the translocation strain; below, the hybrids. F, fertile; ST, sterile. (From Stern.)

be tremendously variable depending on the strains of the parental species used in the cross.

Stern (1929, 1936) has made a very elegant attempt to devise a synthetic model of hybrid sterility within the species *Drosophila melanogaster*. Males devoid of a Y chromosome are sterile, and Stern has found that at least two different sections of this chromosome are concerned with fertility, so that both sections must be present in order that the male may be fertile. Females carrying a whole Y chromosome or a part of it in addition to their X chromosomes are fertile. In a translocation the Y has been broken, and a section of it containing one of the "fertility genes" has become attached to the X. A race can be obtained (Fig. 18, upper right) in which females have two X chromosomes with sections of the Y attached to them, and males have a similar X and a fragment of the Y that is deficient for just the section that is attached to the X. A male of this race is fertile because it carries simultaneously both sections of the Y chromosome that are needed for fertility. If females and males of this artificial race are crossed to each other, no sterile offspring results, and the race breeds true. If normal females are crossed to the males of the artificial race, the resulting offspring are fertile females and sterile males (Fig. 18, lower left); a cross of normal males to females of the artificial race gives rise to a fertile F_1 generation (Fig. 18, lower right).

Mainland (1941) has described in a preliminary note an incipient hybrid sterility in natural populations of *Drosophila macrospina* which seems to parallel very closely Stern's artificial model, although in *D. macrospina* no translocations between the X and the Y chromosomes have been ascertained. *D. macrospina limpiensis* is a form known to occur in a certain mountain range in Texas. Its relatives, *D. macrospina macrospina* and *D. macrospina ohioensis*, occur elsewhere in Texas and in Ohio respectively. The crosses *limpiensis* ♀ × *macrospina* ♂ and *limpiensis* ♀ × *ohioensis* ♂ produce fertile daughters and sterile sons; in the reciprocal crosses the F_1 hybrids are fertile. Backcrosses of the hybrid females to *limpiensis* males produce fertile progenies, while if the hybrid females are crossed back to *macrospina* or to *ohioensis* males, half of the male offspring are sterile. *Macrospina* and *ohioensis* are interfertile. It follows that males carrying a *limpiensis* X must also carry a *limpiensis* Y chromosome in order to be fertile. Another instance of an incipient sterility barrier has been found by Hadjinov (1937). Two strains of *Sorghum vulgare* derived from India are morphologically similar to other known strains of the same species but, nevertheless, produce semisterile hybrids when outcrossed to the latter. Meiosis in the hybrids is normal, but male gametophytes mostly degenerate soon after the meiotic divisions are completed. The backcrosses of these hybrids to the parental strains have, unfortunately, not been analyzed in detail, but the data as presented suggest that only a few genes are involved in the production of the sterility.

CHROMOSOMAL STERILITY WITHIN A SPECIES

The production of sex cells carrying abnormal gene complements in individuals heterozygous for various chromosomal aberrations leads to a certain degree of sterility. Suppose that two normal chromosomes of a species carry the genes *ABCD* and *EFGHI*, respectively. A translocation involving an exchange of sections of these chromosomes takes place, as a result of which two "new" chromosomes, *ABFE* and *DCGHI*, are produced. Homozygous normals and the translocation homozygotes produce sex cells which carry every gene once and only once. But in a translocation heterozygote at least six classes of sex cells can be produced: (1) *ABFE, DCGHI,* (2) *ABCD, EFGHI,* (3) *ABFE, EFGHI,* (4) *ABCD, DCGHI,* (5) *ABFE, ABCD,* and (6) *DCGHI, EFGHI.* Classes 1 and 2 carry normal gene complements, but in classes 3 to 6 certain genes are deficient and other genes are present in duplicate; 1 and 2 are termed regular or orthoploid, and 3 to 6 exceptional or heteroploid gones or sex cells.

The fate of the exceptional gones is different in animals on one hand and in the higher plants on the other. In animals the meiotic divisions are followed by a rapid transformation of the resulting cells into eggs or spermatozoa respectively, and the animal gametes retain their functional ability even if they carry grossly unbalanced gene complements, that is, have deficiencies or duplications for large blocks of genes. The exceptional gametes give rise to zygotes. A proof of the correctness of the propositions just stated has been secured with the aid of simple experiments (Muller and Settles 1927, Dobzhansky 1930b, and others). The chromosomes involved in a translocation are marked by mutant genes, so that the course of every chromosome in the inheritance can be followed by simple inspection of the phenotype of the parents and offspring. Individuals heterozygous for the same translocation are intercrossed. Among the exceptional gametes, it may be noted, classes 3 and 4, and 5 and 6 are complementary to each other, since 3 and 5 are deficient for just the same genes that are carried in duplicate in 4 and 6 respectively, and 4 and 6 lack the genes that are present in excess in 3 and 5. The union of 3 and 5, or 4 and 6, gives rise to zygotes that carry every gene twice; such zygotes develop into viable individuals that can be identified. On the other hand, if translocation heterozygotes

(Fig. 5D) are outcrossed to homozygous normals (A) or to translocation homozygotes (E), the exceptional gametes produce offspring carrying deficiencies for some genes and duplications for others. Such offspring are, as a rule, inviable or abnormal. The sterility of translocation heterozygotes in animals is due to the inviability of a part of their progeny.

In plants the meiotic divisions give rise to female and male gametophytes which undergo a process involving several cell divisions before the generative cells, the gametes proper, are produced. The exceptional gones are here aborted before fertilization can take place; only small duplications, and, rarely, deficiencies may pass through the gametophyte without causing abortion. Translocation heterozygotes are therefore characterized by abortion of a part of the pollen and ovules (Brink 1929, Brink and Burnham 1929, Burnham 1930 in maize, Belling 1927b, Bergner, Satina, and Blakeslee 1933 in *Datura*, Håkansson 1929 in *Pisum*, and many others). In some plants the semisterility is used as a method for the detection of translocations. The translocation homozygotes are, in accordance with expectations, fertile.

The degree of the sterility of a translocation heterozygote is evidently dependent upon the relative frequency of the regular and exceptional gametes it produces. If the six classes of the gametes discussed above should be equally frequent, the regular ones would amount to 33.3 percent of the total, and the translocation would be 66.7 percent sterile. The origin of the exceptional gametes involves, however, the passing of certain sections of chromosomes carrying homologous genes to the same pole of the spindle at the meiotic division; if all homologous sections should disjoin and pass to the opposite poles at the meiotic divisions, only regular gametes could be formed (cf. Figs. 5 and 6). Exceptional gametes are due to nondisjunction of chromosomes or chromosome sections at meiosis. Any factor that raises the frequency of nondisjunction increases sterility, and vice versa. The problem so stated is open to an experimental attack.

A correlation has been detected in translocation heterozygotes in *Drosophila* between the disjunction of the chromosome sections involved and the amount of crossing over taking place in them (Dobzhansky and Sturtevant 1931, Dobzhansky 1933a, Glass 1935,

Pipkin 1940, Brown 1940, and others). It is well known that the amount of crossing over in a chromosome or a chromosome section is constant under normal conditions, that is, in the absence of chromosomal rearrangements and in a definite environment. In translocation heterozygotes, the frequency of crossing over is reduced, especially in the vicinity of the points at which the chromosomes have been broken and reattached. If in a translocation a short section of one chromosome has been transposed to another chromosome, the crossing over in that section is suppressed relatively more than in a long transposed section. The chromosomes and sections that suffer the greatest reduction of the frequency of crossing over undergo nondisjunction at meiosis more frequently than sections in which crossing over remains more nearly normal. The introduction of a factor that suppresses crossing over (e.g., an inversion) in a given chromosome or section leads to an increase of the frequency of nondisjunction. These and other facts have led to a theory according to which the chromosomes and chromosome sections in structural heterozygotes compete with each other for pairing with their homologues at meiosis (Dobzhansky 1931, 1933a, 1934a).

In a normal, structurally homozygous, individual every chromosome has one and only one homologue having an identical gene arrangement. In translocation heterozygotes, some chromosomes consist of sections that are homologous to parts of two or more other chromosomes (Fig. 6). In inversion heterozygotes, certain chromosomes have homologues containing the same genes arranged in a different linear sequence. The meiotic pairing is due to a mutual attraction between homologous loci rather than between chromosomes as such (Belling 1927a, 1928, 1931, and others). In structural heterozygotes, parts of the same chromosome, in an attempt to pair with their respective homologues, may be pulled in different directions simultaneously. Pairing of some chromosome sections may be delayed or not attained at all. The lack of pairing engenders a reduction of the frequency of crossing over, and, as known from cytological observations (cf. Darlington 1931), a failure of disjunction. Short chromosome sections are weaker than long ones in the competition for pairing. Hence, the crossing over is strongly suppressed in short sections, and they frequently undergo nondisjunction, forming exceptional gametes. The more extensive the differences in gene arrangement between the chromosomes of the parents, the greater is the competition for pairing at meiosis, the more frequent are the failures of pairing and disjunction. Other things being equal, a structural heterozygote having chromosomes with more differences in the gene arrangement will produce more gametes with abnormal gene complements than a heterozygote with more nearly similar chromosomes. In different organisms the conditions of the meiotic pairings are, however, not necessarily alike; thus, the translocation heterozygotes in *Oenothera* produce relatively fewer exceptional gametes than the translocations in *Drosophila* (see also Thompson and Thompson 1937).

Failures of the chromosome pairing at meiosis have been observed cytologically in some structural heterozygotes. McClintock (1932, 1933) and Burnham (1932) have found in maize that the chromosome sections adjacent to the loci of breakages in translocation heterozygotes frequently remain unpaired. Short chromosome sections transposed to other chromosomes fail to pair with their homologues more often than long sections. In *Drosophila* the meiotic prophases are technically difficult to study, but the chromosome pairing in the salivary gland nuclei is believed to represent a fairly accurate model of the meiotic pairing process. In translocation and inversion heterozygotes, the pairing is frequently disturbed in the vicinity of the breakage points, although cells with a complete pairing of all sections can sometimes be selected. In complex inversion heterozygotes in *Drosophila pseudoobscura* (Dobzhansky and Sturtevant 1938) long sections of the chromosomes involved may fail to pair, and some short sections remain unpaired in all cells. Oliver and Van Atta (1932) observed a disturbance of the somatic pairing due to translocations and inversions.

In hybrids between races and species, failures of chromosome pairing are, on the whole, proportional to the structural differentiation of the chromosomes. Race A and race B of *Drosophila pseudoobscura* usually differ in four inverted sections, and the chromosomes in the salivary gland nuclei pair except in the vicinity of the breakage points (Tan 1935, Koller 1936a). *D. pseudoobscura* and *D. miranda* differ greatly in gene arrangement, and most nuclei in the hybrids show only a few chromosome sections paired (Dobzhansky and Tan 1936). *D. azteca* and *D. athabasca* have even more profoundly different gene arrangements, and most of the salivary gland cells of the hybrid larvae show no pairing whatever, only exceptional cells having a few short sections paired (Bauer and Dobzhansky, unpublished). There is, however, no doubt in that aside from the differences in the gene arrangements in the parental forms crossed, the chromosome pairing in the hybrids is influenced by genetic factors. Thus, the frequent failure of pairing in the salivary gland chromosomes in the *D. melanogaster* × *D. simulans* hybrids can hardly be accounted for by the nonmatching of the homologous discs in these chromosomes (Kerkis 1936, Horton 1939). Patterson, Stone, and Griffen (1940) found that in the *D. virilis* × *D. americana* and *D. virilis* × *D. texana* hybrids the chromosomes frequently fail to pair in the salivary gland cells, while in *D. americana* × *D. texana* the pairing is good. Although the gene arrangements are different in all these species, the differences between *D. americana* and *D. texana* on the one hand and *D. virilis* on the other are not much more extensive than those between *D. americana* and *D. texana*.

Certain observations seemed to contradict the theory of competitive pairing. Thus, Beadle (1932d) and other workers have shown that the frequency of crossing over may be modified not only in translocation heterozygotes but also in translocation homozygotes, although no competition for pairing can be supposed to take place in the latter. Dubinin, Sokolov, Tiniakov, and Sacharov (1935) and Dobzhansky (1936e) have pointed out, however, that changes in the gene arrangement in the chromosomes may modify the frequency of crossing over not only through the competition for pairing, but also by altering the relative positions of the chromosomes with respect to each other in the nucleus, which is to a certain extent fixed (for example, in at least some organisms the spindle attachments of all chromosomes tend to be adjacent to one another in the resting nucleus as well as during the prophases and telophases). The modifications of the frequency of crossing over in translocation homozygotes may be thus accounted for.

Interesting experiments on the production of isolation between strains of *Drosophila melanogaster* by chromosomal changes have been reported by Kozhevnikov (1936). By combining two different translocations involving the second and the third chromosomes a strain is obtained which Kozhevnikov designates *"Drosophila arti-*

ficialis." This strain has one normal third chromosome and three
other chromosomes composed of sections of the second and third
arranged in a manner indicated in Fig. 19. *D. artificialis* produces
four classes of gametes shown in Fig. 19 (not counting the rare crossovers which take place between the rearranged chromosomes). On
inbreeding *D. artificialis,* sixteen classes of zygotes arise in equal
numbers, twelve of which die on account of deficiencies and duplica-

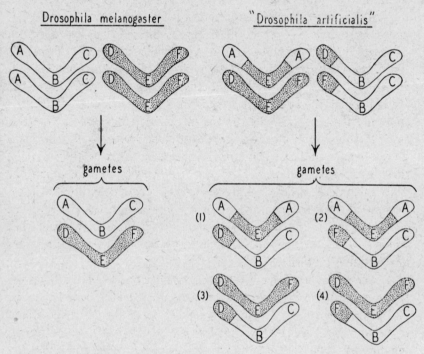

FIG. 19. Arrangement of parts of the second (white) and third (stippled)
chromosomes in *Drosophila melanogaster* and *D. artificialis.* (After
Kozhevnikov.)

tions for chromosome sections, and only four survive. The surviving
ones are, however, identical in chromosome constitution with the
parents. The strain breeds true. A cross *D. melanogaster* ♀ × *D.
artificialis* ♂ produces no viable offspring whatever, since none of
the zygotes formed contain balanced chromosome complements.
Kozhevnikov's model depicts a situation in which a cross between
two strains produces no viable hybrids.

INTERSEXUALITY IN HYBRIDS

Since different genes may produce diverse physiological effects and the processes of gametogenesis may be disturbed in a variety of ways, it is perhaps not unexpected that several physiologically distinct phenomena are subsumed under the general name genic sterility. One of these phenomena is the unbalance of the sex-determining factors, making the hybrids intersexual. We have seen above that the sex of an individual is decided by the balance of the female-determining and the male-determining factors it carries. In *Drosophila*, the genes for femaleness are borne in the X chromosome and those for maleness in the autosomes. In the gypsy moth *Lymantria dispar*, the X chromosome carries maleness, while the factor for femaleness is transmitted, according to Goldschmidt, through the cytoplasm. Within a race the action of the sex-determining genes is so adjusted that only females and males but no intersexes are produced. In *Drosophila*, two X chromosomes combined with two sets of autosomes give a female, and one X chromosome a male. In *Lymantria*, where the female sex is heterozygous, two X's give rise to a male and one X to a female. It can be readily seen, however, that in different races and species the sex genes might vary in strength. In the hybrids, combinations of the female and male determiners may occur that would produce neither females nor males but intersexes. Intersexes are frequently sterile.

A penetrating analysis of the intersexuality observed in crosses between geographical races of *Lymantria dispar* has been made by Goldschmidt (1932a, 1934b). The races from the northern island of Japan (Hokkaido) and from Europe have "weak" sex-determining factors. The sex determiners in strains coming from Russian Turkestan, Manchuria, and southwest Japan are "half weak" or "neutral." Those in the strains from the middle and north Japan are "strong." According to Goldschmidt, an extensive series of multiple alleles of the sex genes underlies the differences between the races, although some modifying genes are also recorded.

A cross weak ♀ × strong ♂ produces in the F_1 generation normal males and females that are intersexual. The reciprocal cross, strong ♀ × weak ♂, gives normal females and males in F_1 but in the F_2 half of the males are intersexual. Denoting the female-determining factor by F, the male determiner by M, the weak and strong alleles by the subscripts w and s respectively, the above results can be interpreted thus:

$F_w M_w$ (weak ♀) × $M_s M_s$ (strong ♂) = $F_w M_s$ (intersex) and $F_w M_s M_w$ (♂)
$F_s M_s$ (strong ♀) × $M_w M_w$ (weak ♂) = $F_s M_w$ (♀) and $F_s M_w M_s$ (♂)

One F is normally sufficient to suppress the effects of a single M and to produce a female; but an F_w is not strong enough to overpower an M_s, hence an $F_w M_s$ individual is an intersex. Likewise, the individuals of the constitution $F_s M_w M_w$ appearing in the F_2 from the cross strong ♀ × weak ♂ are not males but intersexes. The degree of intersexuality may be very different in different crosses. As shown by Goldschmidt and his collaborators, intersexes are individuals that begin their development as representatives of one sex but end it as representatives of the other. The greater the portion of the development which is dominated by either the female or the male determiners, the greater is the resemblance of the resulting individuals to normal females or males respectively. If, however, the turning point falls somewhere in the middle of development, the intersexes possess various mixtures of female and male parts. In some crosses where the "strength" of the sex determiners in the parental races differs only slightly, the intersexes are so much like normal individuals that they remain fertile. Where the difference between the parental races is greater, the intersexes have the gonads, the ducts of the reproductive system, the genitalia, the secondary sexual characters, and the sexual behavior pattern modified so extensively that they are sterile. The degenerative processes in the gonads may be quite extensive, but so far as is known the chromosome behavior at meiosis is unaffected (at least where the cells of the gonads reach the meiotic stages). Finally, the crosses between very strong and very weak races give intersexes that are transformed completely into individuals of the sex opposite to that which they should have had according to their chromosomal constitution (XX instead of XY females, and XY instead of XX males).

The geographical distribution of the *Lymantria* races with weak, neutral, and strong sex determiners has been indicated above. Goldschmidt has studied it with the utmost care; he concludes that races possessing sufficiently different sex genes to produce sterile hybrids when crossed never inhabit adjacent territories. The sole exceptions are north Japan, where very strong races occur, and the neighboring island of Hokkaido inhabited by very weak races; the islands are however separated by the Tsugaru Strait which is broad enough to prevent the mingling of races living on its opposite shores. The attempts of Goldschmidt to detect some correlation between the variations in the sex factors present in a given race and the climatic characteristics of the territory inhabited by it are thus far unavailing.

Sterile intersexual hybrids are known in several groups of animals, although in general they do not appear to be very frequent. In most sterile hybrids the disturbances are confined to the gonads, while in intersexes other parts of the reproductive system and the secondary sexual characters are affected as well. According to Goldschmidt's analysis (1931) of the data of Keilin and Nuttal, the crosses between the head and the body lice (*Pediculus capitis* $\times$ *P. vestimenti*) produce some intersexes in the F_2 and F_3 generations. A similar situation has been observed by Guyénot and Duszynska (1935) in F_2 to F_5 of the cross *Cavia apera* $\times$ *C. cobaya* (guinea pigs), and by Crew and Koller (1936) in the F_1 of the cross *Anas* $\times$ *Cairina* (ducks). In the latter cross, spermatogenesis in the sterile males has been investigated; meiotic chromosome pairing appears to be normal, but various abnormalities in the second spermatocytes are recorded.

Years ago, semisterile F_1 hybrids were obtained by Standfuss from the cross between the moth species *Saturnia pyri* ♀ $\times$ *S. pavonia* ♂. The hybrid males can be backcrossed to *S. pavonia* females; the progeny consists of males and what Standfuss has described as "gynandromorphs." The latter have been shown by Pariser (1927) and Goldschmidt (1931) to be intersexes. The origin of these intersexes is different from those in the *Lymantria* crosses. *S. pavonia* and *S. pyri* have 29 and 30 chromosomes, respectively (haploid). The F_1 hybrid has 59 chromosomes, most of which fail to form bivalents at meiosis (Pariser has counted from 45 to 51 bodies in the spermatocytes of the F_1, which suggests that from 14 to 8 bivalents and from 31 to 43 univalents are formed). Meiosis in the hybrids proceeds apparently according to the scheme described by Federley for *Pygaera* (see above), and the backcross offspring are subtriploid (no complete triploids were observed, presumably because, due to the presence of some bivalents in the F_1 meiosis, no spermatozoa contain the full diploid chromosome complement). The *Saturnia* intersexes are, therefore, comparable to the triploid intersexes in *Drosophila* (cf. Chapter VII). Inasmuch as the sterility of some of the backcross individuals in *Saturnia* is due to their intersexuality, this case may be classed as belonging to the genic sterility type. The lack of chromosome pairing in the gametogenesis of the F_1 may, however, be due either to the dissimilarities in the gene arrangements in the chromosomes of the parental species (chromosomal sterility), or to the effects of complementary genetic factors (genic sterility).

GENIC STERILITY IN *DROSOPHILA PSEUDOOBSCURA*

Lancefield (1929) discovered that race A and race B of *Drosophila pseudoobscura* produce when crossed semisterile daughters and completely sterile sons in the F_1 generation. Although these "races" are practically indistinguishable morphologically, they behave as good species. Their geographical distributions are different but broadly overlapping; no hybrids have been found in nature in the zone of the overlap. They differ in certain physiological characters and in ecological preferences, and display a sexual isolation (p. 264) as well as a hybrid sterility. The shape of the Y chromosome (Dobzhansky 1935b, 1937c) and the gene arrangements (Tan 1935, Koller 1936a) are different.

The cross B ♀ × A ♂ gives in the F_1 hybrid males having visibly small testes; the reciprocal cross, A ♀ × B ♂, produces hybrid males with testes of normal size; in either case the males are completely sterile. The backcrosses of the F_1 females to race A or race B males give progenies in which the males have testes of variable size, ranging from normal to very small. Males with small testes are always sterile, those with large ones are sometimes fertile (Lancefield 1929). The sterility is due to a profound modification of the process of spermatogenesis. The meiotic chromosome pairing is variable; no univalents, some univalents, or only univalents may be present at the first meiotic division. Irrespective of the numbers of the bivalents and univalents formed, only a single meiotic division takes place, which is characterized by an analogous behavior of the spindle. The spermatids degenerate without being transformed into spermatozoa (Dobzhansky 1934b). The disturbances in spermatogenesis are in general greater the smaller the testes in a hybrid. Testis size is therefore a measure of the degree of departure from the normal course of the spermatogenesis that may be observed in a given individual. The disturbances leading to the sterility of the hybrids are confined to their gonads, while the rest of the reproductive system (the sexual ducts, external genitalia) and the secondary sexual characters appear to be entirely normal (Dobzhansky and Boche 1933). The sterile males are therefore not intersexual. Some real intersexes have been found in *Drosophila pseudoobscura,* and they proved to be quite distinct in appearance from hybrid males.

Since races A and B differ in the gene arrangement in their chromosomes, one might surmise that the sterility of their hybrids is chromosomal in the sense defined on p. 293. This conjecture is, however, far fetched, since the differences in the gene arrangement involve only three, or even only two, inversions. In *Drosophila melanogaster,* individuals heterozygous for five inversions are fertile, and in *D. pseudoobscura* itself complex inversion heterozygotes occur in natural populations and manifest no appreciable loss of fertility. A more conclusive evidence that the sterility of race A × race B hybrids is not chromosomal is afforded by observations on the chromosome behavior in tetraploid spermatocytes (Dobzhansky 1933b). Groups of such spermatocytes are frequently encountered in the testes of hybrid males. Their origin is apparently due to the failure of cell fission in one of the spermatogonial divisions, followed by the formation of binucleate cells, and the fusion of the telophasic groups of chromosomes at the next division. Tetraploid spermatocytes contain two full sets of chromosomes of race A as well as of race B. Each chromosome has, consequently, a partner exactly similar to it in gene arrangement. It is known that, in some plant hybrids in which no chromosome pairing is observed in the diploid, the reduplication of the chromosome complement enables all chromosomes to pair and to form bivalents, and the hybrid to become fertile (Chapter VII). The proportion of the chromosomes that become paired in the tetraploid spermatocytes of *D. pseudoobscura* hybrids is however no greater than in the diploid ones. Moreover, after the meiotic division the cells derived from the tetraploid spermatocytes undergo the same series of degenerative changes as their diploid relatives.

Having excluded the hypothesis of chromosomal sterility, we may turn to consideration of the possibility that the sterility of A × B hybrids is genic. Assume that the genetic constitution of race A is *SStt,* and that of race B *ssTT;* the hybrids are *SsTt. S* and *T* are genes or groups of genes; individuals carrying *S* alone, or *T* alone, are fertile, but the simultaneous presence of *S* and *T* makes a male sterile. This hypothesis can be tested experimentally. It is first of all necessary to determine which of the cellular elements carry the theoretically postulated sterility factors. Lancefield (1929) and Koller (1932) have shown that the backcross males carrying an X chromosome similar in racial origin to their father have large testes, while males receiving from their mother the X chromosome of the other race have small testes and are sterile. Since all backcross males normally derive their Y chromosome from the father, the findings of Lancefield and Koller might have suggested that sterile males with small testes are those in which the X and Y chromosomes are of different race. Observations on hybrid males devoid of Y chromosome (XO males) have served to exclude this possibility. Males without a Y have testes of the same size as their sibs carrying a Y. The Y is not connected with hybrid sterility in *Drosophila pseudoobscura* (Dobzhansky 1933d).

In the progenies of F_1 hybrid females backcrossed to males of either parental race, individuals appear that carry various combinations of chromosomes of race A and race B (Figs. 20 and 21). Some have all chromosomes of one race; others have an X chromosome of one race and autosomes of the other; still others carry various mixtures of the chromosomes of both races. Experiments can be so arranged that every chromosome (with the exception of the very small fifth) is marked with a mutant gene; the constellation of the chromosomes present in a given backcross individual is, then, recognizable from a simple inspection of its external appearance. It is a relatively simple matter to determine which combinations of chromosomes cause a male to have small testes and to be sterile, and which permit fertility. Moreover, if the original cross is made by using race A as a female (A ♀ × B ♂), the entire offspring has race A cytoplasm, while the cross B ♀ × A ♂ gives a progeny with race B cytoplasm. Several crosses in which the chromosomes of the parents were marked as indicated above have been studied by Dobzhansky (1936b). The testis size in the backcross males of different genetic constitutions was measured,

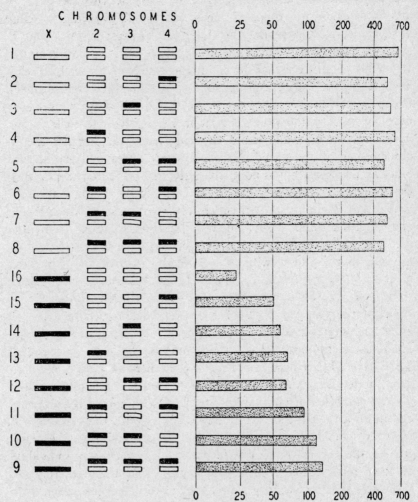

FIG. 20. Testis size in hybrids between race A and race B of *Drosophila pseudoobscura*. Chromosomes of race A are represented white; those of race B, black. (From Dobzhansky.)

and the fertility of some types determined. It became clear at once that fertility or sterility in the backcross males depends upon their chromosomal constitution, and not upon the ultimate source of their cytoplasm. Males whose grandmother was a race A female are similar to those descended from a race B grandmother, provided they have similar chromosome complements.

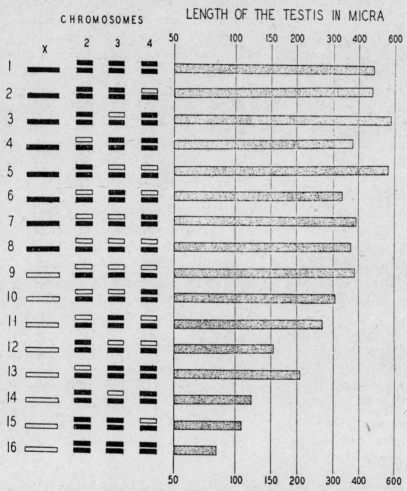

FIG. 21. Testis size in hybrids between race A and race B of *Drosophila pseudoobscura*. Chromosomes of race A are represented white; those of race B, black. (From Dobzhansky.)

Backcross males with X chromosome and autosomes of the same race have large testes and are usually fertile (Figs. 20 and 21). The more dissimilar the X and the autosomes become in racial origin the smaller is the testis size. The smallest testes are observed in males with the X of one race and all autosomes of the other. With a single exception,* all chromosomes act alike, and their action is cumulative. Thus, individuals carrying a race A X and race B autosomes have very small testes (class 16, Fig. 21). The introduction of one fourth or one third or one second chromosome of race A increases the testis size (classes 13-15, Fig. 21). The simultaneous introduction of the fourth and third (class 12), or second and third (class 10), or second and fourth (class 11), or second, third, and fourth (class 9) chromosomes of race A increases the testis size more than each of these chromosomes does alone. Males having all chromosomes of the same race, or having one third or one fourth chromosome of the opposite race from the rest of the chromosomes, are fertile (classes 2 and 3). But if both the third and fourth chromosomes disagree in racial origin with the rest of the complement, the male is sterile.

It is justifiable to conclude that, with the exception of the Y and of the small fifth chromosome, all chromosomes of race A and race B of *pseudoobscura* carry genes concerned with the sterility of the interracial hybrids. Moreover, Dobzhansky (1936b) found that the X, the second, and the third chromosome have each at least two such genes, and unpublished data show that the fourth chromosome has also no less than two. The minimum number of genes concerned with the sterility is therefore eight, but the actual number is almost certainly greater. What the physiological reactions are through which these genes produce their effects culminating in the disturbance of spermatogenesis and in sterility is unknown. The only bit of information on this subject is that the fate of the testis is determined by its own genetic constitution and not by that of the body in which it develops (the transplantation experiments of Dobzhansky and Beadle 1936; see above).

THE "STRONG" AND "WEAK" RACES OF DROSOPHILA PSEUDOOBSCURA

The cross race B ♀ × race A ♂ produces in F_1 sterile sons with small testes. Dobzhansky and Boche (1933) have shown that the exact size of the testes in such hybrids is a function of the strains

---

* The exception is that in backcrosses to race B males the sons having race A third chromosome and race B X chromosome have larger testes than their brothers homozygous for the race B third. This curious relation is due to a maternal effect (cf. Dobzhansky 1936b).

of either race that are used. Certain strains of race B when crossed to the same race A strain, the environmental conditions being kept constant, produce hybrids with markedly larger testes than other strains. Likewise, certain race A strains produce much larger testes in the hybrids than others when crossed to the same race B strain. Strains that tend to give relatively large testes are designated as "weak" and those decreasing the testis size as "strong." The expressions "strength" and "weakness" as applied to *D. pseudoobscura* should not be confused with the similar terminology applied to *Lymantria* races (see above), for in the latter the "strength" of the sex-determining factors is what is being referred to.

The strength of a given strain of *D. pseudoobscura* is an hereditary characteristic. The observed variation in strength is considerable: the linear dimensions of testes of a hybrid from a cross weak B ♀ × weak A ♂ may be three or more times greater than in those from the crosses of strong B ♀ × strong A ♂. The significance of this variation is emphasized by the observation (see above) that the size of the testis in a hybrid is indicative of the degree of the disturbance in spermatogenesis (Dobzhansky 1934b). Although the F_1 hybrid males from crosses between race A and race B are always sterile, the hybrids between weak strains may display a complete chromosome pairing at meiosis, only bivalents being present, while in crosses between strong strains the meiotic pairing fails entirely, and not a single bivalent is formed. The disturbances in the processes following the meiotic division are also somewhat more pronounced in strong A × strong B than in weak A × weak B hybrids.

An analysis of the variations in strength has been undertaken by Dobzhansky (unpublished). The strong and weak races differ in their geographical distribution. In the region inhabited by race A strength increases rather gradually as one moves from northwest to southeast. British Columbia and Washington are populated chiefly by very weak or weak races, while in Mexico very strong variants are encountered. In race B the geographical regularity is less clear than in race A, although the strongest strains seem to come from the coastal regions of Oregon and Washington, and the weakest from the Sierra Nevada mountains. Strains coming from the same locality may differ in strength rather widely. Thus, both intergroup and intragroup variations are present. The genetic basis of the differences in strength is a rather complex one, genes modifying this character being found in all the chromosomes studied. Crosses between two strains of the same race often produce in the F_2 generation some segregants that are weaker or stronger than either parental strain. Wild populations are evidently quite variable with respect to the genes determining strength.

The importance of the above facts is revealed by observations which suggest that the genes determining strength are similar to, or identical with, the sterility genes. If race A × race B hybrid females are backcrossed to males of one of the parental races, one may obtain, in the first or in the later backcross generations, individuals that have most of the chromosomes of one race but carry one chromosome or a section of a chromosome of the other race. Parts of chromosomes or whole chromosomes of race A may be "transferred" by this method to race B, or vice versa. If the transferred chromosome section is long, or carries powerful sterility genes, the male possessing it may be sterile; other sections do not interfere with fertility to an appreciable extent. Sturtevant and the writer (unpublished) have accomplished a number of such "transfers" of chromosome sections to and from either race. The lines of race A and race B known to carry certain chromosome parts of the opposite race may then be tested for strength with the aid of the same method that is used for testing the wild strains coming from nature, i.e., the size of the testes is determined in the F_1 males from the crosses race B ♀ × race A ♂. Experiments of this type conducted by the writer have thus far given quite consistent results: the strength of a line of race A or of race B is decreased by the introduction of chromosomes or chromosome sections of the opposite race.

It has been shown that the sterility of the hybrids between race A and race B is due to the effects of a complex of sterility genes. Now it is known in addition that, by interracial crossing, this complex can be dismembered into elements, and, what is especially important, these elements prove to have the same action as the genes determining the differences in strength between the different lines of the same race. The gap between the interracial differences causing the sterility of hybrids and the intraracial variations is thus bridged. The implications are rather obvious. Within a race we find the genetic elements, the building stones, from which a mechanism causing hybrid sterility may, theoretically, be built. As the situation stands now the analysis is, of course, far from complete. We have not yet succeeded in synthesizing two strains producing sterile hybrids from the genetic elements encountered within a race—a feat that is not beyond the range of possibility in theory. Moreover, the variations in "strength" encountered within a race may be interpreted either as the remains of the store of building materials from which the interracial difference had been built in the history of the species, or else as a sign of an occasional breakdown of the separation between the races. The latter interpretation would involve the assumption that race A and race B of *D. pseudoobscura* sometimes produce hybrids in nature, and that through such hybrids some of the genes of race A are transfused into race B, and vice versa. This possibility cannot be entirely excluded at present, although the fact that the distinction between the races has never been found blurred, even in regions where their geographical distributions overlap, argues against it.

STERILITY IN DROSOPHILA VIRILIS AND ITS RELATIVES

An analysis of the sterility in the hybrids of *Drosophila virilis* and the related species or subspecies *D. americana* and *D. texana* has been published by Patterson, Stone, and Griffen (1940). This sterility proved to be in part genic and in part, apparently, chromosomal. The situation as a whole is sufficiently different from that in *D. pseudoobscura*, making it desirable to consider the *D. virilis* case in some detail. *D. virilis*, *D. americana*, and *D. texana* are rather similar but distinguishable both morphologically and physiologically. Some of the morphological differences (i.e., the grey pupa color of *D. virilis* contrasted with the red one in the two others) are determined by single or by few genes accompanied by systems of modifiers. *D. virilis* is probably native in eastern Asia and introduced in North America, while the others appear to be native in the United States. There is an incomplete sexual isolation, and some complications either with the insemination of the eggs or with the viability of the hybrids between the species (cf. p. 271).

The crosses between *Drosophila virilis*, *D. americana*, and *D.*

texana produce hybrids of both sexes; the fertility of these hybrids varies depending upon the strains of the parental species used, but on the whole it is lower than in the pure species. Only a fraction of the hybrid individuals produce offspring, and this offspring is less numerous than in the nonhybrids. Hybrids in the F_2 and in the backcrosses are likewise semisterile. The causation of the semisterility is apparently multiple. The parental species differ in the gene arrangement (cf. Fig. 13 and p. 143); aside from several inversions which by themselves would be expected to produce only a slight loss of fertility, there are differences in the associations of the chromosome limbs. *D. virilis* has five pairs of rod-shaped chromosomes, one of which is the X; in *D. texana* two of the autosomes, the third and the fourth, are associated to form a V-shaped complex; in *D. americana* the second and the third, and the fourth and the X chromosomes are united into two V-shaped chromosomes (Fig. 13). The interspecific hybrids are, hence, translocation heterozygotes. Although the chromosome disjunction in these hybrids has not been examined, it seems very probable that some gametes with duplications and deficiencies for chromosome sections are produced. Such gametes are expected to give rise to inviable offspring, and hence to a partial sterility of the chromosomal type in both sexes. That this factor alone is not sufficient to account for the semisterility is shown by the observation that the *D. virilis* × *D. americana* and the *D. virilis* × *D. texana* hybrids are relatively more fertile if *D. virilis* is used as the male than if it is used as the female parent. This suggests that either genic or plasmatic effects, or both, are contributing causes of the semisterility. Still another factor enters to produce sterility in certain of the backcrosses.

If *Drosophila virilis* females are crossed to *D. texana* males, and the male hybrids are backcrossed to *D. virilis* females, only about 25 percent of the resulting male progeny are fertile; if the initial cross is made using *D. texana* females, some 82 percent of the backcross males are fertile. The two series of crosses may be represented schematically as follows (X^v and X^t, and Y^v and Y^t, being X and Y chromosomes of *D. virilis* and *D. texana* respectively):

P *virilis* ($X^v X^v$) ♀ × *texana* ($X^t Y^t$) ♂   *texana* ($X^t X^t$) ♀ × *virilis* ($X^v Y^v$) ♂

Backcross *virilis* ($X^v X^v$) ♀ × $X^v Y^t$ ♂   *virilis* ($X^v X^v$) ♀ × $X^t Y^v$ ♂

↓   ↓

$X^v Y^t$ males (25% fertile) $X^v Y^v$ males (82.5% fertile)

The backcross males in both series are similar in that they carry the *Drosophila virilis* X chromosome, but in the series represented on the left they have the *D. texana* Y, and in that on the right the *D. virilis* Y chromosome. Since the chromosomes of *D. virilis* and *D. texana* are distinguishable cytologically owing to the inversions and translocations (see above), it has been possible to determine the constitution of the fertile backcross males by examining the chromosomes in their offspring. Patterson, Stone, and Griffen (1940) found that the fertile males with the *D. texana* Y chromosome invariably possess also the second and the fifth chromosomes of the same species. It seems to follow that the Y, second, and fifth chromosomes of *D. texana* carry complementary genes which must be simultaneously present to enable a male to be fertile. Whether a single or several genes in each of these chromosomes are concerned is unknown. The crosses of *D. virilis* and *D. americana* behave like those of *D. virilis* and *D. texana*, except that only 10 percent of the $X^v Y^a$ backcross males are fertile. With the aid of a cytological examination it has been found that here too a fertile male with a *D. americana* Y chromosome must carry the second and the fifth chromosomes of the same species. In the backcross females, the simultaneous presence of the second and the fifth chromosomes of *D. texana* or *D. americana* is not essential for fertility.

MATERNAL EFFECTS IN HYBRIDS

Differences in the outcome of the reciprocal crosses between the same two species are not rare. For example, the cross *Drosophila melanogaster* ♀ × *D. simulans* ♂ gives females but not males, while the reciprocal one produces male, but few or no female, hybrids (Sturtevant 1920–21). Federley (1929) found that the females from the cross *Chaerocampa elpenor* ♀ × *Metopsilus porcellus* ♂ have a combination of the X chromosome of the latter and the Y chromosome of the former species which acts as a lethal; the reciprocal cross gives rise to viable females that carry the X of *C. elpenor* and the Y of *M. porcellus*. A hybrid inherits its chromosomes from both parents, but its cytoplasm supposedly from the mother only. Interactions between the same chromosome complement and different cytoplasms may give dissimilar results. It must be kept in mind, however, that the characteristics of the cytoplasm of an egg from which a hybrid develops may be determined by its intrinsic properties, independent of the chromosomes it carries or has carried, or else by the properties of the chromosomes that have been present in the egg before the meiotic divisions and fertilization. The former mechanism is spoken of as cytoplasmic inheritance, while the latter, the predetermination of the cytoplasm by the chromosomes, is known as a maternal effect.

The difference between reciprocal crosses of race A and race B of *Drosophila pseudoobscura* proved to be amenable to analysis. The cross B ♀ × A ♂ produces F_1 hybrid males with small testes, while the F_1 hybrids coming from the cross A ♀ × B ♂ have large testes (Lancefield 1929). Males with small testes have consequently the cytoplasm and the X chromosome of race B and the Y chromosome of race A. Hybrid males with large testes have race A cytoplasm and X chromosome, and race B Y chromosome. Both kinds of males have hybrid autosomes, that is one set from race A and the other from race B. Dobzhansky (1933d, 1935c, 1936b) has studied the size of the testes in males coming from backcrosses of the F_1 hybrid females to males of both parental races, and also in males devoid of Y chromosome. The latter type arises from exceptional eggs that carry no X fertilized by X-bearing spermatozoa. The frequency of the production of such exceptional eggs is usually very low, but it is enhanced by treating females with X-rays. The data are summarized in Table 23.

The conclusions that may be deduced from the data presented in Table 23 are as follows: (1) the testis size among the backcross males is determined exclusively by their chromosomal constitution and is independent of the source of their cytoplasm (compare classes 13 and 16, 14 and 17, 15 and 18); (2) the presence or absence of the Y does not influence the testis size (compare 1 and 5, 2 and 6, 4 and 7); (3) males of the same chromosomal constitution in the F_1 generation and in the backcrosses may differ in testis size (compare 3 and 15 and 18); (4) the backcross males have small testes whenever their X chromosome does not agree with the autosomes in racial origin, and large testes when the chromosomes are racially alike; (5) in F_1 males, small testes are found if hybrid autosomes are present with race B cytoplasm (classes 4, 7, 8), or if race B X chromosome is present together with race A cytoplasm (class 9);

hybrid autosomes in race A cytoplasm give large testes in the presence of race A X chromosome (class 3). The role of the cytoplasm in the production of the differences between reciprocal crosses is evident, but it is likewise evident that the properties of the cytoplasm of an egg are determined by the chromosomes that have been present in the body of the mother in which the egg has developed. We have shown above that the sterility of interracial hybrids in *Drosophila pseudoobscura* is due to the action of comple-

TABLE 23

TESTIS SIZE IN *Drosophila pseudoobscura* MALES OF DIFFERENT CONSTITUTION

NO.	RACE OF THE MOTHER	RACE OF THE FATHER	X CHROMOSOME	Y CHROMOSOME	AUTOSOMES	TESTIS SIZE
1	A	A	A	A	A	large
2	B	B	B	B	B	"
3	A	B	A	B	hybrid	"
4	B	A	B	A	"	small
5	A	A	A	none	A	large
6	B	B	B	"	B	"
7	B	A	B	"	hybrid	small
8	B	A	A	"	"	"
9	A	B	B	"	"	"
10	F₁(A♀ ×B♂)♀	A	A	A	A	large
11	"	A	A	A	hybrid	small
12	"	A	B	A	"	"
13	"	B	B	B	B	large
14	"	B	B	B	hybrid	small
15	"	B	A	B	"	"
16	F₁(B♀ ×A♂)♀	B	B	B	B	large
17	"	B	B	B	hybrid	small
18	"	B	A	B	"	"
19	"	A	A	none	A or hybrid	large or small
20	F₁(A♀ ×B♂)♀	A	A	"	"	"

mentary genes contributed by the parental races. It is possible that our conclusions might be better formulated thus: the sterility of the hyrids in question is due to interactions between the chromosomal constitution of the hybrid itself and the properties of the cytoplasm of the egg from which it develops, always keeping in mind that the properties of the latter are determined by the chromosomal constitution of the mother.

Another kind of maternal effect is observed in the progenies from backcrosses of F₁ hybrid females to males of the parental races of

D. pseudoobscura. Deviations from the normal 1:1 sex ratio in these progenies have been recorded by Lancefield (1929) and Sturtevant (1937b); Dobzhansky and Sturtevant have found in addition that the general viability of the backcross individuals is very low in comparison both with the pure races and with the F_1 hybrids. Since a majority of the offspring of the backcrosses have various mixtures of the chromosomes of race A and race B, it was natural to suppose that their decreased vitality is due to the formation of unfavorable recombinations of genes of the parental races. Although this explanation is still not excluded, further studies have shown that it is by no means adequate to account for the whole situation. A sample of the actual data (unpublished) will illustrate the essential features of the phenomenon.

Race A females homozygous for the sex-linked recessive genes beaded (*bd*), yellow (*y*), short (*s*), the dominant Bare (*Ba*, second chromosome), and the recessive purple (*pr*, third chromosome) were crossed to race B males homozygous for the recessive orange (*or*, third chromosome) and heterozygous for the dominant Curly (*Cy*, fourth chromosome). In accordance with expectation, the following results were obtained in the F_1 generation:

$$
\begin{array}{llll}
Ba\,♀\,♀ & 432 \\
Ba\,Cy\,♀\,♀ & 413
\end{array} \Big\} 845
\qquad
\begin{array}{llll}
bd\;y\;s\;Ba\,♂\,♂ & 401 \\
bd\;y\;s\;Ba\,Cy\,♂\,♂ & 385
\end{array} \Big\} 786
$$

Males are somewhat less numerous than females, which is undoubtedly the result of a slight decrease of the viability of the former due to the sex-linked recessives *bd*, *y*, and *s*. The *Ba Cy* hybrid females were backcrossed to race A males homozygous for purple (*pr*) and orange (*or*). It may be noted that the females used have every chromosome, except the small fifth, marked with at least one mutant gene. Therefore in the backcross progeny the genetic constitution of every male may be ascertained from its appearance. Disregarding the crossing over in the X and in the third chromosomes, sixteen classes of males must appear in equal numbers, carrying the combinations of the chromosomes of race A and race B represented diagrammatically in Figs. 20 and 21. Only eight classes of females are distinguishable (since, according to the setting of the experiment, the sex-linked recessive genes do not manifest themselves in the female progeny). The results actually obtained are summarized in Table 24; the column marked "class number" refers to the diagrams in Fig. 20.

Table 24 shows that males are much more scarce than females, and the representatives of the different classes are far from being equally numerous. The number of eggs deposited by an F_1 hybrid female is of the same order of magnitude as in the pure races; and yet the yield of the adult backcross individuals per mother is very

TABLE 24

(*Explanation in Text*)

CLASS NUMBER	MALES		FEMALES	
	Phenotype	Observed	Phenotype	Observed
1	bd y s Ba pr	2	Ba pr	41
2	bd y s Ba pr Cy	—	Ba pr Cy	32
3	bd y s Ba or	4	Ba or	92
4	bd y s pr	7	pr	190
5	bd y s Ba or Cy	1	Ba or Cy	89
6	bd y s pr Cy	7	pr Cy	372
7	bd y s or	14	or	140
8	bd y s or Cy	13	or Cy	336
9	or Cy	147		
10	or	143		
11	pr Cy	62		
12	Ba or Cy	17		
13	pr	58		
14	Ba or	21		
15	Ba pr Cy	14		
16	Ba pr	6		
Crossovers		121	Crossovers	311
Total		637	Total	1603

small. The conclusion follows that some, perhaps a majority, of the backcross individuals die, and, as shown by the results presented in Table 24, the mortality of the representatives of the different classes is selective. An important, and at first sight paradoxical, feature is that class 1 of the males, which consists of individuals having only race A chromosomes, is almost obliterated. If the decrease in viability were due to mixing the chromosomes of the two races in one individual, class 1 would be expected to be the most viable one.

A closer examination of Table 24 shows that the number of individuals of a given class recovered in this backcross is inversely proportional to the number of mutant genes this class carries. All the classes carrying *bd, y,* and *s* are much decreased in frequency. The gene *Ba* also depresses the viability greatly, *pr* follows next, while *or* and *Cy* are relatively innocuous. And yet, the same mutant genes produce no disastrous effects on viability in the pure races and in the F_1 hybrids. The results may be accounted for only if one assumes that the eggs deposited by F_1 hybrid females give rise to individuals that are afflicted with a general constitutional weakness (maternal effect); mutant genes that do not impair greatly the viability of the pure races or of F_1 hybrids act as semilethals in individuals developing from the eggs deposited by hybrid females. To test the above assumption, experiments were so arranged that the class of backcross progeny which is identical in constitution with race A (corresponding to class 1 in Table 24) was free from mutant genes, and the class having hybrid autosomes (corresponding to 9 in Table 24) manifested several mutants. The result was the opposite of that observed in the first experiment: class 9 was depressed in frequency more than class 1.

The decreased viability of the offspring of F_1 hybrid females makes the latter in effect semisterile, and thus entails an intensification of the isolation between the parental species. The degree of the semisterility depends upon the strains used in making the cross; populations of *Drosophila pseudoobscura* carry genetic factors modifying the maternal effects in the hybrids. Dr. G. Gottschewski and the writer (unpublished) found that if certain strains are used the backcross progeny are destroyed entirely. The two race A strains, one homozygous for the sex-linked recessives beaded, yellow, vermilion, singed, and short (*bd y v sn s*), and the other for beaded, miniature, snapt, and sepia (*by m sp se*), are especially remarkable. The strain *bd y v sn s* has been crossed to a wild B race strain (Seattle-6), and also to a race B strain homozygous for the sex-linked gene scutellar. The reciprocal crosses A ♀ × B ♂ and B ♀ × A ♂ have been made in each case, and numerous F_1 hybrids of an apparently good viability were obtained. And yet if the hybrid females are backcrossed to *bd y v sn s* and *bd m sp se* males, respectively, no adult offspring at all are obtained. The F_1 females deposit

numerous eggs some of which give rise to young larvae, but none of
the latter develop to the adult stage. The genetic constitution of the
mothers is evidently such that the eggs produced are virtually inviable when fertilized by spermatozoa of certain males. The same
mothers produce, however, fairly viable offspring when crossed to
males from certain other strains (the race A strain "Texas," for
example).

The outcome of the cross is determined, therefore, by the genetic
constitution of the maternal grandparents, as well as by that of the
father. The eggs of a hybrid female give rise to a weak progeny, but
the degree of weakness may vary depending upon the kind of spermatozoa that fertilize the eggs. The nature of the differences between
the strains of *D. pseudoobscura* that determine the extent of the
deleterious maternal effects in the backcross progenies is unknown,
since the analysis has not been completed. The present hypothesis,
subject to verification in further tests, is that these differences are
due to the genes these strains carry. If this proves to be the case, one
can visualize how an evolutionary change can occur which trans-
forms a pair of species giving rise to hybrids that are sterile in one
sex and fertile in the other to a condition when hybrids of both
sexes will be sterile. Crosses between most strains of race A and
race B of *D. pseudoobscura* give, as we know, sterile males and
fertile females in the F_1 generation. If, however, race A should
uniformly acquire the genetic constitution now present in the
bd y v sn s strain, and race B that present in the Seattle-6 and
scutellar strains, the F_1 hybrid females would be sterile when backcrossed to the race A parents.

Crosses of *Drosophila pseudoobscura* to *D. miranda* produce hybrid males that have very small testes and are completely sterile.
The hybrid females fertilized by males of either parental species
deposit numerous and normal-appearing eggs which, as a rule, give
rise to no larvae; only in crosses between certain strains can a very
small number of backcross hybrids be obtained. The work of Kaufmann (1940b) has made it virtually certain that the sterility of the
hybrid females is due to a kind of maternal effect (the strains used
by Kaufmann give sterile hybrid females). The meiotic divisions
in the hybrid eggs display no striking irregularities, although it has
not been possible to ascertain whether the chromosomes in them are

always united in bivalents. At any rate, female pronuclei are formed which, in at least some instances, contain the haploid number of chromosomes. Spermatozoa enter into the eggs and form male pronuclei. Cleavage mitoses are inaugurated, which occasionally proceed as far as the sixteen-cell stage. The polar bodies, which in normal eggs remain at the periphery and soon degenerate, become, however, active in the hybrid eggs. Their chromosomes rapidly multiply, form irregular mitoses, invade the cytoplasm of the egg, and appear there as scattered masses of clumped chromosomes. The eggs finally die.

What combinations of the chromosomes of the parental species are contained in the female pronuclei of hybrid eggs could not be determined. However, Kaufmann (1940) points out that a random distribution of the chromosomes at the hybrid meiosis must produce some pronuclei containing only *Drosophila pseudoobscura* and other pronuclei with only *D. miranda* chromosomes. Since all the eggs of the hybrid females degenerate, causes other than numerical or qualitative irregularities in the chromosome complements must be responsible. The failure of the development regardless of the chromosomal constitution of the zygote indicates that the chromosomes are unable to function normally in the cytoplasm of an egg produced by a hybrid female.

CHROMOSOMAL STERILITY IN SPECIES HYBRIDS

Chromosome pairing at meiosis in a hybrid may take place either between chromosomes of the different parents (allosyndesis), or among those of the same parent (autosyndesis). If the chromosomes fail to find mates of either kind, univalents are formed. In most hybrids the univalents are distributed at random to the poles of the spindle at the first or at the second meiotic division (see above). The resulting gones may contain unequal or, by chance, equal numbers of chromosomes. In either case they are likely to have mixtures of the chromosomes of both parents, and to be deficient for certain genes and carry duplications for others. Gones bearing an entire haploid set of chromosomes of one species and none of those of the other may sometimes be produced, but the greater the number of chromosomes in the parental species, the smaller is the likelihood of such an event. Since deficiencies, duplications, and incongruous mixtures of the chromosomes of different species frequently act as lethals to the zygotes (in animals) or to the haplonts (in plants), hybrids having univalents at meiosis may be sterile.

Chromosomes of different species may fail to pair and to form bivalents owing either to dissimilarities in the gene arrangement or to a genetic constitution of the hybrid which causes physiological derangements in the meiotic processes. It is not an easy matter to determine which of these causes is responsible for the lack of chromosome pairing and the sterility of a given hybrid. The extent of the differences between species in the gene arrangement is known in only very few instances. The sterility of the hybrids between the "races" of *Drosophila pseudoobscura,* the species of the *D. virilis* group, and *D. pseudoobscura* and *D. miranda* is, as shown above, at least partly genic rather than chromosomal, although the parental species in these cases do differ in the gene arrangement. Known or suspected differences in the gene arrangement in a group of species by no means permit the inference that the sterility of the hybrids between these species can be ascribed directly to these differences. Nevertheless, the existence of the chromosomal sterility can be inferred with a reasonable degree of assurance in certain plant hybrids. The principal source of the evidence is, in these cases, the behavior of the allopolyploid hybrids.

Mostly, or only, univalents are formed at meiosis in the diploid hybrids between radish and cabbage (Karpechenko 1927a, b, 1928; cf. Chapter VII). At the meiotic divisions the univalents are distributed at random, and the gones degenerate. A doubling of the chromosome complement gives rise to the allotetraploid *Raphanobrassica,* in which mostly, or only, bivalents are present at meiosis, the disjunction is normal, and the gones contain uniform chromosome complements. The lack of the bivalent formation in the diploid hybrids may be caused either by dissimilarities of the gene arrangement in the chromosomes of radish and cabbage, or by the genetic constitution of the hybrids. What is, however, the most likely explanation of the restoration of the normal bivalent formation in the tetraploid form? The simplest hypothesis is, unquestionably, that no chromosome of radish is sufficiently similar in the gene arrangement to any cabbage chromosome to insure bivalent formation; the presence of the two sets of radish and of the two sets of cabbage chromosomes in the tetraploid *Raphanobrassica* creates, on the other hand, a situation when every chromosome in the nucleus has one and only one partner with an identical gene arrangement. This hypothesis implies, then, that the sterility of the diploid hybrid is chromosomal. One cannot, however, exclude the possibility that the chromosome pairing in the diploid is suppressed by the hybrid genetic constitution, but that the doubling of the chromosome complement entails a physiological change which removes the hindrance to bivalent formation.

There is no doubt that the doubling of the chromosomes does not necessarily induce bivalent formation in hybrids whose sterility is genic. The gene combination the physiological effect of which is a suppression of the chromosome pairing persists unaltered in the diploid as well as in the tetraploid. Thus, in the tetraploid spermatocytes in A $\times$ B hybrids of *Drosophila pseudoobscura* the proportions of bivalents and univalents are no different from those in the adjacent diploid cells; the spermatids arising in the tetraploid sections of the gonad degenerate, and the hybrids are completely sterile (Dobzhansky 1933b, 1934b; cf. p. 308). The gene arrangements in the chromosomes of *D. melanogaster* and *D. simulans* are relatively similar; spermatogenesis and oögenesis in the hybrids between these species are arrested before the advent of the meiotic stages (Kerkis 1933, 1935); the sterility of these hybrids is genic. Triploid females of *D. melanogaster* and diploid males of *D. simulans* give rise to some triploid female hybrids that carry two chromosome sets from the *D. melanogaster* and one set from the *D. simulans* parent. If the sterility of the diploid hybrids were due to a lack of pairing partners among the chromosomes, one might expect that in the triploid the *D. melanogaster* chromosomes would pair and some functional eggs would be produced. Actually, the triploid hybrids are completely sterile (Schultz and Dobzhansky 1933; cf. Kozhevnikov 1933).

Darlington (1928, 1932a, 1937b) has established a rule applicable to many plant hybrids, the substance of which seems paradoxical and inexplicable except in conjunction with the hypothesis of chromosomal sterility. Sterile diploid hybrids with little or no chromosome pairing at meiosis give rise to allopolyploids that are fertile and display mostly or only bivalents at the meiotic division. Contrariwise, the allopolyploids derived from the diploids that have many bivalents show an irregular chromosome pairing and disjunction. The fertility of an allopolyploid is in general inversely proportional to that of its diploid ancestor (cf. Chapter VII). The occurrence of pairing in a diploid hybrid indicates that the gene arrangement in the chromosomes of the parental species is similar enough for some or all chromosomes of one species to find approximate homologues among those of the other. The doubling of the chromosome complement gives rise to a situation in which each chromosome has one exact homologue and two potential mates that are more or less similar to it. In the competition for pairing that arises at meiosis, the pairing of the chromosomes of the same species is interfered with by the presence of the partial homologues among those of the other. Pairing is variable; bivalents, trivalents, quadrivalents, and univalents are formed in proportions that are inconstant from cell to cell; gones with unbalanced chromosome complements are produced; and the hybrid is more or less sterile. Where the chromosomes of the parental species fail to pair in the diploid on account of extensive dissimilarities in the gene arrangement, every chromosome in the allotetraploid has only one mate, with which it can pair with little or no interference from the chromosomes of the other species. Hence, only bivalents are produced, and meiosis is regular.

Where chromosome pairing in a diploid hybrid is suppressed by the genetic constitution rather than by dissimilarities in the gene arrangement, the same suppression should be encountered in the allotetraploid derived from it. Moreover, the greater the suppression in a diploid hybrid of such kind, the greater it will be in the tetraploid. In other words, Darlington's rule is expected not to apply to hybrids whose sterility is genic. It does not. In weak A × weak B hybrids of *Drosophila pseudoobscura*, only bivalents are present in the diploid spermatocytes, and in the tetraploid ones bivalents, quadrivalents, and some trivalents and univalents are found. Strong A × strong B crosses show little or no chromosome pairing either in diploid or in tetraploid spermatocytes.

A hybrid whose behavior seems difficult to account for is *Primula verticillata* × *P. floribunda* (= *P. Kewensis*). According to Newton and Pellew (1929) and Upcott (1939), the diploid has mostly bivalents, and yet it is nearly sterile; the tetraploid has again bivalents (with an occasional quadrivalent) and is fertile, although not quite true breeding. The hypothesis of chromosomal sterility still furnishes the most plausible explanation of this exceptional behavior. The gene arrangements in the chromosomes of *P. verticillata* and *P. floribunda* are probably different, but not different enough to prevent their pairing in the diploid hybrid. In the tetraploid hybrid each chromosome has a homologue with an exactly similar gene arrangement, and also two partial homologues. Due to competition for pairing, the complete homologues will unite to form bivalents more frequently than the partial ones. In a few cells, quadrivalents may however arise owing to the chance occurrence of pairing between parts of chromosomes of the two species. Now, the meiotic disjunction in the tetraploid will give rise to gones most of which will contain a full haploid set of *verticillata* and a full set of *floribunda chromosomes*. The gones formed in the diploid will have equal numbers of chromosomes, but a majority of them will be mixtures, including some of *verticillata* and some of *floribunda*. Gones with a pure complement of one species will sometimes also be produced, but the proportion of such gones will be low. If gones with mixtures of the chromosomes of the parental species are eliminated, the hybrid will be sterile. Another hybrid the sterility of which appears to have a similar basis is that of *Saxifraga adscendens* × *S. tridactylites* (Drygalski 1935).

The species whose origin through allopolyploidy is known, or suspected, show as a rule only bivalents at meiosis; exceptions are known but they are on the whole rare. And yet in an allopolyploid most genes must be supposed to be represented four (tetraploid) or more times. The formation of multivalent chromosome associations is prevented by the competition for pairing: every chromosome is more likely to pair with its complete homologue than with a partial one.

Through the occurrence of parthenogenesis the egg of a polyploid may develop and give rise to an organism that is haploid with respect to its progenitor. But if the progenitor is itself a polyploid, the "haploid" derived from it has two or more sets of chromosomes that are in part homologous. Thus, Gaines and Aase (1926) have obtained a haploid from the wheat *Triticum compactum;* since *T.*

compactum is a hexaploid, the "haploid" plant has in reality three sets of seven chromosomes each. None of the chromosomes in such a haploid has an exact homologue, but as many as three bivalents may be formed at meiosis, evidently due to the association of partly homologous chromosomes from different sets. From 5 to 12 bivalents have been observed by Jorgensen (1928) in the "haploid" derived from the hexaploid species *Solanum nigrum* ($2n = 72$, basic number 12). Similar observations have been made by Chipman and Goodspeed (1927) and Lammerts (1934b) in the haploid *Nicotiana tabacum* ($2n = 48$, basic number 12), and by Buxton and Darlington (1932) in the haploid *Digitalis mertonensis* ($2n = 112$, basic number 7). Some chromosome pairing may be observed also in haploids derived from species that are not suspected of being polyploids (Emerson 1929, Catcheside 1932). Unless a nonhomologous pairing like that discovered in maize by McClintock (1933) is here involved, these cases must be due to the presence of homologous segments in the different chromosomes of the same diploid set, similar to the "repeat" segments in the chromosomes of *Drosophila* (Bridges 1935; cf. Chapter IV).

In hybrids between polyploid and diploid species, or in those between polyploid ones, several chromosome sets of different origin are brought together. Such hybrids may show at meiosis only bivalents, or both bivalents and univalents, or only univalents. Pairing may take place between chromosomes of different parents (allosyndesis) or between those of the same parent (autosyndesis). As pointed out in Chapter VII, it is not always easy to determine the origin of the bivalents in a particular hybrid, but in some favorable objects the discrimination between the alternatives is possible. Autosyndetic pairing is what interests us at present, since its occurrence indicates a partial homology between chromosomes of the same species. The cross between two species of poppy, *Papaver nudicaule* ($n = 7$) and *P. striatocarpum* ($n = 35$), gives a fertile hybrid with 42 chromosomes that unite to form 21 bivalents at meiosis (Ljungdahl 1924). We are compelled to conclude that 7 chromosomes of *nudicaule* have paired with 7 of *striatocarpum*, and that the remaining 28 chromosomes of the latter species have formed 14 more bivalents. Since in the pure *P. striatocarpum* ($2n = 70$) 35 bivalents and no quadrivalents or higher associations are reported at meiosis, the pairing of the partially homologous chromosomes must be prevented by the competition of the complete homologues. In the hybrid, where complete homologues are absent, the partial homology asserts itself in the form of pairing.

Autosyndetic pairing is found also in the hybrid *Digitalis lutea* (n = 48) × *D. micrantha* (n = 24), which is described as absolutely sterile despite the presence of 36 bivalents and no univalents at meiosis (Haase-Bessel 1921). The sterility is here caused probably by the same mechanism as that in the diploid *Primula Kewensis*. A partial autosyndesis is observed in the hybrids between diploid and octoploid strawberries (Yarnell 1931), and also in those between species of wheats (Kihara and Nishiyama 1930, Kihara and Lilienfeld 1932, Liljefors 1936), *Crepis biennis* × *C. setosa* (Collins, Hollingshead and Avery 1929), species of violets (J. Clausen 1931a), and species of cotton (Skovsted 1935).

It may be noted that all the hybrids whose sterility is supposed to be chromosomal belong to the plant kingdom. This suggests that hybrid sterility is usually chromosomal in plants and genic in animals, but so broad a generalization is decidedly premature at present. The apparent prevalence of chromosomal sterility among plants may be due simply to the fact that it has been inferred from observations on fertile allopolyploids. Allopolyploids are at least rare in animals, for reasons discussed in Chapter VII. In general, the discrimination between chromosomal and genic sterility is as yet possible in so few hybrids that any statistical treatment of the data would rest on too insecure a foundation.*

* P. Hertwig (1936) in her book on species hybrids in animals distinguishes between "Hemmungssterilität" and "Konjugationssterilität," which correspond to our genic and chromosomal sterility. She places all hybrids in which a failure of chromosome pairing is observed (except the A × B hybrids in *Drosophila pseudoobscura*) in the latter category. The validity of this classification is doubtful, since disturbances of the meiotic pairing can be produced by gene action as well as by differences in gene arrangements.

X: PATTERNS OF EVOLUTION

INTRODUCTION

THE PROCEDURE of science is to dismember natural phenomena into their constituent parts, and, after duly examining the parts and assaying their properties, to reconstruct the original order. It is hoped that by so doing a more communicable, if not a more profound, insight into the nature of things may be gained than it is possible to secure with the aid of other than scientific methods. Some scientists obtain the greatest satisfaction from analysis and examination of parts, and others from synthesis of the whole from the parts; the former are attracted by the diversity and the latter by the unity of things. In the field of evolution, some investigators strive to discover the most widespread mechanisms of evolutionary changes, and others to detect the peculiarities of the evolutionary patterns in the separate lines of descent. It behooves us to recognize the legitimacy of both methods of approach.

Gene mutation, chromosome changes, restriction of the population size, natural selection, and development of isolating mechanisms are the known common denominators of many, if not all, evolutionary histories. Different phylogenetic lines vary, however, in that one or the other of these evolutionary agents may become limiting at different stages of the process. Polyploidy, self-fertilization, apogamy, and asexual reproduction create very special conditions, to which some references have been made in the foregoing chapters. In the present chapter the subject will be considered more systematically.

SELECTION IN POPULATIONS OF DIFFERENT SIZES

As shown by Wright (cf. Chapter V), gene frequencies in small populations do not remain constant even in the absence of mutation and selection. They oscillate within limits that are inversely correlated with the population number, N, and a fraction of the unfixed genes equal to $1/2N$ is eliminated in every generation because some alleles are lost while others reach the fixation level. It is a matter of chance which alleles are lost and which reach fixation. On the other hand, selection is intrinsically opposed to random variations in gene frequencies; it tends toward fixation of alleles possessing the highest adaptive values. The processes of the genetic drift and of selection are, consequently, pitted against each other, and the outcome in any one population depends upon the relative strength of the opposing forces.

The interrelations of selection and the genetic drift have been examined in a series of papers by Wright (1931a, 1940a, b, and others). His mathematical arguments are too abstruse to be presented here, but his conclusions are simple enough. The smaller the effective population size, the greater are random variations in gene frequencies, and the less effective becomes selection pressure. In small populations, alleles most favored by selection may be lost and the less favored ones may reach fixation. Evolutionary changes may at times proceed against the selection pressure. In very large populations, even very small selective advantages and disadvantages will eventually be effective; but a more rigorous selection must be applied to overcome the genetic drift in small populations.

The relations between population size and selection intensity are illustrated in the diagrams in Fig. 22. In these diagrams the abscissae indicate the gene frequencies from o (loss) to 1 (fixation). The ordinates may be interpreted in any one of the three following ways. First, we may consider the fate of the different variable genes in a single population, for natural populations may vary with respect to many genes. Some of these genes may reach fixation, others may be lost, and still others may remain unfixed, that is to say, they are represented by two or more alleles with different frequencies $(0 < q < 1)$. The ordinates in the diagrams indicate, then, the frequencies of the different gene frequencies in a population. Second, one may follow the fate of the same gene in different populations, for example, in the subgroups of the same species, that is to say, in the isolated colonies into which the species is broken up. The ordinates in Fig. 22 refer then to the frequencies of the subgroups in which a given gene frequency is reached. Third, the ordinates

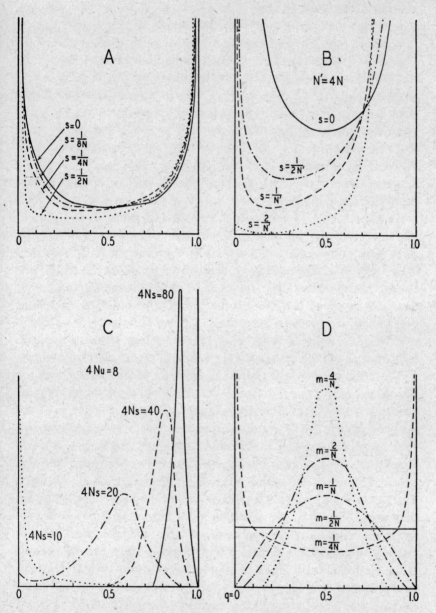

FIG. 22. Distribution of gene frequencies in populations of different size under different selection, mutation, and migration pressures. Further explanation in text. (From Wright.)

may be interpreted to show how often, in the long run, any one gene comes to possess a given frequency.

In small populations. (Fig. 22A) the gene frequency curves are U-shaped. This means that in such populations a majority of the variable genes are either fixed or lost most of the time; in a majority of the colonies into which a species may be subdivided any given gene is either totally absent, or else present to the exclusion of all but one of its possible alleles (cf. p. 168). The curves show that the effectiveness of selection is very low in small populations. With selection coefficients of the order $s = 1/8N$ to $s = 1/2N$, the shape of the curves is little modified. Genes are lost or fixed at random, with little reference to the selection pressure. Fig. 22B represents the action of a selection of the same absolute intensity as in Fig. 22A, but in a population that is four times larger ($N' = 4N$). Here a selection of the order $s = 2/N'$ is rather effective; the curve is no longer U-shaped but has a definite maximum at the right, indicating that the gene alleles favored by selection mostly reach fixation and supplant the less favored ones. The equation describing this family of curves is, according to Wright (1931a), $y = Ce^{4Nsq} q^{-1} (1-q)^{-1}$, where e is the base of natural logarithms, q the gene frequency, s the selection coefficient, and N the population number.

The interaction of the mutation pressure with selection and the population size factor presents naturally an even more complex problem. Under certain conditions, namely, if the selection pressure is of the same order of magnitude as the mutation rate, and both are very small, the random variations of the gene frequencies in small populations become most important. The curve of the gene frequencies is U-shaped, indicating that gene alleles are likely to reach fixation or loss largely irrespective of the mutation and selection pressures. Mutation and selection rates that may be regarded as small are such as make the products $4Nu$ and $4Ns$ smaller than unity. The greater the mutation and selection pressures, the greater is their effectiveness. An example borrowed from Wright (1931a) is reproduced in Fig. 22C. It refers to a population of an intermediate size with a moderate mutation rate ($4Nu = 8$) opposed by a selection of varying intensity. With selection of the order $4Ns = 10$, the mutation pressure gets the upper hand. The allele favored by selection is mostly lost. A doubling of the selection intensity ($4Ns = 20$) changes the situation very appreciably. The gene frequencies fluctuate over a great range of values. In a species segregated into numerous isolated subgroups this means a great differentiation of the species population into local races, some of which will possess characteristics favored by selection and others the relatively unfavorable ones. With a selection becoming more stringent ($4Ns = 40$ and $4Ns = 80$), the amplitude of variation is gradually restricted, the gene frequencies being kept within rather narrow limits centered upon the equilibrium values. The equation describing the curves is $y = Ce^{4Nsq} q^{-1} (1-q)^{4Nu-1}$, where u is the mutation pressure.

The biologically highly significant corollary of the above analysis is that a species, broken up into isolated colonies, may differentiate mainly as a result of the restriction of the population size in these colonies. Even if the environment is homogeneous for all the colonies, and selection and mutation rates are the same and the initial composition of the populations identical, a sufficient lapse of time will bring about a differentiation. It must be stressed that the differentiation need not, theoretically, be of an adaptive kind. The latter point, however, must be much qualified by the consideration that in practice the separate colonies are exposed to a variety of environments. Although in the abstract the differentiation may be pictured as taking place under the influence of the restriction of the population size alone, or under the influence of the selection alone, in nature the process is going on because of both these factors, one or the other gaining the upper hand, probably only temporarily. The genetic equilibrium in a living species population seems to be a delicately balanced system which can be modified by a number of agents.

The problem of the subdivision of the species population into colonies has already been discussed in Chapter V, and the meager observational evidence bearing on it has been reviewed there. It remains now only to point out that the genetic differentiation of the populations in the colonies, by whichever factors it may be caused, is counteracted by migration, that is, by the interchange of individuals between the colonies. A complete isolation of colonies of one species from each other is probably a rather exceptional condition in nature. Whether the colonies are isolated geographically (which is probably the commonest method) or in any other way (for instance by the difference in the breeding seasons), a certain number of individuals from one colony is likely to pass to the adjacent one and to join its breeding population. If the gene frequencies in the colonies are different, this migration pressure will evidently tend to decrease and eventually to level the difference. The racial differentiation in the semi-isolated colonies can therefore proceed only so long as the factors provoking it are more effective than the opposing migration pressure.

How large the migration pressure may be without annulment of the genetic differentiation in semi-isolated colonies has been studied mathematically by Wright (1931a). Let the frequency of a certain gene in the species population as a whole be 50 percent ($q = 0.5$); the species is broken up into semi-isolated colonies, each exchanging the proportion m of its population with a random sample of the population of the species as a whole. With $m = 0$ (that is, isolation being complete), the gene frequency in the separate colonies will eventually become different, q reaching zero in some and unity in other colonies. A similar result is accomplished with m = 1/4N, as shown by the U-shaped curve in Fig. 22D. With $m = 1/2N$, a critical value for the migration coefficient is reached, since above this the random fixation or loss of the gene alleles in the separate colonies is unlikely. The value of 1/2N is a very low one, for it means an exchange of a single breeding individual every other generation. Wright points out, however, that an exchange between a colony and a random sample of the species population as a whole is only a rather theoretical situation, and that in practice migration occurs almost entirely between adjacent colonies. In a widely distributed species, subdivided into very many local populations, migration coefficients even greater than 1/2N will permit a considerable drifting apart of the genetic composition in the subgroups.

PROGRESSIVE EVOLUTION

As pointed out in Chapter I, genetic studies are confined to microevolutionary changes, that is, to alterations in the composition of populations observable within a human lifetime. Inferences regarding macroevolution which may be drawn from genetic data are of necessity extrapolations. Nevertheless, a geneticist can hardly eschew trying to sketch some sort of a general picture of evolution, the more so since Goldschmidt (1940) published his challenging theory of systemic mutations.

Wright (1932) has devised a symbolic picture of the field of gene combinations which may serve as an aid in arriving at clear-cut statements of evolutionary problems. In an organism possessing 1,000 genes each capable of producing 10 alleles, the number of potentially possible combinations is 10^{1000}. These combinations constitute the "field" within which evolutionary changes can be enacted. The adaptive values of the different combinations are, of course, not alike. Some, probably a vast majority, are discordant and unfit for survival, while others are suitable for occupation of different ecological niches in various environments. Related gene combinations which differ in only a few genes tend, on the whole, to be similar in adaptive value. If, then, the field of the possible gene combinations is graded with respect to the adaptive value, we may find numerous "adaptive peaks" separated by "valleys." The "peaks" are the groups of related gene combinations that make their carriers fit for survival in a given environment; the "valleys" are the more or less unfavorable combinations. Each living species or race may be thought of as occupying one of the available peaks in the field of gene combinations. The evolutionary possibilities are twofold. First, a change in the environment may make the old genotypes less fit than they were before. Symbolically we may say that the "field" has changed, some of the old peaks have been leveled off, and some of the old valleys or pits have risen to become peaks. The species may either become extinct, or it may reconstruct its genotype to arrive at the gene combinations that represent the new "peaks." The second type of evolution is for a species to find its way from one of the adaptive peaks to the others in the available field, which may be conceived of as remaining relatively constant in its general relief.

The entire field of the potentially possible gene combinations is by no means immediately available to the species. Some gene combinations have never been formed and tried out—this is obvious from the fact that the number of possible combinations far exceeds the number of individuals in any species or group of species. There are in the environment unoccupied ecological niches as well as niches whose occupants are not in a perfect harmony with their surroundings. The validity of the foregoing statements is rather obvious on a priori grounds—it means essentially nothing more than that the existing world is not the best of all possible ones. A proof is furnished by the rapid spread of many species of animals and plants introduced from foreign countries. The ability of such invaders not only to take root in a foreign soil but sometimes to displace the native species means that before the invader's arrival there had existed either an empty ecological niche or a niche whose occupant was less efficient than the invader. Man-made changes in the environment have led to the extinction of many "wild" species and to the manifold increase in populations of other species to the point of their becoming pests, weeds, or commensals. The species that died out were evidently unable to effect the necessary readjustment rapidly enough, while those that spread either evolved new adaptive genotypes or else happened to be "pre-adapted" to conditions created by man. The availability of an ecological niche does not in itself insure occupation by an organism (Turesson 1931, cf. p. 200). There is no obvious reason why mammals could not have existed in the environment of the Palaeozoic time, but actually they did not appear until the close of the Mesozoic era. What prevents or postpones the formation of certain adaptive gene combinations?

Here one must emphasize a very important point. It is known (Chapter III) that species, genera, and higher groups differ in large numbers of genes. Moreover, the genes are organized into genotypic systems, and the adaptive value is a property of the system as such rather than of the constituent genes. Evolutionary changes involve not merely additions and subtractions of genes, but development and integration of gene systems. Hence, a shift from one adaptive peak to another, which may be even higher than the first, may require a thorough rebuilding of the genotype. The difficulty of this process appears to be that the stages intermediate between the two or more adaptive gene systems may represent unbalanced genotypes. Adaptive peaks may be separated by adaptive valleys (Fig. 23), and transition from peak to peak may require a trial and error mechanism on a grand scale which would enable the species to "explore" the region around its own adaptive peak in order finally to encounter gradients leading toward the other peaks in the field. This difficulty in a neo-Darwinian conception of evolution has been realized by many biologists for some time; to Goldschmidt it appears insuperable.

Let us consider first the evolutionary possibilities of a very large undivided species (Fig. 23 A, B, C), in which the effective population is such that either the products 4Nu and 4Ns are much larger than unity, or the exchange of individuals between the colonies is so rapid that no isolation obtains. In such a species, each gene ultimately reaches an equilibrium frequency determined by the interaction of the mutation and the selection pressures. An increase of mutation or a relaxation of selection increases the variance in a nonadaptive fashion. The field occupied by the species (Fig. 23A) spreads along the slopes of its adaptive peak. If the spread is sufficiently great, the species may find its way to a neighboring adaptive peak and occupy it as well. Any new favorable mutations that may occur will be used to increase the height of the existing adaptive peak. A decrease of the mutation rate, or an increase in the stringency of selection (Fig. 23B), will force the species to withdraw to the highest level of its adaptive peak. The variability is reduced, but the average adaptive level of the individuals is increased. The possibility of a progressive evolution is curtailed, except through mutations that may be favorable at the very start. Since such mutations are probably very rare, this condition leads to an extreme specialization which may prove fatal if the environment changes.

A change in the environment provokes an alteration of the relief of the adaptive field. The relative elevations of the peaks and valleys may change, or the location of the peaks may shift in any direction (Fig. 23C). In extreme cases the adaptive peak may, figuratively speaking, escape from under the species, which may be left in a valley instead. To escape extinction, an evolutionary change may become essential. A species with a large variable population will probably undergo a reconstruction consonant with the new demands of the environment, the genes will gradually reach new equilibrium values, and the new adaptive peak thus arrived at may prove to be higher than the old one.

A restriction of the population size which renders the breeding population very small (4Nu and 4Ns less than unity, Fig. 23D) leads to a depletion of the supply of the hereditary variability, and to fixation of genes more or less irrespective of their adaptive values. The part of the field occupied by the species is much reduced and the adaptive peak may be abandoned. This is a way to extinction. With an intermediate population size (Fig. 23E), the effect is about the same as with a relaxation of selection or increase of mutation in a large population; the species begins to wander on the slopes of the adaptive peak, and may. find a gradient leading

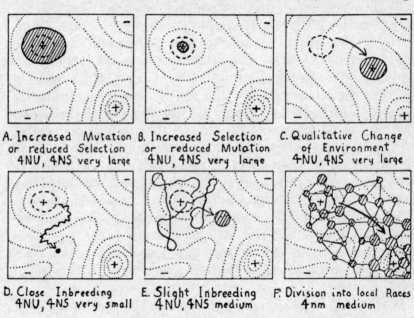

A. Increased Mutation or reduced Selection 4NU, 4NS very large

B. Increased Selection or reduced Mutation 4NU, 4NS very large

C. Qualitative Change of Environment 4NU, 4NS very large

D. Close Inbreeding 4NU, 4NS very small

E. Slight Inbreeding 4NU, 4NS medium

F. Division into local Races 4nm medium

Fig. 23. Fate of populations of different size and under different conditions in the "field" of gene combinations. Further explanation in text. (From Wright.)

to a new one. The important difference is that a large population continues to occupy its old peak as well, while a smaller one moves in a body. The chance of extinction is obviously greater in the latter case, which consequently is unfavorable for evolution.

As pointed out by Wright (1931a, 1932, 1940a, b), conditions most favorable for progressive evolution seem to obtain in a species subdivided into a large number of local populations at least some of which have medium or small effective sizes (Fig. 23F). The behavior of such populations, considered separately, may be similar to that shown in Figs. 23D and E, that is, some or most of them may drift off too far from the adaptive peak and face extinction. In some of the populations the store of the variability may be depleted, with the result that only a limited number of gene combinations will occur, while in others the variability may remain intact. Different gene combinations may become established in different colonies. Compared to a large undivided species, the intrapopulational variability will be on the average lower, but, because the separate local populations drift apart, the total variability of the species as such will be high. Perhaps the most important feature is that gene combinations whose adaptive value is somewhat lower than the average of the whole species may be temporarily preserved in some of the colonies, rather than eliminated as they would be in an undivided species. Most of these denizens of the slopes of their adaptive peaks will eventually drift down into the valleys and be lost, but perhaps a small minority may conceivably encounter a gradient leading to a different peak. Once that has happened, the population may climb the new peak relatively rapidly, increase in numbers, and either supplant the old species, or, more likely, form a new one that owes its allegiance to the new peak. Natural selection will deal here not only with individuals of the same population (intragroup selection) but also, and perhaps to a greater extent, with colonies as units (intergroup selection). In case of an environmental change, the colony first reaching the vicinity of the new adaptive peak will obviously have the best chance of being the victorious one. Here, then, conditions are given both for differentiation of a single species into derived ones, and for a movement of the species as a whole to a new status. At any one time the average adaptive level of a species broken up into small populations is liable to be lower than that of a large undivided one; evolutionary plasticity must be purchased at the price of sacrificing some adaptive uniformity (cf. Chapter V).

A superficial observer is prone to assume that a species which is common, widespread, and displays a great variability within the population of every locality is in the throes of evolutionary change and is about to produce a crop of evolutionary novelties. This is not necessarily true; the forms of life which have been successful to the extent of becoming the dominant species densely occupying unbroken expanses of territory today may not be the inheritors of the world of tomorrow. Systematists are inclined to regard the geographical differentiation of a species into local races, rather than a high intrapopulational variability, as the precursor of the formation of new species. A thorough examination of the evolutionary patterns in different groups of animals and plants in the light of available data on their ecology, breeding behavior, and especially on the effective population sizes, would seem to be a most promising task for modern systematists. Unfortunately, we are at present in possession of only scattered and disconnected observations of this type, which are, nevertheless, highly suggestive. It appears that, at least in the temperate and subtropical zones, the maximum diversity of species and races of land forms is found usually in mountainous countries rather than on the plains (for example, Kinsey 1937a). Territories with a complex topography frequently prove to be the cradles in which the variety of forms of a given group of organisms has developed (cf. Vavilov 1928 and other works). Anyone who has observed animals and plants in mountains and deserts can hardly fail to be impressed with the extraordinary patchiness of their distributions and the frequently obvious smallness of their colonies. It seems very probable that in such colonies new gene combinations could be formed, established, and tried out. The great variety of environmental conditions in topographically complex territories furnishes, of course, a further stimulus to evolutionary changes.

Dr. E. Mayr informs me that some differences in the kind of speciation observed in various groups of birds may be correlated with their breeding behavior. Many species of geese are highly differentiated into local races and form complex "Rassenkreise"; some species of ducks, for example, the mallard *Anas boschas*, tend to be geographically undifferentiated. The data on migratory behavior show that geese return faithfully to the localities in which they have been born or have bred in previous years; in ducks the attachment to a territory is less pronounced, and males and females form pairs in their winter quarters sometimes regardless of their geographical origin. The breeding behavior of geese would, therefore, tend to make small, and that of ducks to make large, effective population sizes. Among ladybird beetles (*Coccinellidae*) certain species which are common, widespread, and gregarious during hibernation show a high intrapopulational but a limited geographical variability; the reverse is observed in many species which are restricted to definite habitats and do not assemble in large numbers in the same place for hibernation.

Certain generalizations arrived at by palaeontologists should be seriously pondered by geneticists. The fossil record indicates that the tempo of evolution within a phyletic line is not uniform in time: periods of an explosive proliferation of new forms are succeeded by a more gradual development. A circumstance that is most irksome to a student of phylogenetic histories is that major evolutionary advances, the first appearances of new families, orders, and classes, seem to occur suddenly, with few or no intermediates between the new groups and their putative ancestors being preserved as fossils. The "missing links" are, indeed, seldom found. Schindewolf (1936), in his brilliant and provocative discussion of the bearing of palaeontological findings on theories of evolution, stresses this sudden emergence of the radically new organic forms and infers that evolution takes place in part by what seems to correspond to Goldschmidt's systematic mutations.* The facts at hand can, however, be accounted for without recourse to Goldschmidt's assumptions.

Transition from one adaptive peak to another quite remote from the first in the field of gene combinations entails a radical reconstruction of the genotype. In general, the more radical the reconstruction the less likely are the intermediate stages of the rebuilding process to represent harmonious genotypic systems. Goldschmidt and Schindewolf have correctly pointed out (as others have done before them) that when observing two sufficiently different types of organization, each of which is harmonious in itself, it is frequently difficult to visualize functional systems intermediate between the two. As stated above, the roads leading from one adaptive peak to

---

* The resemblance between the theories of Schindewolf and Goldschmit is, however, a limited one. According to both authors, genetic changes leading to the emergence of higher categories occur through modifications of the early embryonic stages. This point of view is supported by evidence from comparative anatomy, embryology, and in part from developmental genetics, and may very well prove to be correct. Goldschmidt believes, however, that such changes lead at once to the appearance of adult systemic mutants which represent new species, genera, or higher groups physiologically isolated from their ancestors, and, hence, breeding *inter se*. Schindewolf does not seem to be committed to such a doctrine. If I understand him aright, the embryonic changes need not immediately alter the adult stage, and do so only relatively gradually in the course of the phylogeny.

others usually cross adaptive valleys. The "missing links" are, therefore, expected to be creatures able to subsist only in certain special environments, and hence rare in nature. Rare species are evidently seldom preserved and discovered as fossils. In as much as the effective population sizes in species that are rare or confined to strictly circumscribed types of habitat are likely to be smaller than in common and widespread species, the rates of evolution may be greater on the average in the former than in the latter. In a sense, evolution may at times defeat its own ends: successful types multiply, spread, conquer vast territories, but in so doing they run the risk of losing the very population structure which enabled them to become successful.

SPECIALIZATION AND RUDIMENTATION

It has been pointed out (p. 160) that natural selection is opportunistic: genetic changes become established if they confer an advantage on their carriers at a given time and place, regardless of whether such changes might be favorable or otherwise in the future. Any adaptive peak, however temporary, will be occupied by a species, provided only that the peak is accessible. Adaptation to specialized environments may decrease the importance of certain organs and physiological functions which are vital in other environments. Such organs and functions may become vestigial or disappear altogether. There are two possible ways to account for vestigial structures. Weismann and other classical evolutionists have introduced the idea of the struggle of parts of the body: since it takes energy to build an organ, genetic changes which dispose of a superfluous organ entail a saving of effort and thereby acquire a positive adaptive value. On the other hand, the frequencies of mutations tending to weaken or to destroy an organ may be higher than those of the reverse mutations which strengthen it. So long as the functioning of an organ remains vital to the species, the destructive mutations are opposed by natural selection; when an organ ceases to be vital, selection is relaxed and the mutation pressure alone might lead to rudimentation (Wright 1940a).

Some of the best examples of specialization and rudimentation are encountered among cave inhabitants. Reduction and disappearance of the eyes and of the pigmentation of the body, development of the organs possessing tactile functions and of certain peculiar behavior patterns are observed in cave animals belonging to various subdivisions of the animal kingdom, from the vertebrates to insects, crustaceans, and flatworms. The work of Hubbs (1938b), De Lattin (1939), Kosswig and Kosswig (1940), Vandel (1938b) and others has shed interesting light on the relations between the subterranean species and their surface relatives. The instances in which the same or closely related species occur in, as well as out, of the caves are particularly important, since here the processes of adaptation to the subterranean life may be studied. The variability of the structure of such organs as the eyes within the population of a single cave may be striking. Some individuals have fully developed eyes, while in others only rudiments are present; some individuals are fully pigmented and others colorless. Aberrant individuals resembling in certain particulars the cave forms may be found in the surface populations as well, but their frequency outside the caves is small. Although some of these variations have been proven to be hereditary, no less important is the extraordinary phenotypic plasticity of certain characters of cave animals. Kammerer (1912) showed that the salamander *Proteus anguinus,* which, when kept in the dark, has vestigial eyes and little or no black pigmentation, develops apparently functional eyes and a black pigmentation when grown under light. The genotype of an organism is, in general, so adjusted as to insure a standard development of vital organs and physiological functions in a variety of environments that are likely to be encountered; a deterioration of this adjustment may be one of the first steps of the rudimentation process.

Perfection of certain organs may confer so great an advantage on a species by making it an undisputed possessor of a definite ecological niche that other organs whose functions are not entirely lost may undergo rudimentation. According to Murphy (1939), the species of man-o'-war (*Fregata*) may be regarded among the most common and successful types of marine birds in the tropical zone. Yet, these unsurpassed fliers and accomplished fish hunters are awkward anywhere out of the air because of their nearly rudimentary legs. "The birds sometimes lose their balance and, before they can launch into flight, slither helplessly down the branches . . . to a lingering death made certain by their inability to clamber out of the tangles to some jumping-off place." They are even more help-less in water; they can neither swim nor rise into the air from water surface or from flat ground, and their plumage easily becomes waterlogged. This example shows once more that the adaptive value is an attribute of the genotype as a whole and not of its parts taken separately. The application of this principle to the evolution of the domesticated species, and to that of man himself, is obvious.

MORPHOLOGICAL AND PHYSIOLOGICAL DIFFERENTIATION

Although any change in bodily structures is of necessity a sequel to physiological developmental processes, the customary distinction between morphological and physiological characters possesses a certain descriptive value. Some structures appear to have an intrinsic adaptive significance, others are merely the visible signs or by-products of biologically important physiological reactions, and still others seem to be completely neutral. Physiological differences, whether adaptive or neutral, are sometimes not accompanied by any detectable changes in the visible characteristics. A systematist is per-force confined to describing chiefly the structural differences in his materials, although he realizes that evolutionary processes may entail changes of any or all of the above types. His hope that exclusively or predominantly morphological description does accurately reflect the magnitude of the differences between races, species, and higher categories implies the assumption that a certain constant fraction among the genetic differences that arise and become established in populations are of the visible kind. Nevertheless, in some groups, races and species may be formed that appear to be altogether in-distinguishable morphologically. Such races and species are spoken of as "biological," "physiological," or "ecological"; very lucidly written reviews of the subject have been published by Thorpe (1930, 1940).

In some instances the failure to detect structural differences between species is due to an incomplete study. The malarial mos-quito *Anopheles maculipennis,* and also certain other mosquito species, are now known to represent complexes of "biological races" differing in geographical distribution, habitat preferences, inclination to attack man or other animals, and in their roles as vectors of malaria (a review of the rather voluminous literature of this subject in Hackett 1937). As shown by De Buck, Schoute, and Swellen-grebel (1934), there is a strong sexual isolation between some of these "races," as well as a sterility in their hybrids, so that they should be more properly considered separate species. These species were originally believed to be morphologically indistinguishable, but it is known at present that they can be differentiated rather easily by visible characteristics of the larvae and especially of the eggs. In other cases the lack of morphological differentials between species appears, however, to be real. The A and B "races" of *Drosophila pseudoobscura* so often referred to in this book are distinct species by any criterion except the absence of reliable morphological differentials (Mather and Dobzhansky 1939). The "biological races" of the wasp *Trichogramma minutum* parasitize different hosts and in most cases fail to produce offspring when crossed; the visible differences between them are confined to slight variations in color, which apparently arise from only a few genetic factors (Harland and Atteck 1933). According to Emerson (1935), two species of the termite *Nasutitermes* differ only in the number of bristles on the thorax of the soldier cast and in that their nests attract different species of termitophile organisms. The classical "species" of the well-known infusorians *Paramecium* and *Euplotes* are split into noninterbreeding "mating groups" which are, as far as known, alike both morphologically and ecologically, and distinguishable solely through their mating reactions (Sonneborn 1939, Jennings 1939, Kimball 1939). The mating groups are equivalent to species in other organisms. (For further examples of "biological races" see Thorpe 1930, 1940.)

A real, and an as yet untouched, problem concerning the "biological species" is whether the extent of the genetic differences between them is smaller than that between related species which are visibly distinct. The attainment of the species rank by two or more related populations signifies that the exchange of genes between them is limited or discontinued, owing to the presence of physiological isolating mechanisms (cf. Chapter XI). Theoretically it is conceivable that physiological isolation appears automatically as soon as a certain amount of genetic difference between populations has accumulated. If this were the case, one would have to conclude that in some organisms the proportion of genetic changes producing visible external effects is higher than in others. On the other hand, it is possible that the amount of genetic change preceding the development of physiological isolating mechanisms varies greatly from group to group. In this case, species would comprise much larger units in some groups than in others, in the sense that, to put it crudely, the numbers of genes differentiating related species in one genus would be large and in another genus relatively small. For the time being we can do nothing more than to recognize the existence of the above possibilities. The fact which is, however, plain is that the species of some genera differ strikingly enough to be distinguished by a layman, while in other genera species distinctions appear trifling to our eyes.

INTROGRESSIVE HYBRIDIZATION

The efficiency of physiological isolating mechanisms which hinder the exchange of genes between species inhabiting the same territory is sometimes incomplete. Their occasional breakdown leads to the appearance in nature of interspecific hybrids. Many such hybrids are on record, especially in the botanical literature (cf. Lotsy 1916, Du Rietz 1930, Wiegand 1935). Hybrids may appear as exceptional individuals, so that the limits of species are only slightly blurred, or the territory where two species meet may be populated with "hybrid swarms." The parental species may be almost completely lost in a mass of intermediates and of new types that presumably arose through recombination of the genes of two species. The "hybrid swarms" remind one of the complex segregations obtained in the F_2 and further generations of experimental interspecific hybrids (cf. Chapter III). The population of *Salix* inhabiting Greenland is described as consisting almost exclusively of hybrids between several species, while the putative parents are encountered rarely or not at all (Du Rietz 1930). The evidence on the basis of which certain individuals are judged to be hybrids is usually circumstantial and not always convincing. Presence in certain populations of a species A of individuals possessing some characteristics usually associated with species B does not necessarily prove that these individuals are hybrids; they may be the remnants of the ancestral population from which the species A and B have differentiated. Furthermore, some of the mutants arising in the species A may resemble some of the characters of the species B. Nevertheless, there can be no doubt that interspecific hybridization does occur in nature.

In a series of recent papers, Anderson and his collaborators (Anderson 1936b, 1939a, Anderson and Hubricht 1938, Riley 1939) have reëmphasized the rather high frequency and the possible importance of introgressive hybridization in some plant genera. By "introgression" is meant infiltration of the germ plasm of one species into another. Thus, populations of *Tradescantia occidentalis* growing in localities where other species of the same genus (especially *T. canaliculata*) are common may contain individuals displaying certain structural characters resembling these other species. In the Ozark region *T. canaliculata* grows mostly in locations exposed to sun at the top of cliffs, and *T. subaspera* on rich shaded soils at the foot of the same cliffs.This ecological isolation breaks down and hybrids are produced along the ravines made by erosion in such cliffs. Until recently most investigators have favored a theory according to which the cultivated maize (*Zea mays*) has arisen through mutation and artificial selection from the teosinte (*Euchlaena mexicana*), a plant now found as a semiweed in Central America and Mexico. Mangelsdorf and Reeves (1939) have evolved an alternative view, in support of which they have mustered a considerable array of evidence. The wild progenitors of the cultivated maize must be looked for in the Andean region of South America, where a primitive agriculture based on maize is known to have existed since antiquity. The spread of maize cultivation northward to Central and North America brought maize in contact with species of the grass *Tripsacum* indigenous in these lands. Incompletely sterile *Zea* × *Tripsacum* hybrids have been obtained experimentally. Owing to the spontaneous formation of such hybrids in nature and their repeated backcrossing to *Zea,* an introgression of the *Tripsacum* genes into *Zea* has presumably taken place. Far from being the progenitor of cultivated maize, teosinte is now regarded as a *Zea* × *Tripsacum* recombination product. Indeed, the differences between maize and *Euchlaena* seem to be carried in a limited number of choromosome segments, the genetic residuum being rather similar in both forms (Arnason 1936, Mangelsdorf and Reeves 1939, and others).

It is impossible at present to appraise the evolutionary role of introgressive hybridization. As we have seen in Chapter VIII, physiological isolation between species might develop in response to the challenge of hybridization, provided the hybrids or the recombination products are inferior in viability or fertility to the parental species. Introgressive hybridization may, then, be a passing stage in the process of species formation. On the other hand, the adaptive value of hybrids may be as high as that of their parent; introgressive hybridization may lead to obliteration of the differences between the incipient species and their fusion into a single variable one, thus undoing the result of the previous divergent development. If the environments in which the incipient species were formed have ceased to exist, some of the recombination products may be more fit in the new environment than the parental species; introgressive hybridization may, then, result in emergence of superior genotypes. There is evidence that the last of the above possibilities is realized in some instances: Wiegand (1935), Anderson and Hubricht (1938), and Riley (1939) point out that introgressive hybridization is observed most frequently in localities which have been interfered with by man. The introgressive hybrids in *Tradescantia* are weeds or semiweeds, and they occur relatively rarely on virgin land. It may also be noted that, with few exceptions (for example, Boettger 1922 and Franz 1928 in the molluscs *Cepaea* and *Viviparus*, respectively, and Blair 1941 in *Bufo*), introgressive hybridization seems to be much commoner in the plant than in the animal kingdom. Whether this impression is due to faulty data or to a greater average efficiency of the isolating mechanisms between fully formed animal species is a matter that can be determined only through further studies.

POLYPLOIDS

Speciation through polploidy is, as pointed out in Chapter VII, one of the most aberrant among the known evolutionary patterns. A new species arises suddenly, and is at once at least partially isolated from its progenitor or progenitors. We shall now consider another peculiarity of polyploidy which concerns the mutation process.

Whether a species is an auto- or an allopolyploid, it has at least a part of its genes represented more than twice in the somatic cells and more than once in the gametes. Thus, an einkorn wheat is A^1A^1, an emmer $A^1A^1A^2A^2$, and vulgare $A^1A^1A^2A^2A^3A^3$, where A^1, A^2, and A^3 are the alleles of the same gene located in the different semihomologous sets of chromosomes of these plants. A mutation from A to a recessive allele a can easily manifest itself in the einkorn wheat, since a heterozygote A^1a^1 will produce on inbreeding one-quarter of the offspring homozygous for $a^1(a^1a^1)$. A similar mutation in an emmer wheat will not be detectable. An individual $a^1a^1A^2A^2$, despite being homozygous for a^1, carries two dominant alleles A^2 which suppress the effects of a^1. The same argument is applicable *a fortiori* to a mutation in a hexaploid vulgare wheat, where the effects of the recessive a^1 are suppressed by those of the two pairs of dominants A^2 and A^3. The phenotypic manifestation of recessive mutant genes in the emmer and vulgare wheats may become possible only if similar mutations take place in the two or three chromosome sets, respectively, which is, however, a rather improbable event.

Indirect evidence corroborating the above deduction is afforded by the experiments of Nilsson-Ehle (1911) and others on the identical (polymeric) genes in the polyploid species of cereals. For in the vulgare wheats some characteristics (for example the seed color) are determined by three pairs of identical factors. A cross between a recessive strain ($a^1a^1a^2a^2a^3a^3$) and a strain carrying three dominants ($A^1A^1A^2A^2A^3A^3$) gives in the F_2 generation a segregation in the ratio 63 dominants:1 recessive. Polymeric genes appear to be very common in polyploids (Müntzing 1937b), although they occur as an exception also in organisms that are regarded as diploids (e.g., *Drosophila*). Their presence in diploids may conceivably be due to the existence of the repeat regions in some chromosomes (Chapter IV), which make a generally diploid species polyploid for some chromosome sections.

The mutation frequencies in related species having different chromosome numbers have been compared by Stadler (1929, 1932). The diploid oats *Avena brevis* and *A. strigosa* ($n = 7$) were given similar amounts of X-ray treatments as the hexaploid *A. byzantina* and *A. sativa* ($n = 21$). Fourteen mutations were obtained in the former and none in the latter in approximately equally large samples. The experiments with wheat species gave comparable results. Stadler expresses the mutation frequency in terms of the number of mutations obtained per unit of the X-ray treatment (r-unit). The resulting figures are 10.4×10^{-6} for the diploid *Triticum monococcum*, 2.0×10^{-6} and 1.9×10^{-6} for the tetraploids *T. dicoccum* and *T. durum*, respectively. No mutations were obtained in the hexaploid *T. vulgare*. Stadler concludes that the data "support the hypothesis that the reduced frequency of mutation observed in polyploid species is low because of gene reduplication."

The suppression of the effects of a recessive mutant gene appearing in one of the chromosome sets of a polyploid by normal alleles lying in other chromosome sets precludes the phenotypic manifestation of the mutant and prevents its detection. This mechanism need not, however, decrease the mutation rates of the genes as such. It is reasonable to suppose, in the absence of any evidence to the contrary, that the genes in the chromosomes of a polyploid mutate just as frequently as they do in the diploid. A majority of the mutations are, however, deleterious in nature. In a diploid, deleterious mutations are eliminated, or at least are kept down in frequency, by natural selection. In a polyploid, an unfavorable recessive mutation, even a lethal or a gene deficiency, arising in one of the chromosome sets is "sheltered" from natural selection by the presence of the normal alleles in the other sets. Only the dominant mutations, or such recessives as have appeared in all chromosome sets, can be kept under control by selection.

The sheltering of the destructive mutations produces a dislocation in the usual relationships between the mutation and the selection processes. It would seem that polyploidy must inexorably lead to a progressive deterioration of the germ plasm. And yet polyploid species not only exist in nature, but are sometimes more successful than their diploid relatives. A suggestion put forward to resolve this apparent paradox is that the initially homologous genes lying in the different chromosome sets will mutate in different directions, and will gradually become so distinct as to be no longer allelic. Such a differentiation of the chromosome sets might eventually transform a polyploid into a species that has most genes represented only once in the gametes and twice in the zygotes, and thus would in effect restore the diploid status despite the altered chromosome number. The presence of the duplicate, triplicate, and other multiple genes may be regarded as a temporary condition which is overcome by mutation. Polyploidy is thus a mechanism whereby both the gene number and the gene variety are increased. Unfortunately, nothing is known about the kind of mutation that might make the once allelic genes nonallelic; the concept of allelism is in general one of the weak spots in the genetic theory.

However that may be, an at least temporary effect of polyploidy is virtually equivalent to a limitation or suppression of the gene mutation process. This drying up of the major source of evolutionary change is bound to have profound influence on the evolutionary perspectives of a polyploid species. Yet, the occurrence of polyploidy may, as we know (Chapter VII), be accompanied by a considerable modification of the reaction norm; the combination of the germ plasms of two or more species in an allopolyploid may create a genotype superior in adaptive value to those of the ancestral species. To sum up: polyploidy may make a new adaptive peak suddenly available to the species, but, as noted by Manton (1932), "high polyploidy, however much it may figure in elaboration of specific forms, is a barrier to true progress." Babcock and Stebbins (1938) and Stebbins (1940) in their lucid analysis of the role of polyploidy in evolution came to a similar conclusion: "There is every reason to believe that one of the principal causes of the great abundance of polyploid types among Angiosperms at present is the great variation in climate that accompanied the last glaciation. In other words, polyploidy is largely a 'short cut' by which a species or genus may adapt itself easily to a rapidly changing environment."

RETROGRESSION OF SEXUALITY

Weismann has pointed out as early as 1892 that, owing to recombination of the germ plasms available in a panmictic population, the genetic variability is increased by sexual reproduction. This increase of the variability Weismann considered to be an important evolutionary advantage of sexuality. Modern genetics has confirmed this prophetic view. The process of evolution entails changes in gene systems; a gene which on a certain genetic background has an unfavorable viability effect may be neutral or favorable in combination with other genes. Evolutionary potentialities of a species depend upon how great a variety of gene combinations the species is capable of producing; the larger the area of the field of gene combinations available, the greater is the chance that a new adaptive peak may be discovered. Darlington (1932a, 1939) has put forward an ingenious theory according to which the development in phylogeny of the whole complex machinery of chromosome and cell division, chromosome pairing, crossing over, and meiotic reduction may be regarded as a series of adaptations devised to secure the advantages of gene recombination. And yet, in many phylogenetic lines in the animal, and especially in the plant, kingdom the sexuality has been permitted to degenerate to the point where its basic evolutionary function is lost; moreover, this retrogression has taken place in many different ways.

The simplest form of retrogression of sexuality is self-fertilization. The outward appearance of sexual reproduction is retained, the chromosome cycle is normal, functional gametes are formed, but a union of gametes of a single hermaphrodite individual, instead of the fusion of gametes produced by different individuals, takes place. The danger of self-fertilization is inherent in hermaphroditism, and many hermaphrodites have developed various devices to prevent selfing: separation of female and male sexual ducts, flower structure making self-pollination difficult or impossible, gametes of one sex maturing earlier than those of the other, and, finally, genic self-sterility. Nevertheless, some hermaphrodites reproduce facultatively or obligatorily through self-fertilization. Facultative selfing, if it occurs rarely, has the same effect on a population as an occasional close inbreeding: homozygotes become more frequent than they would be under random mating, recessive genes with deleterious effects are eliminated more rapidly, and the supply of the hereditary variability is somewhat reduced in local populations. On the whole, the breeding structure is not materially different from that obtaining under panmixia. If, however, self-fertilization becomes the predominant or the only method of reproduction, populations of a species consist mostly of homozygotes. Mutations, whether dominant or recessive, manifest themselves in the phenotype soon after their origin, and those among them that are deleterious in the given genetic or secular environment are eliminated. If the effects of a mutation are favorable, the new type will successfully compete with the old ones. The formation of favorable gene combinations is, however, made difficult, for this requires the occurrence of a series of mutations in the same line of descent. If each mutation is favorable *per se*, the task may be accomplished at the expense of a great loss of time; otherwise the potentially possible evolutionary change may never become realized. Obligatory or habitual selfing robs the species of evolutionary plasticity, transforming it into a complex of genetically homogeneous strains (pure lines) which do not exchange their genes.

Apomixis is a common name for several methods of procreation in which the sexual structures (sexual ducts, genitalia, flowers) may be retained, but in which development is initiated without fertilization. Where the specialized reproductive cells—eggs in animals and macrospores in plants—give rise to the embryo, we are dealing with parthenogenesis. Diploid parthenogenesis, in which the reproductive cells contain the diploid chromosome complement, is most frequent. In plants the sporophyte may arise without fertilization from a vegetative cell of the gametophyte (apogamy), or the gametophyte may develop from a cell other than a spore (apospory), or from somatic cells of the nucellus (nucellar embryogony). Apomixis is accompanied by a remarkable variety of chromosome behavior, the situation being frequently different not only in species of the same genus, but even within a species (Rosenberg 1930, Darlington 1937b, Gentcheff and Gustafsson 1940; see these works for further references). The point which is important for us here is that the meiotic chromosome pairing in most apomicts is partly or completely suppressed; the eggs come to possess the same chromosome complement which is present in the mother, and therefore the genotype of the entire progeny of an individual uniformly resembles that of the progenitor. Binary fission, procreation through adventitious buds, sprouts, stolons, bulbs, and other forms of asexual reproduction are in this respect analogous to apomixis. Apomixis and asexual reproduction, like self-fertilization, eventually lead to formation of groups of individuals having identical genotypes and not exchanging genes with other similar groups; such groups are termed clones. But in another respect the effects of apomixis and asexual reproduction are the antithesis of self-fertilization. Prolonged selfing may give rise to a virtually completely homozygous pure line; apomictic or asexual clones retain whatever heterozygosis may be present in their ancestors.*

In many protozoans, coelenterates, some worms, crustaceans (*Cladocera*), insects (*Aphids* and others), and in certain plants, sexually reproducing generations alternate more or less regularly with asexual or diploid parthenogenetic generations. In many other plants, sexual, apomictic, and asexual reproduction are facultative and occur side by side. So long as cross-fertilization takes place not too infrequently in the pedigree of any given strain composing the species, the evolutionary situation remains rather similar to that in purely cross-fertilizing forms. Omission of the sexual process in some generations entails a certain loss of the opportunity to form novel gene patterns; the patterns that have been formed are, however, multiplied and thoroughly tested by natural selection before they are returned to the melting pot of sexual reproduction (cf. Banta 1939). The species remains a unit, since all strains composing it are at least potentially capable of exchanging genes with each other.

Where apomixis or asexual reproduction are the rule, very peculiar evolutionary situations may be created. Many genetic conditions that are known to arise by mutation in the wide sense of that term cannot become established with cross-fertilization. Here belong polyploids with odd numbers of chromosome complements (triploids, pentaploids, etc.) which cannot breed true sexually, owing to the impossibility of forming only bivalents and no univalents at meiosis. Autopolyploids and allopolyploids coming from hybridization between closely related species may have even numbers of chromosome sets, and yet variable multivalent associations at meiosis may lead to production of gametes with various deviations from the standard chromosome number. Reduplications and losses of certain chromosomes of a single set may give rise to aneuploids, monosomics, and polysomics; individuals carrying such chromosome complements, if reproducing sexually, form more than one type of gametes, and a segregation is observed in their offspring.

* Under certain exceptional conditions retention of heterozygosis is compatible with self-fertilization. Some species of *Oenothera* and certain other plants are permanent hybrids in which two gene complexes are perpetuated owing to a system of translocations and balanced lethals (Cleland 1937). These species propagate by facultative self- and cross-fertilization.

Nevertheless, such unbalanced chromosome complements may create reaction norms which are favorable in certain environments. Retention and fixation of an inherently unstable chromosomal or genic condition is a problem the solution of which is difficult with sexual reproduction; apomixis and asexuality offer, according to Darlington's (1939) figure of speech, an "escape." This escape has, indeed, been made use of by many plants and by some animal species.

A review of the extremely complex and variable chromosomal conditions encountered in apomictic and asexual forms may be found in Darlington's well-known book (1937b). A few examples will suffice here. The basic chromosome number in the genus *Rubus* (blackberry) is seven; Gustafsson (1939) found two diploids, three triploids, thirty-three tetraploids, and four pentaploids among the types belonging to the section of the genus known as "Eubati veri"; in the section "Corylifolii" from eastern Sweden, seventeen types were tetraploid and six pentaploid. Among the American representatives of the genus *Crepis*, having eleven chromosomes as the basic number, diploids, triploids, tetraploids, pentaploids, heptaploids, octoploids, and aneuploids (45, 76, and 86 chromosomes) have been found (Babcock and Stebbins 1938). In the genus *Poa*, sexual and apomictic strains are found; chromosomal conditions may be quite irregular and inconstant within the progeny of a single plant. The basic chromosome number is seven, but in the apomictic strains of *Poa alpina* the following numbers were found: 28, 33, 34, 35, 36, 37, 38, 39, 41, 45, 49, 52, 64, 65, 66, 67, 72, 73, and 74, the commonest being 33, 35, 37, and 38 (Müntzing 1940). It is important to note that in several plant genera most or all diploid species reproduce sexually, while their polyploid and aneuploid relatives are mostly or entirely apomictic or asexual. A causal connection between the establishment of unbalanced chromosomal conditions and apomixis may reasonably be inferred.

There can be no doubt that some apomictic and asexual types are successful in the struggle for existence: in some plant genera, diploid species occur as relics while larger territories are populated by swarms of apomicts. Each apomictic type taken separately displays, however, a limited individual variability and appears narrowly specialized to fit a certain restricted environment (Gustafsson 1935).

According to Babcock and Stebbins (1938), "An agamic complex is a 'closed system,' whose ultimate fate is bound up in the fate of its sexual members. It can give rise to nothing new, and can keep abreast of changing conditions only through the activity of the latter forms." Retrogression of sexuality is a striking example of evolutionary opportunism, an escape, according to Darlington, in a phylogenetic blind alley.*

The method of sex determination in which females are diploid and males haploid has been ascertained in some rotifers, *Acarina, Homoptera,* and especially in *Hymenoptera* (Schrader and Hughes-Schrader 1931). The population genetics of these forms is little known, so that the evolutionary consequences of their sex-determining mechanisms are unclear. Provided the genes that are recessive in females have similar phenotypic effects in both sexes, there must be a rapid elimination of unfavorable mutant genes during passage through the haploid males. This would limit the supply of hereditary variation, although freedom to form gene combinations need not be affected, because the chromosome behavior in the diploid females is apparently normal.

MAN

No adequate treatment of so complex a subject as evolutionary patterns in man can, obviously, be given here, but a few remarks may be appropriate. We refrain from consideration of the old problem of the relative importance of nature and nurture in determining the characters differentiating human individuals and populations; the vicious and notoriously unscientific polemics of the last two decades have merely confused the problem still further. The situation seems to be that as far as psychic characters, such as intelligence and temperament, are concerned, the evidence on their causation is simply not good enough to be accepted as critical or even indicative, and hence whoever has a regard for truth must defer judgment (a viewpoint which is equally abhorrent to good racialists and to environmentalists). Nobody doubts, however, that certain human traits are inherited, and the mode of the transmission of some "normal" as well as pathological characters has been estab-

---

* The obligatory asexual groups of lower organisms (certain fungi, algae, and perhaps bacteria) are believed to be derived secondarily from sexually reproducing ancestors. The primitive asexual types appear to be extinct.

lished. A practical issue of great importance is how to investigate and describe the intrapopulational variation and the interpopulational differences in man, so that the resulting data may most effecticely elucidate the statics and the dynamics of the human species.

Physical anthropology has accumulated an enormous mass of information consisting chiefly of accurate measurements of various bodily dimensions and, to a certain extent, of measurements of physiological and psychological characteristics of human races. This information has permitted the compilation of an inventory of the subdivisions of the species *Homo sapiens,* and, in conjunction with historical, archaeological, linguistic, and other data, has revealed a fascinating story of the distribution and migration of man on the earth's surface. No geneticist should presume to disparage the value of this information. The difficulty, however, is that, as pointed out in Chapter III, the concept of race as a system of character averages logically implies a theory of continuous, rather than of particulate, germ plasm. Such a concept is obviously outmoded and incapable of producing much insight into the causative factors at work in human populations. Although the genic basis of relatively few human traits is known, it seems that following up the distribution of these few traits could tell us more about the "races" than a great abundance of measurements. Furthermore, the concealed genic variability can no longer be disregarded. Populations of any species which reproduce sexually, in which genes are subject to mutation, and in which there is no very close inbreeding are bound to accumulate hereditary variability in their germ plasms. In so far as this variability consists of recessive genes, only a part of it, and often a very small part, is manifested in the phenotype, and yet the concealed portion is neither immaterial for the welfare of the species nor useless as a tool for investigation (Chapters III and V).

How large are the genetically effective sizes of human populations at present, and how large were they in the past? To what extent has the racial differentiation of the human species been determined by mutation pressure, genetic drift, migration and selection? What are the present trends in these genetic agents? No answers to these and many related questions are available, not alone because the problems involved are inherently difficult, but also because little work has been done that could bring about their solution. A start in the right direction has been made by Wahlund (1928) and Dahlberg (1929, 1938), who point out that the number of individuals among which a person may choose his or her mate is necessarily limited by geographical, social, and other factors. This number measures an "isolate"; the concept of isolate is, therefore, related to Wright's concept of N, the effective population size. The sizes of isolates are evidently variable not only in different countries and social groups, but they change in the course of time.

Attempts to estimate the isolates numerically could be made through studies on the frequencies of consanguineous marriages in different populations. If marriages between relatives of a certain degree are not discriminated against by social usage, the frequency of such marriages is a function of the size of the isolate and of the average number of relatives of that particular degree. The necessary demographic data exist for very few populations, and their accuracy is so low that at best only the order of magnitude of the isolates may be arrived at. According to Dahlberg, an average isolate in western European countries could hardly be less than 400 or more than 3,000 individuals (i.e., a person has between 200 and 1,500 potential mates). The same data are, however, more reliable in showing the trends of change in the isolates. Thus, in Prussia, the frequency of cousin marriages, which was 0.71 percent in 1875–80, fell to 0.20 percent in 1921–26, and in Bavaria it fell from 0.87 percent in 1876–80 to 0.20 percent in 1926–33. In cities, cousin marriages occur consistently less often than in country districts. The isolates are larger in urban than in rural communities, and they are growing with time. This is, of course, the expected result of an increasing population density and the development of communications (an interesting fact in this connection is that in rural France the frequency of cousin marriages did not decrease between 1898 and 1910).

It is important that the incidence of hereditary defects of a type approaching semilethality may be geographically not uniform in human populations (see, in Sjögren 1931, the data on the distribution of amaurotic idiocy in Sweden). This indicates that the isolates in man are, or recently were, sufficiently small to permit a geographical differentiation owing to genetic drift (cf. Chapter V). The systematic increase of the average stature observed in populations of many countries over the past several decades or century is usually attributed to improvements in the diet and in hygienic conditions; Dahlberg (1938) points out that it may also be due, at least in part, to the increase in the size of isolates and the consequent heterosis. Indeed, a certain amount of heterosis is expected to accrue to a species as a result of interbreeding of local populations which had differentiated owing to limitation of the effective population size (cf. Chapter V); at the same time the infestation of the germ plasm with recessive mutant genes producing deleterious effects is expected to increase.

In the absence of reliable data on the physiological and ecological significance of the characters distinguishing human races and ethnic groups, it is idle to speculate on the relative importance of various genetic agents that have brought about the differentiation of our species. Agents tending toward geographical diversification (mutation, limitation of the effective population size, selection) are always pitted against those tending toward geographical unification (migration, relaxation of selection). The outcome depends upon the balance of the forces in the course of time. It seems that in the past this balance was on the diversifying side, while in modern times it has definitely turned toward unification of mankind; the future can only be conjectured.*

* Goldschmidt (1940) considers it preposterous to suppose that human races might be incipient species. It is, indeed, absurd to class them as distinct species, but it is rash to deny that they could not become species if the processes of diversification should continue for a long time (on a quasi-geological scale). In fact, human races are an illustration of the correctness of the general proposition of the lack of an absolute determination in evolution: a process of speciation once having got under way does not follow an inexorably predestined course, but can be arrested and even turned back. Only after species distinctions have become fixed by a complete physiological isolation may we suppose that a relatively irreversible stage has been reached.

XI: SPECIES AS NATURAL UNITS

BIOLOGICAL CLASSIFICATION

THE PROCESS of evolution has two aspects, since it involves the development of diversity as well as that of discontinuity in the living world. The aspect of discontinuity should be emphasized, not because it is the more important of the two, but because it is the less obvious one to a superficial observer. The characteristics of discontinuity as a static phenomenon have been dealt with in Chapter I. The essential point stressed there is that the variation observed among organisms living at any given time level does not form a single distribution, but rather an array of discrete distributions. Moreover, the variation is hierarchical, since the small discrete arrays are grouped into larger ones, these into still larger ones, and so on. The discontinuity is preserved throughout the hierarchy of arrays. The discontinuous variation of morphological and physiological characteristics of organisms is a fact given us in experience, an objective phenomenon rather than a projection on nature of some concepts created by the investigator.

The scientific classification of organisms is founded on the discontinuity and the hierarchy of variation, or, to put it more precisely, these properties of variation have been used for the purpose of making a classification. The fact that this is not the only possible kind of classification should not be lost sight of. Books in a library may be classified according to contents, name of the author, year of publication, size, or color of the cover; which of these methods is selected depends on convenience. The same principle may be applied to the classification of organisms. In fact, Pliny did reject the system of animals proposed before him by Aristotle, which happened to be fairly similar to the modern one, and subdivided the animals into those living in water, on land, and in the air. One might just as well use as a basis of classification such characters as usefulness or harmfulness to man, or occurrence in different climates. It is amusing that at least one contemporary biologist has apparently in all serious-ness suggested that an "ecological" classification might be superior to the one now in use. The pragmatism of the existing classification is openly acknowledged by many systematists; this attitude seems not very consistent with the claims to the effect that it is also the only "natural" one, and that its naturalness must be preserved at all costs. A natural and a convenient system need not necessarily be identical.

The concept of a "natural" system is far from being always made clear. Being told that an organism belongs to the genus *Drosophila* we may safely predict that its body consists of segments, that it re-spires with the aid of tracheae, that it has a legless larva, is likely to have certain wing veins, bristles on the thorax, a branched arista, a short period of development, a rather low number of chromosomes, and the rest. The position of an organism in the system of Pliny, or one like it, would not define so many of its characteristics. This seems to be the reason why our system is more natural than that of Pliny. A knowledge of the position of an organism in an ideal natural system would permit the formation of a sufficient number of deduc-tive propositions for its complete description. Hence, a system based on the empirically existing discontinuities in materials to be classi-fied, and following the hierarchical order of the discontinuous arrays, approaches most closely to the ideal natural one. Every subdivision made in such a system conveys to the student the greatest possible amount of information pertaining to the objects before him. The modern classification of organisms uses the principles on which an ideal system could be built, although it would be an exaggeration to think that the two are consubstantial.

On the other hand, since the time of Darwin and his immediate followers the term "natural classification" has meant in biology one based on the hypothetical common descent of organisms. The forms united together in a species, genus, class, or phylum were supposed to have descended from a single common ancestor, or from a group of very similar ancestors. The lines of separation between the sys-tematic categories were, hence, adjusted, at least in theory, not so much to the discontinuities in the observed variations as to the branching of real or assumed phylogenetic trees. And yet the classifi-cation has continued to be based chiefly on morphological studies of the existing organisms rather than of the phylogenetic series of fossils. The logical difficulty thus incurred is circumvented with the aid of an hypothesis according to which the similarity between the organisms is a function of their descent. In other words, it is believed that one may safely base the classification on studies of the structures and functions of the organisms existing at our time level, in the assurance that if such studies are sufficiently complete, a picture of the phylogeny will emerge. The validity of this hypothesis can evidently be tested only through palaeontological data, by comparing the theoretically constructed phylogenies with the actual ones. Such a comparison seems to show that in general the morphologically similar creatures existing at our time level have descended from more similar or identical ancestors. In some groups no appreciable morphological convergence is, however, observed if one compares more and more remote ancestors of a given complex of forms. Rather, the development takes place along parallel lines, in such a way that several genealogical strains pass in the course of time through a certain sequence of stages; analogous stages may, however, be reached at different time levels in the different lines of descent. The result is that if one makes a morphological comparison of the entire series of forms regardless of their geological age, the consecutive stages of the development within a genealogical line may be less similar than analogous stages in different lines. Two classifications become possible: a "vertical" one uniting all types within a genealogical line, and an "horizontal" one combining analogous stages of different genealogical lines (Schindewolf 1936, Arkell and Moy-Thomas 1940, Gilmour 1940; see these papers for further references).

Fortunately, the difficulty just stated is more abstract than real. The fact is that the classification of organisms that existed before the advent of evolutionary theories has undergone surprisingly little change in the times following it, and such changes as have been made have depended only to a trifling extent on the elucidation of the actual phylogenetic relationships through palaeontological evidence. The phylogenetic interpretation has been simply superimposed on the existing classification; a rejection of the former fails to do any violence to the latter. The subdivisions of the animal and plant kingdoms established by Linnaeus are, with few exceptions, retained in the modern classification, and this despite the enormous number of new forms discovered since then. The new forms were either included in the Linnaean groups, or new groups have been created to accommodate them. There has been no necessity for a basic change in the classification. This fact is taken for granted by most systematists, and frequently overlooked by the representatives of other biological disciplines. Its connotations are worth considering. For the only inference that can be drawn from it is that the classification now adopted is not an arbitrary but a natural one, reflecting the objective state of things.

To avoid misunderstanding, it is necessary to define in what sense the classification may be said to have remained constant. The system of Linnaeus recognized only four hierarchical ranks: species, genus, order, and class. Two new categories were added very early: the family and the phylum. The number of categories now used is large indeed: species are subdivided into subspecies and combined into subgenera, sections, tribes, subfamilies, families, superfamilies, suborders, etc. Among insects, for example, most of the Linnaean genera are now treated as families. What has remained virtually unaltered through all these metamorphoses is the recognition that a given complex of forms represent a natural group. The rank ascribed to a group has been changed repeatedly, and individual authorities are quite likely to be at odds in their opinions on such matters, but the delimitation of the groups is much less frequently a subject of contention. The evaluation of a group as a genus, tribe, subfamily, or a family is determined purely by convenience; an investigator is, within limits, free to exercise his choice. The number of discontinuities of different orders in the organic world is so large that more and more categories can be created to describe them, just as branches of a tree can be classified only into major and minor ones, or else into primary, secondary, tertiary, and the rest.

There is, however, a systematic category which, in contrast to others, has withstood the changes in the nomenclature with a singular tenacity. This is the category of species. To be sure, some of the species described by Linnaeus have been split into two or more new ones, and yet a majority of the Linnaean species are still treated as species, not as subgenera, genera, or anything else. In animal and plant groups which are taxonomically well understood, and excepting the so-called "difficult" ones (which constitute a special problem to be discussed below), the delimitation of species usually is subject to no dispute at all (Mayr 1940). To be sure, a few taxonomists have from time to time succumbed to the temptation of assigning the species rank to any local race distinct enough to permit every specimen to receive a determination label. Excesses of this sort were frequent, for example, among mammalogists and specialists on certain genera of butterflies, but a salutary reaction has apparently started against them. The notion, entertained by some biologists unfamiliar with the subject, that species are arbitrary units like all other systematic categories is unfounded. In fact, no category is arbitrary so long as its limits are made to coincide with those of the discontinuously varying arrays of living forms. The category of species has certain attributes peculiar to itself that restrict the freedom of its usage, and consequently make it methodologically more valuable than the rest.

GENETIC BASIS OF CLASSIFICATION

Before proceeding further with our discussion of species as natural units, it may be useful to make a short digression to consider certain prolegomena on which this discussion must be based. Let us examine first an imaginary situation, a living world in which all possible gene combinations are represented by equal numbers of individuals. Under such conditions no discrete groups and no hierarchy of groups could occur, since the single gene differences producing striking phenotypical effects, like some of the mutations in *Drosophila*, would be the sole remaining source of discontinuity. Disregarding these, the variability would become a perfect continuum. The most "natural," although not the only possible, classification would be a sort of a multidimensional periodic system, with a number of dimensions equal to that of the variable genes.

Clearly, the existing organic world is unlike the above imaginary one. As pointed out in Chapters VIII and X, only an infinitesimal fraction of the possible gene combinations is, or has ever been, realized among living individuals. According to a conservative estimate given by Wright (1932), the number of possible combinations of genes is of the order of 10^{1000}, while the estimate of the number of electrons in the visible universe is of the order of 10^{100}. Furthermore, the existing gene combinations are grouped into more or less compact arrays attached to one or to several related "adaptive peaks" in the field. The arrays are therefore complexes of fairly similar gene combinations that make their carriers fit to survive in the environments encountered by them in nature. The "adaptive valleys" intervening between the peaks correspond to discordant gene combinations, most of which would be nearly or completely inviable. A promiscuous formation of gene combinations would give mainly a mass of freaks, something like the primeval monsters in the poetic myths of Empedocles and Lucretius.

The discontinuous variation in the organic world is therefore not a superficial appearance, but the consequence of a fundamental discontinuity in the genetic make-up of organisms. The discontinuity and the hierarchical character of the empirically observed variation may be viewed as a response of living matter to the pressure of the secular environment. Each race, species, genus, or any other group embraces a certain array of gene combinations attached to an "adaptive peak," or to several neighboring peaks. The fact that one group may be distinguished from the related ones implies that the gene combinations lying in the field between the peaks are formed rarely or not at all. Now, if the representatives of the different groups were to interbreed at random, all the gene combinations that are now rare or absent would be produced—given a sufficient number of individuals—within a few generations from the start of random breeding. That would mean a breakdown of the separation of the groups, and an emergence of a continuous variability over a part of the field. If all the organisms were to interbreed freely, a perfect continuum would result, as postulated above.

The conclusion that is forced on us is that the discontinuous variation encountered in nature, except that based on single gene differences, is maintained by means of preventing the interbreeding of representatives of the now discrete groups. This conclusion is evidently applicable to discrete groups of any rank whatever, beginning with minor races of a species and up to and including classes and phyla. The development of isolating mechanisms is therefore a *conditio sine qua non* for emergence of discrete groups of forms in evolution (cf. Chapter VIII). This conclusion is certainly not vitiated by the well-known fact that the isolation between groups may be complete or only partial. An occasional exchange of genes, not attaining to the frequency of a random interbreeding, results in the production of some intergrades, without, however, entirely swamping the differences between the groups.

We have endeavored to show that the category of species is more "natural" than other categories used by systematists. It is a matter of convenience which groups we designate subgenera, genera, or families, but ever since the time of Linnaeus biologists have felt that there is something about species that makes them more definite entities than all other groups. Bateson (1922) expressed this vague feeling most concisely: "Though we cannot strictly define species, they yet have properties which varieties have not, and . . . the distinction is not merely a matter of degree." In apparent contradiction to this stands the fact that systematists have never succeeded in evolving universally valid criteria which would permit a decision to be reached in all cases on whether or not two given forms are already separate species or are still races of a single species. Some species are recognized as such without hesitation by any competent systematist; with respect to others a decision on the species-race alternative can be reached only after a careful study; there remains, however, a certain residue of cases which seem to defy analysis and in which the decision is largely a matter of taste. The North American bird fauna, which is comparatively very well known, comprises 755 species and 1,367 races; according to Mayr (1940) at least 94 of these species, or 12.5 percent, might as well be considered races of certain of the remaining 661 species.

The relative facility with which most species can be separated and delimited offered no great difficulty for explanation in pre-Darwinian days. If species arose through separate acts of creation, each species is, then, a primordial entity, and the task of an investigator is merely to learn to discriminate between true species and their secondary subdivisions. Discerning systematists quickly realized that the well-nigh impossibility of distinguishing certain species from races is not an accident but is inherent in the material itself. The only reasonable explanation of this phenomenon ever offered is that given by Darwin: species evolve from races through a process of accumulation of genetic changes. Races, species, genera, and families are nothing more than different degrees of separation in the process of phylogenetic divergence. This divergence being a gradual one, instances must be found, and are found, when two or more races have become so distinct as to approach, but not to attain completely, the species rank. Once the process of speciation is accomplished, species can no longer be mistaken for races. What to systematists has been a source of vexation has become the keystone of evolutionary theory.

Darwin's explanation continues to be accepted by a tremendous majority of biologists. We know a method, namely polyploidy, whereby species arise from one another by a single sudden change; but species formation through polyploidy is, on the whole, an exception. A far more general method, encountered in all groups of organisms and believed, in most of them, to be the only one, is through accretion of gene mutations and chromosomal reconstructions. Evolutionary theory has been, however, recently challenged by Goldschmidt (1940). According to his view, species do not evolve; they arise at once through catastrophic systemic mutations. The necessary corollary of this view evidently is that, contrary to Darwin, species do not come from races. The incipient species, the races that stand on the threshold of species, are a delusion: real species can never be mistaken for races, or vice versa. The proposition that races may be (although not all races necessarily are) incipient species has become so thoroughly a part of the biologist's convictions that it is taken almost for granted; Goldschmidt's challenge is stimulating because it disturbs this complacency.

According to Goldschmidt (1940, p. 149), "The subspecific differences are always of the same order of magnitude; i.e., shifts in a few directions within the general pattern of organization of the species. If these are incipient species, the closely related species must be different in the same way, though on a larger scale. But actually the specific differences are on a completely different level of organization, the result of completely different materials, as Anderson expressed it." Species are separated by "bridgeless gaps," and "between the species even the basic patterns are different." The present writer thoroughly agrees with Goldschmidt in that if races are incipient species their differences must be commensurable; in the writer's opinion they are, in Goldschmidt's they are not. The question is which opinion is supported by the available evidence. Goldschmidt believes to have found "bridgeless gaps" between the species *Lymantria dispar*, *L. monacha*, and *L. mathura*. These species differ in the color patterns, shape, size, and hairiness of the body of the adult as well as of the larvae and pupae, in the structure of the genitalia, feeding and egg-laying habits, instincts, chromosomes, and so on. The two species *Ascaris megalocephala* and *A. lumbricoides* are so different histologically that any organ and sometimes a single cell can be determined as belonging to one or the other of them.

What, however, is the meaning of the assertion that differences between species "are on a completely different level of organization" from the racial ones? If this means anything at all, it signifies that the differences between species are so pervasive that, no matter what body part or physiological function we may choose to investigate, more or less dissimilarity will be found; it may also mean that the characteristics of each species are so integrated that a simple substitution of a certain structure or function of the species A for that of B would result in a disharmony of the whole. The more integration of this kind we find, the less conceivable becomes, however, the conjecture that these integrated systems of structural and functional traits could have arisen from each other by single leaps—that is, unless these leaps are miraculously premeditated, chiseled out, and delivered into being. That may, possibly, be a matter of opinion, but it is a matter of fact that there is no universally valid scale or "level of organization" applicable to all species. Nobody, either before or after Darwin, has doubted that certain species are profoundly distinct; the gist of the evolutionist's argument has been that some species are very different, others are less different, and still others are so little different that they may as well be considered very distinct races. To prove Goldschmidt's thesis it is absolutely essential to show that the *entire* living world is divisible into groups separated by "bridgeless gaps"; this is exactly what systematists have strived to do for nearly two hundred years and what they have so signally failed to accomplish. Since Goldschmidt himself not only did not attempt to demonstrate the feasibility of such a paragon of systematics but has eschewed giving any indication of a method whereby the "bridgeless gaps" can be discovered, the main premise of his theory is wholly unacceptable.

Examples of groups which stand on the boundary between species and race can be given by systematists working on almost any group of organisms (except the groups which are old and relictual, and in which formation of new species is no longer actively going on). Of necessity, we must confine ourselves to a single example dealing with materials repeatedly mentioned in this book. Despite the smallness of the visible morphological differences between them, *Drosophila azteca* and *D. athabasca* would be considered distinct species by any systematist or geneticist (cf. p. 148); *D. pseudoobscura* and *D. miranda* are more similar still, but probably nobody familiar with the evidence would doubt their specific distinctness either. But how shall we evaluate the differences between the A and B "races" of *D. pseudoobscura* or between the "subspecies" *virilis, americana,* and *texana* of *D. virilis?* If they too are regarded as separate species, what are *D. macrospina macrospina* and *D. macrospina limpiensis* (cf. pp. 143, 297, 315)? The plain fact is that the A and B "races" of *D. pseudoobscura* and the "subspecies" of *D. virilis* are at the evolutionary stage when races become species. In the opinion of the writer, the A and B "races" should be considered as having accomplished the transition, the "subspecies" of *D. virilis* as at the boundary, and *D. macrospina macrospina* and *D. macrospina limpiensis* as still on the race side of the boundary. Others may not share the opinion just stated, but there can be no doubt whatever that the "order of magnitude" of the differences between groups of *Drosophila* populations varies continuously from the racial to the specific level.

DEFINITION OF SPECIES IN SEXUALLY REPRODUCING ORGANISMS

There has been no shortage of attempts, to give a definition of what constitutes a species. The lack of intergrades between species and their presence between races has been frequently depended upon, but there are some very distinct species the intergrades between which occasionally occur, and there are obviously closely related races and variations produced by a single Mendelian gene that are discrete. Among insects, differences in the genitalia were assumed to mark species, but such differences may be present in races and absent in species. The geographical distributions of species frequently overlap, while those of races do not—but again there are exceptions. Experimental biologists have naturally looked in a somewhat different direction for criteria of species distinction. The sterility of hybrids has been frequently supposed to be confined to species crosses. Thus Standfuss (1896) gives the following definition: "Arten sind Gruppen von Individuen, die sich in ihren geschlechtlich entwickelten Formen nicht mehr dergestalt kreuzen können, dass sich die aus dieser Kreuzung hervorgehenden vollkommen ausgebildeten Tiere unbeschränkt miteinander fortzupflanzen vermögen." Yet hybrids between some apparently "good" species seem to be fully fertile. Writers inclined toward eclecticism prefer to believe that none of the above criteria are sufficient when taken singly, but that a satisfactory result may be obtained by combining them. Of late, the futility of attempts to find a universally valid criterion for distinguishing species has come to be fairly generally, if reluctantly, recognized. This diffidence has prompted an affable systematist to propose something like the following definition of species: "a species is what a competent systematist considers to be a species."

The cause of this truly amazing situation—a failure to define species which is supposedly one of the basic biological units—is not too difficult to fathom. All of the attempts mentioned above have strived to accomplish a patently impossible task, namely to produce a definition that would make it possible to decide in any given case whether two given complexes of forms are already separate species or are still only races of a single species. Such a task might be practicable if species were separate acts of creation or arose through single systemic mutations. If species evolve rather than suddenly appear, there will necessarily be a residue of situations intermediate between species and races (see above). This need not, however, deter biologists from attempting to elucidate the nature of species, provided it is clearly realized that no rigid standard of species distinction can be secured.

An interesting trial of this kind has been made by Lotsy (1931), who regards a "syngameon" (which he defines as "an habitually interbreeding community of individuals") to be the fundamental unit among systematic categories. Syngameons are, however, not identical with species, since a territorially isolated colony, and not the whole species, is "an habitually interbreeding community." We have seen (Chapter VIII) that the exchange of genes between populations may be prevented either by geographical separation or by reproductive isolating mechanisms of various kinds. Although a geographical isolation may be just as complete as a reproductive one, its effectiveness is limited in time. If the discreteness of groups of organisms were guarded by geographical isolation alone, every locality might then be inhabited by one and only one kind of living beings: for, as soon as two discrete groups came together in the process of expanding their distribution areas the interchange of genes would lead to a fusion of the once distinct groups. In reality, discrete groups frequently coexist in the same territory, because their interbreeding is prevented through a single physiological isolating mechanism or a combination of several of them (Chapters VIII and IX). Reproductive isolation causes a more or less permanent fixation of the organic discontinuity.

The stage of the evolutionary process at which the fixation of the discontinuity takes place is fundamentally important, and the attainment of this stage signifies the advent of species distinction. Dobzhansky (1935e) has therefore proposed to define species as that stage of evolutionary process, "at which the once actually or potentially interbreeding array of forms becomes segregated in two or more separate arrays which are physiologically incapable of interbreeding." This definition differs from those hitherto proposed in that it lays emphasis on the dynamic nature of the species concept. The species is a stage in a process, not a static unit. This difference is important, for it frees the definition of the logical difficulties inherent in any static one. At the same time, it cannot pretend to offer to a systematist a fixed yardstick with the aid of which he can decide in any given case whether two or more groups of forms have or have not reached the species rank. This drawback is unavoidable. A systematist is forced to describe the changing patterns of life in terms of abstract static conceptions. His task is first of all a practical one, viz., to classify and to systematize. To put it crudely, he wishes to be able to write a determination label under every specimen. Instances of groups of forms caught at our time level in the transition stage between races and species are interesting and at the same time are a hindrance in practice. And yet systematists have intuitively grasped the existence of species as natural units. Hence, a dynamic definition may be of value for systematists, if it substitutes an analytical judgment for the less communicable judgment of intuition.

The above definition of species—or variants which retain the basic idea—has been adopted by Emerson (1938), Epling (1939), Timofeeff-Ressovsky (1940a), Thorpe (1940), and Mayr (1940).* Since the stage of the evolutionary process at which physiological isolating mechanisms develop and the genetic discontinuity reaches fixation is undoubtedly important, species so defined are tangible natural phenomena. It is pertinent, however, to inquire whether they correspond to the species established by nearly two centuries of usage of this term in descriptive biology. Fortunately, there is enough evidence to show that the correspondence is rather far reaching. Although in separating species, the systematists, with rare exceptions, have no direct information on the ability of the forms concerned to interbreed, the criteria used by them are capable of producing indirect evidence bearing on this point. Some of these criteria are reviewed below.

Separate species possess different cycles of variability in morphological and physiological characters. The variations in at least some characters usually do not overlap, so that a hiatus is formed. Varieties, especially those occurring in the same geographical region with the "type" form, differ from each other mostly in single, although sometimes striking, characters. Geographical races, and especially species, differ in complexes of traits, some of which may be less striking to the eye than varietal differences. As might be expected theoretically, and is actually found to be the case in the few instances studied, the differences between geographical races and species are due to the coöperation of numerous genes. The differences between nongeographical variations are more frequently monogenic. Now,

---

* Among the critics, at least one misunderstood the writer's definition as meaning that species hybrids are necessarily sterile. A reference to the list of physiological isolating mechanisms on p. 257 dispels this misapprehension; physiological isolation can be induced by any heritable property which limits or prevents the exchange of genes between populations. Doubtless, some species may cross and produce fertile offspring in experiments; what matters is whether populations do so in nature, and if not, whether it is prevented by a mere geographical separation or by some intrinsic properties as well. Other critics have argued that species in different organisms are so diverse that no definition can be valid. This is a logical fallacy since diversity does not necessarily preclude possession of some common properties. On the other hand, it is admitted that the definition in question is applicable only to sexual and cross-fertilizing forms.

the existence of discrete forms differing in complexes of genes is possible only provided they are debarred from interbreeding. The reverse is true for the nongeographical varieties, since there the interbreeding does not result in any decrease in the extent of the difference.

The geographical criterion of species distinction is regarded by some systematists as no less decisive than the presence of a hiatus in morphological and physiological characteristics (Semenov-Tian-Shansky 1910). The geographical distributions of races (subspecies) as a rule do not overlap. In species with a continuous distribution the races may merge into each other by a series of almost imperceptible gradations (Rensch 1929); or else races may be fairly definite entities separated from each other by more or less pronounced physical barriers; intermediate situations are likewise encountered, where the intergradations are localized in a narrow stretch of territory in which races meet. On the other hand, the geographical distributions of species overlap very frequently, without hybrids or intermediates being formed in the territory common to two or more species. In fact, the area of one species may be included in that of another without decreasing the sharpness of the separation. The presence of physiological isolating mechanisms is the only possible explanation of the preservation of differences between species with overlapping distributions. The occurrence of introgressive hybridization or of the "hybrid swarms" on the boundaries between the distribution areas of species (Chapter X) does not invalidate the general concept. Occasional hybridization may be a stimulus hastening the development of isolating mechanisms (Chapter VIII); furthermore, the possibility that physiologically incompletely isolated species may sometimes fuse together and be degraded to a single variable population cannot be disregarded. It is justifiable to conclude that if species separation is defined as the stage of the evolutionary divergence at which reproductive isolating mechanisms develop, the species so delimited and the species of systematists will largely coincide. Aside from apomictic and asexually reproducing organisms (see below), discrepancies will occur only in those relatively rare groups in which the appearance of physiological isolating mechanisms is not accompanied by a morphological divergence (Chapter X). Most systematists have, however, become reconciled to the idea that these "biological species" or "biological races" are equivalents of the ordinary "morphological species," although the former are indistinguishable in museum practice.

The importance of the presence or absence of interbreeding as a criterion of the species distinction is shown in a striking manner by the so-called "rings of races." Two distinct forms may coexist in the same territory without giving rise to intergrades, and yet they may be united by a series of races inhabiting other territories and

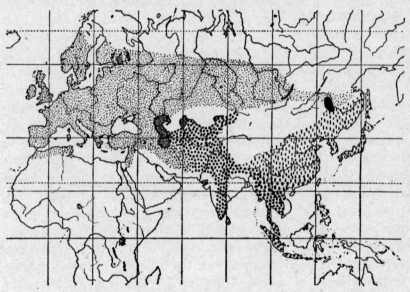

FIG. 24. The geographical distribution of *Parus major* and its relatives. *Parus major*—finely stippled; *P. bokharensis*—coarsely stippled; *P. minor* —vertical dashes; the area in which both *P. major* and *P. minor* occur side by side is shown in black. (From Rensch.)

imperceptibly grading into each other and into the extreme members of the series. The Asiatic titmouse *Parus minor* occupies the territory from Amur and Japan to Southern China, where it intergrades with *P. bokharensis*. The latter inhabits southern Asia from the Sunda Islands, through India, to Turkestan, and in Iran intergrades with the European *P. major*. The distribution of *P. major* extends across Siberia, and in the Amur region meets that of *P. minor;* in that region both forms occur in the same territory without inter-gradation (Stegmann 1931, Rensch 1933; see Fig. 24). If the species were to die out in India, for example, or anywhere along the "ring" of countries it occupies, the forms *major* and *minor* would doubtless be considered separate species, since they coexist in the same territory without hybridization and are, consequently, physiologically isolated (although the particular isolating mechanism which keeps them separate is not known). As the situation actually stands, a systematist is confronted with the impossibility of drawing. the "line" anywhere between the two. The nomenclatorial difficulty need not, however, obscure the evolutionary importance of the fact that the end members of the series have attained the stage at which interbreeding no longer takes place. A quite analogous situation has been described by Forbes (1928) in the butterfly *Junonia*. *Junonia lavinia coenia* inhabits the United States; in Mexico it intergrades with another race, which in turn intergrades with *Junonia lavinia zonalis* inhabiting the northern part of South America and the Antilles. In Cuba, however, both *coenia* and *zonalis* occur in the same territory without intergradation. Among the gall wasps *Cynips* rings of races appear to be extremely common (Kinsey 1936, 1937b). Species which coexist in the same region (as the United States) without interbreeding are frequently connected by a series of intermediate links inhabiting other regions (as Mexico or Central America); the discontinuities, which are quite striking if the fauna of only one region is studied, decrease and sometimes vanish when the entire diversity of forms of the genus is taken into account. (Other examples of rings of races may be found in Fischer-Piette 1935, Meise 1936, Stresemann 1936, and especially in Rensch 1933.)

As might be expected, different authors have made different evaluations of the phenomenon of racial rings. To Kinsey (1936, 1937b) the nomenclatorial difficulties involved seemed so important that he went to the length of proposing that the term species be applied only to the smallest distinguishable population unit. The "species" of Kinsey are, therefore, equivalent to races of other authors, while what is generally known as species he considers to be "higher categories." Goldschmidt (1940) ascribes no importance to the lack of interbreeding between extreme members of the chains in rings of races: "As a taxonomist, do with them what appears to be practical. But as an evolutionist, treat them as members of one species, which they most clearly are, though they do not interbreed in some localities, just as the Brahmin does not interbreed with a Pariah, his own near biological relative." We agree with the first part of Goldschmidt's advice, but emphatically do not agree with the second: as evolutionists we must treat the end members of the racial rings as different species, which they most clearly are.

"SPECIES" IN ASEXUAL ORGANISMS

An occasional, or regularly periodic, occurrence of self-fertilization, apogamy, or asexual reproduction in an organism need not cause any essential alteration in its evolutionary pattern (Chapter X). A species remains a group of populations which are actually or potentially able to exchange genes, and the species genotype as a collective unit continues to be a reality. The situation changes entirely as soon as selfing, apogamy, or asexual reproduction becomes predominant or obligatory instead of facultative or periodic. The resulting pure lines or clones consist of individuals which, barring mutation, are similar in genotype to each other and to their ancestors. On the other hand, these pure lines or clones do not exchange genes with each other, as such an exchange is precluded by their very method of reproduction. The genotype of each line is a closed system isolated from other similar ones and capable of changing only through mutation or through reversal to sexuality. It is not surprising that the groups of organisms recognized as being uncommonly "difficult" from the standpoint of delimiting species have proved to be mainly those in which asexual reproduction or self-fertilization are the only, or the predominant, modes of propagatior The standard examples of such "difficult" groups are the plant genera *Crataegus, Hieracium* and *Rubus*. The opinions of different authorities on what constitutes a species in these genera vary so widely that it is not uncommon to find that one investigator unites under a single specific name a complex of forms that is divided by others into numerous "species." Crow (1924) in his work on *Cyanophyceae* (algae) emphasizes that in this asexually reproducing group "the differences between closely related species rarely show that discontinuity which is apparent in many other groups of organisms," and that "individuals transitional between species are exceedingly common among the Cyanophyceae." The subdivision of the mass of clones into the species *Bacterium coli, B. typhi,* and *B. enteridis* is purely a matter of taste; one might just as well regard all of them as a single species (Baur 1930). The same is true for the lichen genus *Cladonia* and the related ones, in which a clear separation of species is impossible (but in which, nevertheless, a tremendous number of "species" have been described). Baur rightly points out, however, that such genera, constituting a "crux et scandalum botanicorum," are found mainly among the asexually reproducing forms.

The above statements should not be misunderstood as implying that the variation in asexually reproducing groups is absolutely continuous. On the contrary, we find there aggregations of numerous more or less clearly distinct biotypes, each of which is constant and reproduces its like if allowed to breed. These constant biotypes are sometimes called elementary species, but they are not united into integrated groups that are known as species in the cross-fertilizing forms. The term "elementary species" is therefore misleading and should be discarded. The existing biotypes obviously do not embody all the potentially possible combinations of genes. As in cross-fertilizing organisms, the biotypes in the asexual ones are clustered around some of the "adaptive peaks" in the field of gene combinations, while the "adaptive valleys" remain more or less uninhabited. Furthermore, the clusters are arranged in an hierarchical order, in a way which is again analogous to that encountered in sexual forms. The different clusters may, then, be designated some as species, others as subgenera, still others as genera, and so on. Which one of these ranks is ascribed to a given cluster is, however, decided by considerations of convenience, and the decision is in this sense purely arbitrary. In other words, the species as a category which is more fixed and therefore less arbitrary than the rest is lacking in asexual and obligatorily self-fertilizing organisms. All the criteria of species distinction (see above) utterly break down in such forms.

The binominal system of nomenclature, which is applied universally to all living beings, has forced systematists to describe "species" in the sexual as well as in the asexual organisms. Two centuries have rooted this habit so firmly that a radical reform is beyond practical possibility. Nevertheless, systematists themselves have come to the conclusion that sexual species and asexual ones or "agamospecies" must be distinguished (Du Rietz 1930). All that is saved by this method is the word "species." As pointed out by Babcock and Stebbins (1938), "The species, in the case of a sexual group, is an actuality as well as a human concept; in an agamic complex it ceases to be an actuality."

LITERATURE

LITERATURE

The following abbreviations of the names of periodicals are used below.

A.E.—Roux' Archiv für Entwicklungs-mechanik der Organismen
A.N.—American Naturalist
B.B.—Biological Bulletin (Woods Hole)
B.Z.—Biologisches Zentralblatt
B.Zh.—Biologichesky Zhurnal (Moscow)
C.—Cytologia
G.—Genetics
H.—Hereditas
J.E.Z.—Journal of Experimental Zoology
J.G.—Journal of Genetics
J.H.—Journal of Heredity
P.N.A.S.—Proceedings of the National Academy of Sciences (U.S.A.)
P.VI.C.G.—Proceedings of the VI International Congress of Genetics (Ithaca)
S.—Science
U.C.P.B.—University of California Publications, Botany
V.K.V.—Verhandlungen des V. Internationalen Kongresses für Vererbungswissenschaft (Berlin)
Z.i.A.V.—Zeitschrift für induktive Abstammungs- und Verebungslehre
Z.Z.m.A.—Zeitschrift für Zellforschung und mikroskopische Anatomie

Alpatov, W. W. 1929. Biometrical studies on variation and races of the honey bee (Apis mellifera L.). Quart. Rev. Biol., 4:1–58.

—— 1932. Egg production in *Drosophila melanogaster* and some factors which influence it. J.E.Z., 63:85–111.

Altschuler, V. 1930. Investigation on the variation of sublethality. Proc. USSR Congr. Genetics, Plant and Animal Breeding, 2:127–138.

Anderson, Edgar, 1924. Studies on self-sterility. VI. The genetic basis of cross-sterility in Nicotiana. G., 9:13–40.

—— 1936a. The species problem in Iris. Ann. Missouri Bot. Garden, 23: 457–509.

—— 1936b. An experimental study of hybridization in the genus Apocynum. Ann. Missouri Bot. Gardens, 23:159–167.

—— 1939a. Recombination in species crosses. G., 24:668–698.

—— 1939b. The genetic coefficients of specific difference. Ann. Missouri Bot. Garden, 26:325–348.

—— and L. Hubricht. 1938. Hybridization in Tradescantia. The evidence for introgressive hybridization. Amer. J. Bot., 25: 396–402.

—— and K. Sax. 1936. A cytological monograph of the American species of Tradescantia. Bot. Gazette, 97:433–476.

—— and T. W. Whitaker. 1934. Speciation in Uvularia. J. Arnold Arboretum, 15:28–41.

—— and R. E. Woodson. 1935. The species of Tradescantia indigenous to the United States. Contr. Arnold Arboretum, 9:1–132.

Arkell, W. J., and J. A. Moy-Thomas. 1940. Palaeontology and the taxonomic problem. Huxley's New Systematics, pp. 395–410.

384 LITERATURE

Arnason, T. J. 1936. Cytogenetics of hybrids between *Zea mays* and *Euchlaena mexicana*. G., 21:40–60.

Artom, Ch. 1931. L'origine e l'evoluzione della partenogenesi attraverso i differenti biotipi di una specie collettiva (*Artemia salina L.*) con speciale riferimento al biotipo diploide partenogenetico di Sète. Mem. Reale Accad. Italia, Fis. Mat. Nat., 2:1–57.

Avery, Priscilla. 1938. Cytogenetic evidences of Nicotiana phylesis in the alata-group. U.C.P.B., 18:153–194.

Babcock, E. B., and M. S. Cave. 1938. A study of intra- and interspecific relations of Crepis foetida L. Z.i.A.V., 75:124–160.

—— and M. Navashin. 1930. The genus Crepis. Bibliogr. Genetica, 6:1–90.

—— and G. L. Stebbins, Jr. 1938. The American species of Crepis. Carnegie Inst. Washington, Publ., 504.

Balkaschina, E. I., and D. D. Romaschoff. 1935. Genetische Struktur der Drosophila Populationen. I. Swenigoroder Populationen von *D. phalerata Meig., transversa Fall.* und *vibrissina Duda.* B.Zh., 4:81–106.

Banta, A. M. 1929. Studies on the physiology, genetics, and evolution of some Cladocera. XII. Adaptation and evolution. Carnegie Inst. Washington, Publ., 513:253–264.

—— and T. R. Wood. 1927. A thermal race of Cladocera originating by mutation. V.K.V., 1:397–398.

—— and T. R. Wood. 1939. Genetic studies in sexual reproduction. Carnegie Inst. Washington, Publ., 513:131–181.

Barulina, H. I., and H. A. Dombrovskaya. 1937. Genetic differentiation in geographical races. Bull. Appl. Bot. Gen., Plant Breeding, Ser. 2, 7:277–338.

Bateson, W. 1895 (1928). On the colour variations of a beetle of the family Chrysomelidae, statistically examined. Proc. Zool. Soc. 1895 (reprinted in: Scientific papers of William Bateson, Cambridge, University Press).

—— 1922. Evolutionary faith and modern doubts. S., 55:55–61.

Bauer, H. 1936. Beiträge zur vergleichenden Morphologie der Speicheldrüsenchromosomen. Zool. Jahrb. allg. zool. Physiol., 56:239–276.

—— 1939. Röntgenauslösung von Chromosomenmutationen bei *Drosophila melanogaster*. I. Bruchhäufigkeit, -verteilung und- rekombination nach Speicheldrüsenuntersuchungen. Chromosoma, 1:343–390.

—— M. Demerec, and B. P. Kaufmann. 1938. X-ray induced chromosomal alterations in *Drosophila melanogaster*. G., 23:610–630.

Baur, E. 1924. Untersuchungen über das Wesen, die Entstehung und die Vererbung von Rassenunterschieden bei Antirrhinum majus. Bibliotheca Genetica, 4:1–170.

—— 1925. Die Bedeutung der Mutationen für das Evolutionsproblem. Z.i.A.V., 37:107–115.

Baur, E. 1930. Einführung in die Vererbungslehre. 7–11 Aufl., Borntraeger, Berlin.

—— 1932. Artumgrenzung und Artbildung in der Gattung Antirrhinum, Sektion Antirrhinastrum. Z.i.A.V., 63:256–302.

Beadle, G. W. 1930. Genetical and cytological studies of Mendelian asynapsis in *Zea mays*. Cornell Univ. Agr. Exp. Sta., 129:1–23.

—— 1931. A gene in maize for supernumerary cell divisions following meiosis. Cornell Univ. Agr. Exp. Sta., 135:1–12.

—— 1932a. A gene for sticky chromosomes in *Zea mays*. Z.i.A.V., 63: 195–217.

—— 1932b. Genes in maize for pollen sterility. G., 17:413–431.

—— 1932c. A gene in *Zea mays* for failure of cytokinesis during meiosis. C., 3:142–155.

—— 1932d. A possible influence of the spindle fibre on crossing-over in Drosophila. P.N.A.S., 18:160–165.

—— 1933. Further studies of asynaptic maize. C., 3:269–287.

Belgovsky, M. L. 1937. A comparison of the frequency of induced mutations in *Drosophila simulans* and in its hybrid with *D. melanogaster*. Genetica, 19:370–386.

Beljajeff, M. M. 1927. Ein Experiment über die Bedeutung der Schutzfärbung. B.Z., 47:107–113.

—— 1930. Die Chromosomenkomplexe und ihre Beziehung zur Phylogenie bei den Lepidopteren. Z.i.A.V., 54:369–399.

Bellamy, A. W. 1922. Breeding experiments with the viviparous teleosts *Xiphophorus helleri* and *Platypoecilus maculatus*. Anat. Rec., 23:98–99.

Belling, J. 1927a. Configurations of bivalents of Hyacinthus with regard to segmental interchange. B.B., 52:480–487.

—— 1927b. The attachment of chromosomes at the reduction division in flowering plants. J.G., 18:177:205.

—— 1928. The ultimate chromomeres of Lilium and Aloe with regard to the number of genes. U.C.P.B., 14:307–318.

—— 1931. Chromomeres of Liliaceous plants. U.C.P.B., 16:153–170.

—— and A. F. Blakeslee. 1926. On the attachment of non-homologous chromosomes at the reduction division in certain 25-chromosome Daturas. P.N.A.S., 12:7–11.

Berg, R. L. 1937. The relative frequency of mutations in different chromosomes of *Drosophila melanogaster*. I. Lethal mutations; II. Sterility mutations. G., 22:225–240, 241–248.

Bergner, A. D., and A. F. Blakeslee. 1932. Cytology of the ferox-quercifolia-stramonium triangle in Datura. P.N.A.S., 18:151–159.

—— 1935. Chromosome ends in Datura discolor. P.N.A.S., 21:369–374.

—— J. L. Cartlege, and A. F. Blakeslee. 1934. Chromosome behavior due to a gene which prevents metaphase pairing in Datura. C., 6:19–37.

—— S. Satina, and A. F. Blakeslee. 1933. Prime types in Datura. P.N.A.S., 19:103–115.

Birkina, B. M. 1938. The effect of low temperature on the mutation process in *Drosophila melanogaster*. B.Zh., 7:653–660.

Blair, A. P. 1941. Variation, isolating mechanisms, and hybridization in certain Toads. G., 26:(in press).

Blair, W. F. 1940a. Home ranges and populations of the meadow vole in southern Michigan. J. Wildlife Management, 4:149–161.

—— 1940b. A study of prairie deer-mouse populations in Southern Michigan. Amer. Midland Natur., 24:273–305.

Blakeslee, A. F. 1922. Variations in Datura due to changes in chromosome number. A.N., 56:16–31.

—— 1929. Cryptic types in Datura due to chromosomal interchange and their geographical distribution. J.H., 20:177–190.

—— 1932. The species problem in Datura. P.VI.C.G., 1:104–120.

—— and A. G. Avery. 1937. Methods of inducing doubling of chromosomes in plants. J.H., 28:393–411.

—— and J. Belling. 1924. Chromosomal mutations in the Jimson weed, *Datura stramonium*. J.H., 15:194–206.

—— J. Belling, and M. E. Farnham. 1923. Inheritance of tetraploid Daturas. Bot. Gazette, 76: 329–373.

—— A. D. Bergner, and A. G. Avery. 1937. Geographical distribution of chromosomal prime types in *Datura stramonium*. C., Jubilee Volume: 1070–1093.

—— and R. E. Cleland. 1930. Circle formation in Datura and Oenothera. P.N.A.S., 16:177:189.

—— G. Morrison, and A. G. Avery. 1927. Mutations in a haploid Datura. J.H., 18:193–199.

Bleier, H. 1928. Genetik und Cytologie teilweise und ganz steriler Getreidebastarde. Bibliogr. Genetica, 4:321–400.

—— 1933. Die meiosis von Haplodiplonten. Genetica, 15:129–176.

—— 1934. Bastardkaryologie. Bibliogr. Genetica, 11:393–485.

Boettger, C. 1922. Über freilebende Hybriden der Landschnecken *Cepaea nemoralis* L. und *Cepaea hortensis Müll.* Zool. Jahrb. Systematik, 44: 297–336.

Bonnier, G. 1924. Contributions to the knowledge of intra- and interspecific relationship in Drosophila. Acta Zool., 5:1–122.

—— 1927. Species-differences and gene-differences. H., 9:137–144.

Boveri, Th. 1904. Ergebnisse über die Konstitution der Chromatischen Substanz des Zellkerns. Gustav Fisher, Jena.

Boyce, A. M. 1935. The codling moth in Persian walnuts. J. Econ. Entom., 28:864–873.

Boyd, W. C. 1939. Blood groups. Tabulae Biologicae, 17 (2):113–240.

Boyes, J. W., and W. P. Thompson. 1937. The development of the endosperm and embryo in reciprocal interspecific crosses in cereals. J.G., 34:203–227.

Braun, W. 1938. Opposite effect of environmental factors on similar phenotypes. A.N., 72:189–192.

Bridges, C. B. 1917. Deficiency. G., 2:445–465.

—— 1919. Duplications. Anat. Record, 15:357.

—— 1923. The translocation of a section of chromosome II upon chromosome III in Drosophila. Anat. Record, 24:426–427.

—— 1935. Salivary chromosome maps. J.H., 26:60–64.

—— 1936. The bar "gene" a duplication. S., 83:210–211.

Brieger, F. 1928. Über die Verdoppelung der Chromosomenzahl bei Nicotiana Artbastarden. Z.i.A.V., 47:1–53.

—— 1930. Selbststerilität und Kreuzungssterilität im Pflanzenreich und Tierreich. J. Springer, Berlin.

—— 1935. Genetic analysis of the cross between the self-fertile *Nicotiana langsdorfii* and the self-sterile *N. sanderae*. J.G., 30:79–100.

Brierley, J. 1938. An exploratory investigation of the selective value of certain genes and their combinations in Drosophila. Biol. Bull., 75: 475–493.

Brink, R. A. 1929. The occurrence of semi-sterility in maize. J.H., 20: 266–269.

—— and C. R. Burnham, 1929. Inheritance of semi-sterility in maize. A.N., 43:301–316.

Brooks, W. K. 1899. The foundations of zoology. Columbia University Press, New York.

Brown Suche, M. 1940. The relation between chiasma formation and disjunction. Univ. Texas Publ., 4032:11–64.

Buchholz, J. T., L. F. Williams, and A. F. Blakeslee. 1935. Pollen-tube growth of ten species of Datura in interspecific pollinations. P.N.A.S., 21:651–656.

Buchmann, W., und N. V. Timofeeff-Ressovsky. 1935. Über die Wirkung der Temperatur auf den Mutationsprozess bei Drosophila melanogaster. II. Behandlung der Männchen mit Temperaturschocks. Z.i.A.V., 70: 130–137.

—— Über die Wirkung der Temperatur auf den Mutationsprozess bei *Drosophila melanogaster*. III. Behandlung der Weibchen mit Temperaturschocks. Z.i.A.V., 71:335–340.

Buck, A. de, E. Schoute, and N. H. Swellengrebel. 1934. Cross-breeding experiments with Dutch and foreign races of *Anopheles maculipennis*. Riv. Malariologia, 13:237–263.

Burnham, C. R. 1930. Genetical and cytological studies of semisterility and related phenomena in maize. P.N.A.S., 16:269–277.

—— 1932. An interchange in maize giving low sterility and chain configurations. P.N.A.S., 18:434–440.

Burt, W. H. 1940. Territorial behavior and populations of some small mammals in southern Michigan. Misc. Publ. Mus. Zool. Univ. Mich., 45:1–58.

Buxton, B. H., and W. C. F. Newton. 1928. Hybrids of *Digitalis ambigua* and *Digitalis purpurea*, their fertility and cytology. J.G., 19:269–279.

Buxton, B. H., and C. D. Darlington. 1932. Behaviour of a new species, *Digitalis mertonensis*. New Phytol., 31:225–240.

Bytinski-Saltz, H. 1933. Untersuchungen an Lepidopterenhybriden. II. Entwicklungsphysiologische Experimente über die Wirkung der disharmonischen Chromosomenkombinationen. A.E., 129:356–378.

Carlson, J. G. 1941. An analysis of X-ray induced single breaks in neuroblast chromosomes of the grasshopper (Chortophaga viridifasciata). P.N.A.S., 27:42–47.

Carothers, E. 1917. The segregation and recombination of homologous chromosomes as found in two genera of Acrididae (Orthoptera). J. Morphology, 28:445–521.

—— 1931. The maturation divisions and segregation of heteromorphic homologous chromosomes in Acrididae (Orthoptera). B.B., 61:324–349.

Cartlege, J. L., M. J. Murray, and A. F. Blakeslee. 1935. Increased mutation rate from aged Datura pollen. P.N.A.S., 21:597–600.

Catcheside, D. G. 1932. The chromosomes of a new haploid Oenothera. C., 4:68–113.

—— 1938. The effect of X-ray dosage upon the frequency of induced structural changes in the chromosomes of *Drosophila melanogaster*. J.G., 36:307–320.

Chapman, Frank M. 1936. Further remarks on Quiscalus with a report on additional specimens from Louisiana. The Auk, 53:405–417.

—— 1939. Quiscalus in Mississippi. The Auk, 56:27–30.

Chipman, R. H., and T. H. Goodspeed. 1927. Inheritance in *Nicotiana tabacum* VIII. Cytological features of purpurea haploid. U.C.P.B., 11:141–158.

Chopard, L., and R. Bellecroix. 1928. Dimorphisme alaire chez les Gryllides, répartition géographique des formes macroptères et brachyptères. Bull. Biol. France Belgique, 62:157–163.

Clark, F. J. 1940. Cytogenetic studies of divergent meiotic spindle formation in Zea mays. Amer. J. Botany, 27:547–559.

Clausen, J. 1927. Chromosome number and the relationship of species in the genus Viola. Ann. Bot., 41:677–714.

—— 1931a. Cyto-genetic and taxonomic investigations on Melanium violets. H., 15:219–308.

—— 1931b. Genetic studies on Polemonium. III. Preliminary account on the cytology of species and species hybrids. H., 15:62–66.

—— 1933. Cytological evidence for the hybrid origin of *Penstemon neotericus Keck*, H., 18:65–76.

—— D. D. Keck, and W. M. Hiesey. 1940. Experimental studies on the nature of species. I. Effects of varied environments on western North American plants. Carnegie Inst. Washington, Publ., 520: 1–452.

Clausen, R. E. 1928a. Interspecific hybridization in Nicotiana. VII. The cytology of hybrids of the synthetic species, *digluta,* with its parents, *glutinosa* and *tabacum.* U.C.P.B., 11:177–211.

—— 1928b. Interspecific hybridization and the origin of species in Nicotiana. V.K.V., 1:547–553.

—— and T. H. Goodspeed. 1925. Interspecific hybridization in Nicotiana. II. A tetraploid *glutinosa-tabacum* hybrid, an experimental verification of Winge's hypothesis. G., 10:278–284.

Cleland, R. E. 1937. Species relationships in Onagra. Proc. Amer. Philos. Soc., 77:477–542.

—— and A. F. Blakeslee. 1931. Segmental interchange, the basis of chromosomal attachments in Oenothera. C., 2:175–233.

Collins, J. L., L. Hollingshead and P. Avery. 1929. Interspecific hybrids in Crepis. III. Constant fertile forms containing chromosomes derived from two species. G., 14:305–320.

Correns, C. 1902. Über Bastardirungsversuche mit Mirabilis-Sippen. Ber. Deutsch. Bot. Ges., 20:549–608.

—— 1937. Nicht mendelnde Vererbung. Handbuch Vererbungswiss., 22(II,H), Borntraeger, Berlin.

Cott, H. B. 1940. Adaptive coloration in animals. Methuen & Co., London.

Cousin, G. 1934. Sur la fécondité normale et les caractères des hybrides issus du croisement de deux espèces de Gryllides. C.R. Acad. Sci. Paris, 198:853–855.

Crampton, H. E. 1916. Studies on the variation, distribution, and evolution of the genus Partula. The species inhabiting Tahiti. Carnegie Inst. Washington, Publ., 228:1–311.

—— 1932. Studies on the variation, distribution, and evolution of the genus Partula. The species inhabiting Moorea. Carnegie Inst. Washington, Publ., 410:1–335.

Cretschmar, M. 1928. Das Verhalten der Chromosomen bei der Spermatogenese von *Orgyia thyellina* Btl. und *antiqua* L., sowie eines ihrer Bastarde. Z.Z.m.A., 7:290–399.

Crew, F. A. E., and P. C. Koller. 1936. Genetical and cytological studies of the intergeneric hybrid of *Cairina moschata* and *Anas platyrhyncha platyrhyncha.* Proc. R. Soc. Edinburgh, 56, III:210–241.

Crew, F. A. E., and R. Lamy. 1935. Linkage groups in *Drosophila pseudoobscura.* J.G., 30:15–29.

Crow, J. F. 1941. Studies in Drosophila speciation: I. The *Drosophila mulleri* group. G., 26:146.

Crow, W. B. 1924. Variation and species in Cyanophyceae. J.G., 14:397–424.

Csik, L. 1935. Die Wirkung einiger Genkombinationen auf die Lebensfähigkeit von *Drosophila melanogaster.* Z.i.A.V., 68:209–221.

Cuénot, L. 1933. La seiche commune de la Méditerranée; étude sur la naissance d'une espéce. Arch. Zool. Exp. Gén. 75:319–330.

Dahlberg, G. 1929. Inbreeding in man. G., 14:421–454.

—— 1938. On rare defects in human populations with particular regard to inbreeding and isolate effects. Proc. R. Soc. Edinburgh, 58:213–232.

Darlington, C. D. 1928. Studies in Prunus, I and II. J.G., 19:213–256.

—— 1929a. Chromosome behaviour and structural hybridity in the Tradescantiae. J.G., 21:207–286.

—— 1929b. Ring-formation in Oenothera and other genera. J.G., 20:345–363.

—— 1931. Meiosis in diploid and tetraploid Primula sinensis. J.G., 24:65–96.

—— 1932a. Recent advances in cytology. Blakiston's, Philadelphia.

—— 1932b. The control of the chromosomes by the genotype and its bearing on some evolutionary problems. A.N., 66:25–51.

—— 1936. Crossing over and its mechanical relationships in Chorthippus and Stauroderus. J.G., 33:465–500.

—— 1937a. Chromosome behaviour and structural hybridity in the Tradescantiae. II. J.G., 35:259–280.

—— 1937b. Recent advances in cytology. Second edition, Blakiston's, Philadelphia.

—— 1939. Misdivision and the genetics of the centomere. J.G., 37:341–364.

—— 1940. The origin of iso-chromosomes. J.G., 39:351–361.

—— and A. E. Gairdner. 1937. The variation system in Campanula persicifolia. J.G., 35:97–128.

Demerec, M. 1929a. Genetic factors stimulating mutability of the miniature-gamma wing character of Drosophila virilis. P.N.A.S., 15:834–838.

—— 1929b. Cross sterility in maize. Z.i.A.V., 50:281–291.

—— 1933. What is a gene? J.H., 24:369–378.

—— 1934. Biological action of small deficiencies of X-chromosome of Drosophila melanogaster. P.N.A.S., 20:354–359.

—— 1935a. Unstable genes. Bot. Reviews, 1:233–248.

—— 1935b. Cytogenetic evolutionary processes and their bearing on evolutionary theory. A.N., 69:125–138.

—— 1936. Frequency of "cell-lethals" among lethals obtained at random in the X-chromosome of Drosophila melanogaster. P.N.A.S., 22:350–354.

—— 1937a. A mutability stimulating factor in the Florida stock of Drosophila melanogaster. G., 22:190.

—— 1937b. Frequency of spontaneous mutations in certain stocks of Drosophila melanogaster. G., 22:469–478.

—— 1939. L'importanza di alcuni loci per l'organismo. Scientia Genetica, 1:123–128.

—— and U. Fano. 1941. Mechanism of the origin of X-ray induced Notch deficiencies in Drosophila melanogaster. P.N.A.S., 27:24–31.

—— B. P. Kaufmann, and M. E. Hoover. 1938. The gene. Carnegie Inst. Washington, Year Book, 1938:40–47.

Demerec, M., and M. E. Hoover. 1936. Three related X-chromosome deficiencies in Drosophila. J.H., 27:207–212.

—— and M. E. Hoover. 1939. Hairy-wing—a duplication in *Drosophila melanogaster*. G., 24:271–277.

Detlefsen, J. A. 1914. Genetic studies on a cavy species cross. Carnegie Inst. Washington, Publ., 205:5–134.

Dice, L. R. 1931. The occurrence of two subspecies of the same species in the same area. J. Mammalogy, 12:210–213.

—— 1933. Fertility relationships between some of the species and sub-species of mice in the genus Peromyscus. J. Mammalogy, 14:298–305.

—— 1939a. Variation in the cactus mouse, Peromyscus eremicus. Con-trib. Lab. Vert. Gen. Univ. Mich., 10:1–27.

—— 1939b. Variation in the deer mouse (Peromyscus maniculatus) in the Columbia Basin of southeastern Washington and adjacent Idaho and Oregon. Contrib. Lab. Vert. Gen. Univ. Mich., 12:1–22.

—— 1939c. Variation in the wood mouse, *Peromyscus lencopus,* from several localities in New England and Nova Scotia. Contrib. Lab. Vert. Gen. Univ. Mich., 9:1–16.

—— 1939d. An estimate of the population of deer mice in the Black Hills of South Dakota, and Wyoming. Contrib. Lab. Vert. Gen. Univ. Mich., 10:1–5.

—— 1940a. Ecologic and genetic variability within species of Peromyscus. A.N., 74:212–221.

—— 1940b. Speciation in Peromyscus. A.N., 74:289–298.

—— and P. M. Blossom. 1937. Studies of mammalian ecology in south-western North America with special attention to the colors of desert mammals. Carnegie Inst. Washington, Publ., 485.

Dickson, R. C. 1940. Inheritance of resistance to hydrocyanic acid fumi-gation in the California red scale. Hilgardia, in press.

Digby, L. 1912. The cytology of Primula kewensis and of other related Primula hybrids. Ann. Bot., 26:357–388.

Diver, C. 1939. Aspects of the study of variation in snails. J. Conchology, 21:91–141.

—— 1940. The problem of closely related species living in the same area. Huxley's New Systematics, pp. 303–328.

—— A. E. Boycott, and S. Garstang. 1925. The inheritance of inverse symmetry in *Limnaea peregra*. J.G., 15:113–200.

Dobzhansky, Th. 1927. Studies on manifold effect of certain genes in *Drosophila melanogaster*. Z.i.A.V., 43:330–388.

—— 1930a. The manifold effects of the genes Stubble and stubbloid in *Drosophila melanogaster*. Z.i.A.V., 54:427–457.

—— 1930b. Translocations involving the third and the fourth chromo-somes of *Drosophila melanogaster*. G., 15:347–399.

—— 1931. The decrease of crossing over observed in translocations, and its probable explanation. A.N., 65:214–232.

Dobzhansky, Th. 1932. Studies on chromosome conjugation. I. Translocations involving the second and the Y-chromosome of *Drosophila melanogaster*. Z.i.A.V., 60:235–286.

—— 1933a. Studies on chromosome conjugation. II. The relation between crossing over and disjunction of chromosomes. Z.i.A.V., 64:269–309.

—— 1933b. On the sterility of the interracial hybrids in *Drosophila pseudoobscura*. P.N.A.S., 19:397–403.

—— 1933c. Geographical variation in lady-beetles. A.N., 67:97–126.

—— 1933d. Rôle of the autosomes in the *Drosophila pseudoobscura* hybrids. P.N.A.S., 11:950–953.

—— 1934a. Studies on chromosome conjugation. III. Behavior of duplicating fragments. Z.i.A.V., 68:134–162.

—— 1934b. Studies on hybrid sterility. I. Spermatogenesis in pure and hybrid *Drosophila pseudoobscura*. Z.Z.m.A., 21:169–223.

—— 1935a. *Drosophila miranda*, a new species. G., 21:377–391.

—— 1935b. The Y-chromosome of *Drosophila pseudoobscura*. G., 20: 366–376.

—— 1935c. Maternal effects as a cause of the difference between the reciprocal crosses in *Drosophila pseudoobscura*. P.N.A.S., 21:443–446.

—— 1935d. Fecundity in *Drosophila pseudoobscura* at different temperatures. J.E.Z., 71:449–464.

—— 1935e. A critique of the species concept in biology. Philosophy of Science, 2:344–355.

—— 1936a. Induced chromosomal aberrations in animals. Biol. Effects of Radiation. 2:1167–1208.

—— 1936b. Studies on hybrid sterility. II. Localization of sterility factors in *Drosophila pseudoobscura* hybrids. G., 21:113–135.

—— 1936c. Position effects of genes. Biol. Reviews, 11:364–384.

—— 1936d. L'effet de position et la théorie de l'hérédité. Hermann, Paris.

—— 1936e. The persistence of the chromosome pattern in successive cell divisions in *Drosophila pseudoobscura*. J.E.Z., 74:119–135.

—— 1937a. Genetic nature of species differences. A.N., 71:404–420.

—— 1937b. Further data on *Drosophila miranda* and its hybrids with *Drosophila pseudoobscura*. J.G., 34:135–151.

—— 1937c. Further data on the variation of the Y-chromosome in *Drosophila pseudoobscura*. G., 22:340–346.

—— 1939a. Genetics of natural populations. IV. Mexican and Guatemalan populations of *Drosophila pseudoobscura*. G., 24:391–412.

—— 1939b. Experimental studies on genetics of free-living populations of Drosophila. Biol. Reviews, 14:339–368.

—— 1940. Speciation as a stage in evolutionary divergence. A.N., 74: 312–321.

—— 1941. Discovery of a predicted gene arrangement in *Drosophila azteca*. P.N.A.S., 27:47–50.

Dobzhansky, Th., and G. W. Beadle, 1936. Studies on hybrid sterility. IV. Transplanted testes in *Drosophila pseudoobscura*. G., 21:832–840.

—— and R. D. Boche. 1933. Intersterile races of *Drosophila pseudoobscura Frol*. B.Z., 54:314–330.

—— and P. C. Koller. 1938. An experimental study of sexual isolation in Drosophila. B.Z., 58:589–607.

—— and M. L. Queal. 1938. Genetics of natural populations. II. Genic variation in populations of *Drosophila pseudoobscura* inhabiting isolated mountain ranges. G., 23:463–484.

—— and D. Socolov. 1939. Structure and variation of the chromosomes in *Drosophila azteca*. J.H., 30:3–19.

—— and A. H. Sturtevant. 1931. Translocations between the second and third chromosomes of Drosophila and their bearing on Oenothera problems. Carnegie Inst. Washington, Publ., 421:29–59.

—— and A. H. Sturtevant. 1935. Further data on maternal effects in *Drosophila pseudoobscura* hybrids. P.N.A.S., 21:566–570.

—— and A. H. Sturtevant. 1938. Inversions in the chromosomes of *Drosophila pseudoobscura*. G., 23:28–64.

—— and C. C. Tan. 1936. Studies on hybrid sterility. III. A comparison of the gene arrangement in two species, *Drosophila pseudoobscura* and *Drosophila miranda*. Z.i.A.V., 72:88–114.

—— and S. Wright. 1941. Genetics of natural populations. V. Relations between mutation rate and accumulation of lethals in populations of *Drosophila pseudoobscura*. G., 26:23–51.

Donald, H. P. 1936. On the genetical constitution of *Drosophila pseudoobscura*, race A. J.G., 33:103–122.

Donchenko, V. V., and N. N. Medvedev. 1935. A case of dependence of success of interspecific hybridization upon a single gene. C. R. (Doklady) Acad. Sci. URSS, 2:67–70.

Dowdeswell, W. H., R. A. Fisher, and E. B. Ford. 1940. The quantitative study of populations in the Lepidoptera. I. *Polyommatus icarus Rott*. Ann. Eugenics, 10:123–136.

Drygalski, U. V. 1935. Über die Entstehung einer tetraploiden, genetisch ungleichmässigen F_2 aus Kreuzung Saxifraga adscendens L. × Saxifraga tridactylites L. Z.i.A.V., 69:278–300.

Dubinin, N. P. 1930. On the origin of deleted X-chromosomes. J. Exp. Biol. (Russian), 6:365–368.

—— 1931. Genetico-automatical processes and their bearing on the mechanism of organic evolution. J. Exp. Biol. (Russian), 7:463–479.

—— 1934. Experimental reduction of the number of chromosome pairs in *Drosophila melanogaster*. B.Zh., 3:719–736.

—— 1936. Experimental alteration of the number of chromosome pairs in *Drosophila melanogaster*. B.Zh., 5:833–850.

—— M. A. Heptner, Z. A. Demidova, and L. I. Djachkova. 1936. The genetical structure of the population and its dynamics in wild *Drosophila melanogaster*. B.Zh., 5:939–976.

Dubinin, N. P., and D. D. Romaschoff. 1932. Die genetische Struktur der Art und ihre Evolution. B.Zh., 1:52–95.

—— D. D. Romashov (Romaschoff), M. A. Heptner, and Z. A. Demidova. 1937. Aberrant polymorphysm in *Drosophila fasciata Meig*. (Syn.-melanogaster Meig). B.Zh., 6:311–354.

—— and B. N. Sidorov. 1935. The position effect of the hairy gene. B.Zh., 4:555–568.

—— N. N. Sokolov, and G. G. Tiniakov. 1936. Occurrence and distribution of chromosome aberrations in nature. Nature, 138:1035–1036.

—— N. N. Sokolov, and G. G. Tiniakov. 1937. Intraspecific chromosome variability. B.Zh., 6:1007–1054.

——N. N. Sokolov, G. G. Tiniakov, and W. W. Sacharov. 1935. On the problem of chromosome conjugation. B.Zh., 4:175–204.

—— and fourteen collaborators. 1934. Experimental study of the ecogenotypes of *Drosophila melanogaster*. B.Zh., 3:166–216.

Dubovskij, N. V. 1935. On the question of the comparative mutability of stocks of *Drosophila melanogaster* of different origin. C.R. Acad. Sci. URSS, 4:95–97.

Dunn, L. C. 1921. Unit character variation in rodents. J. Mammalogy, 2:125–140.

—— 1937a. Studies on spotting patterns. II. Genetic analysis of variegated spotting in the house mouse. G., 22:43–64.

—— 1937b. A third lethal in the T (Branchy) series in the house mouse. P.N.A.S., 9:474–477.

—— and W. Landauer. 1934. The genetics of the rumpless fowl, with evidence of a case of changing dominance. J.G., 29:217–243.

—— and W. Landauer. 1936. Further data on genetic modification of rumplessness in the fowl. J.G., 33:401–405.

Du Rietz, G. E. 1930. The fundamental units of botanical taxonomy. Svensk. Bot. Tidskrift, 24:333–428.

East, E. M. 1916. Inheritance in crosses between *Nicotiana langsdorfii* and *Nicotiana alata*. G., 1:311–333.

Eisentraut, M. 1934. Markierungsversuche bei Fledermäusen. Zeits. Morph. Ökol. Tiere, 28:553–560.

Ellison, W. 1938. The occurrence of quadrivalents in certain diploid and tetraploid Avena hybrids. J.G., 36:515–522.

Elton, C. S. 1924. Periodic fluctuations in the numbers of animals: their causes and effects. Brit. J. Exp. Biol., 2:119–163.

—— 1927. Animal ecology. Macmillan, New York.

Emerson, A. E. 1935. Termitophile distribution and quantitative characters as indicators of physiological speciation in British Guiana termites (Isoptera). Ann. Entom. Soc. America, 28:369–395.

—— 1938. The origin of species. Ecology, 19:152–154.

Emerson, Sterling. 1929. The reduction division in a haploid Oenothera. La Cellule, 39:159–165.

—— 1939. A preliminary survey of the Oenothera organensis population. G., 24:524–537.

—— and A. H. Sturtevant. 1931. Genetic and cytological studies on Oenothera. III. The translocation interpretation. Z.i.A.V., 59:395–419.

Emsweller, S. L., and H. A. Jones. 1938. Crossing over, fragmentation, and formation of new chromosomes in an Allium species hybrid. Bot. Gaz., 99: 729–772.

Ephrussi, B. 1934. The absence of autonomy in the development of the effects of certain deficiencies in Drosophila melanogaster. P.N.A.S., 20: 420–422.

—— B., et G. W. Beadle. 1935. La transplantation des ovaires chez la Drosophile. Bull. Biol. France Belgique, 69:492–502.

Epling, Carl. 1939. An approach to classification. Sci. Monthly, 49:1–8.

Erickson, M. M. 1938. Territory, annual cycle, and numbers in a population of wren-tits (Chamaea fasciata). Univ. Calif. Publ. Zool., 42:247–333.

Fabergé, A. C. 1940. An experiment on chromosome fragmentation in Tradescantia by X-rays. J.G., 39:229–248.

Fankhauser, G. 1938. Triploidy in the newt, Triturus vividescens. Proc. Amer. Philos. Soc., 79:715–739.

—— 1939. Polyploidy in the Salamander, Eurycea bislineata. J.H., 30: 379–388.

Federley, H. 1913. Das Verhalten der Chromosomen bei der Spermatogenese der Schmetterlinge Pygaera anachoreta, curtula und pigra sowie einiger ihrer Bastarde. Z.i.A.V., 9:1–110.

—— 1914. Ein Beitrag zur Kenntnis der Spermatogenese bei Mischlingen zwischen Eltern verschiedener systematischer Verwandtschaft. Öfv. Finska Veten. Soc. Förhandl., 56:1–28.

—— 1915a. Chromosomenstudien an Mischlingen. I. Die Chromosomenkonjugation bei der Gametogenese von Smerinthus populi var. austauti × populi. Öfv. Finska Veten. Soc. Förhandl., 57, No. 26:1–36.

—— 1915b. Chromosomenstudien an Mischlingen. II. Die Spermatogenese des Bastards Dicranura erminea ♀ × D. vinula ♂. Öfv. Finska Veten. Soc. Förhandl., 57, No. 30:1–26.

—— 1916. Chromosomenstudien an Mischlingen. III. Die Spermatogenese des Bastards Chaerocampa porcellus ♀ × elpenor ♂. Öfv. Finska Veten. Soc. Förhandl., 58, No. 12:1–17.

—— 1928. Das Inzuchtsproblem. Handbuch der Vererbungswissenschaft, Borntraeger, Berlin.

—— 1929a. Über subletale und disharmonische Chromosomenkombinationen. H., 12:271–293.

—— 1929b. Metoden zur Erforschung der Vererbung bei den Lepidopteren. Abderhalden Handb. biol. Arbeitsmethoden, Abt. 9, 3:637–690.

Federley, H. 1931. Chromosomenanalyse der reziproken Bastarde zwischen *Pygaera pigra* und *P. curtula* sowie ihrer Rückkreuzungsbastarde. Z.Z.m.A., 12:772–816.

—— 1932. Die Bedeutung der Kreuzung für die Evolution. Jenaische Zeits. Naturwiss., 67:364–386.

—— 1938. Chromosomenzahlen finnländischer Lepidopteren. I. Rhopalocera. H., 24:397–464.

—— 1939. Geni e chromosomi. Sci. Genetica, 1:186–205.

Fischer-Piette, E. 1935. Les patelles d'Europe et d'Afrique du nord. J. Conchyliologie, 79:5–66.

Fisher, J., and Vevers, H. G. 1939. The world distribution and numbers of breeding gannets. Bull. Brit. Ornith. Club, 60:39–41.

Fisher, R. A. 1922. On the dominance ratio. Proc. R. Soc. Edinburgh, 42: 321–341.

—— 1928. The possible modification of the response of the wild type to recurrent mutations. A.N., 62:115–126.

—— 1930. The genetical theory of natural selection. Clarendon Press, Oxford.

—— 1931. The evolution of dominance. Biol. Reviews, 6:345–368.

—— 1932. The evolutionary modification of genetic phenomena. P.VI.C.G., 1:165–172.

—— 1935. Dominance in poultry. Philos. Trans. R. Soc. London. 225: 195–226.

—— 1936. The measurement of selective intensity. Proc. R. Soc. London, Serie B, 121:58–62.

Flovik, K. 1938. Cytological studies on arctic grasses. H., 24:265–376.

—— 1940. Chromosome numbers and polyploidy within the flora of Spitzbergen. H., 26:430–440.

Forbes, W. T. M. 1928. Variation in Yunonia lavinia (Lepidoptera, Nymphalidae). J. New York Entom. Soc., 36:305–320.

Ford, E. B. 1930. The theory of dominance. A.N., 64:560–566.

—— 1937. Problems of heredity in the Lepidoptera. Biol. Reviews, 12: 461–503.

—— 1940a. Polymorphism and taxonomy. Huxley's New Systematics. Clarendon Press, Oxford.

—— 1940b. Genetic research in the Lepidoptera. Ann. Eugenics, 10:227–252.

Fox, H. M. 1937. The activity and metabolism of poikilothermal animals in different latitudes. I. Proc. Zool. Soc. London, 1936:945–955.

—— 1939. The activity and metabolism of poikilothermal animals in different latitudes. Proc. Zool. Soc. London, A, 109:141–156.

Frankel. O. H. 1937. Inversions in Fritillaria. J.G., 34:447–462.

Franz, V. 1928. Über Bastardpopulation in der Gattung Paludina (recte: Viviparus). B.Z., 48:79–93.

Friesen, H. 1936. Röntgenomorphosen bei Drosophila. A.E., 134:147–165.

Frisch, Karl von. 1927. Aus dem Leben der Bienen. Julius Springer, Berlin.

Frolova, S. L. 1936. Several spontaneous chromosome aberrations in Drosophila. Nature, 138:204–205.

Fulton, B. B. 1933. Inheritance of song in hybrids of two subspecies of Nemobius fasciatus (Orthoptera). Ann. Entom. Soc. America, 26:368–376.

Gaines, E. F., and H. C. Aase. 1926. A haploid wheat plant. Amer. J. Bot. 13:373–385.

Gairdner, A. E. and C. D. Darlington. 1931. Ring formation in diploid and polyploid Campanula persicifolia. Genetica, 13:113–150.

Gaisinovich. 1928. A study on the phenomenon of malelessness in Drosophila falerata Meig. J. Exp. Biol. (Russian), 4:233–250.

Galtsoff, P. S. 1930. The role of chemical stimulation in the spawning reactions of Ostrea virginica and Ostrea gigas. P.N.A.S., 16:555–559.

Ganesan, D. 1939. Cytological studies in a chromosome ring-forming diploid Natonia grandiflora Dc. J.G., 38:493–516.

Gause, G. F. 1934. The struggle for existence. Williams & Wilkins, Baltimore.

Geitler, L. 1938. Weitere cytogenetische Untersuchungen an natürlichen Populationen von Paris quadrofolia. Z.i.A.V., 75:161–190.

Gentcheff, G., and Å. Gustafsson. 1940. The balance system of meiosis in Hieracium. H., 26:209–249.

Gerhardt, U. 1938. Zur Frage der Sexualbiologie und Artzugehörigkeit von Limax albipes Dumont und Mortillet. Zeits. Morph. Ökol., 34:79–88.

—— 1939. Neue biologische Untensuchungen an Limaciden. Zeits. Morph. Ökol., 35:183–202.

Gershenson, S. 1934. Mutant genes in a wild population of Drosophila obscura Fall. A.N., 68:569–571.

—— 1940. Induction of directed mutations in Drosophila. C.R., Acad. Sci. URSS, 25:236–238.

Giles, N. 1940. Spontaneous chromosome aberrations in Tradescantia. G., 25:69–87.

Gilmour, J. S. L. 1940. Taxonomy and philosophy. Huxley's New Systematics, Clarendon Press, Oxford.

Glass, H. B. 1935. A study of factors influencing chromosomal segregation in translocations of Drosophila melanogaster. Univ. Missouri Agric. Exp. Sta., Res. Bull., 231:1–28.

—— 1940. Differential susceptibility of the sexes of Drosophila to the effect of X-rays in producing chromosome aberrations. G., 25:117.

Godlewski, E. 1926. L'inhibition réciproque de l'aptitude à féconder de spermes d'espèces éloignées comme conséquence de l'agglutination des spermatozoides. Arch. Biologie, 36:311–350.

Goldat, S. J., and V. N. Beliaieva. 1935. Artificial induction of mutations in *Drosophila melanogaster* through hydrochloric acid. B.Zh., 4:379–384.

Goldschmidt, R. 1921. Erblichkeitsstudien an Schmetterlingen III. Der Melanismus der Nonne, *Lymantria monacha L.* Z.i.A.V., 25:89–163.

—— 1924. Erblichkeitsstudien an Schmetterlingen IV. Weitere Untersuchungen über die Vererbung des Melanismus. Z.i.A.V., 34:229–244.

—— 1929a. Untersuchungen zur Genetik der geographischen Variation II. A.E., 116:136–201.

—— 1929b. Experimentelle Mutationen und das Problem der sogenannten Parallel-Induktion. B.Z., 49:437–448.

—— 1931. Die sexuellen Zwischenstufen. J. Springer, Berlin.

—— 1932a. Untersuchungen zur Genetik der geographischen Variation III. Abschliessendes über die Geschlechtsrassen von *Lymantria dispar*. A.E., 126:277–324.

—— 1932b. Untersuchungen zur Genetik der geographischen Variation. IV. Cytologisches. A.E., 126:591–612.

—— 1932c. Untersuchungen zur Genetik der geographischen Variation. V. Analyse der Überwinterungszeit als Anpassungscharakter. A.E., 126: 674–768.

—— 1933a. Untersuchungen zur Genetik der geographischen Variation. VI. Die geographischen Variation der Entwicklungsgeschwindigkeit und des Grössenwachstums. A.E., 130:266–339.

—— 1933b. Untersuchungen zur Genetik der geographischen Variation. VII. A.E., 130:562–615.

—— 1933c. Some aspects of evolution. S., 78:539–547.

—— 1934a. Die Genetik der geographischen Variation. P.VI.C.G., 1: 173–184.

—— 1934b. Lymantria. Bibliogr. Genetica, 11:1–186.

—— 1935. Gen und Ausseneigenschaft. Z.i.A.V., 69:38–131.

—— 1937. Spontaneous chromatin rearrangements and the theory of the gene. P.N.A.S., 23:621–623.

—— 1938. Physiological genetics. McGraw-Hill, New York.

—— 1939. Mass mutation in the Florida stock of *Drosophila melanogaster*. A.N., 73:547–559.

—— 1940. The material basis of evolution. Yale University Press.

—— J. Seiler, and H. Poppelbaum. 1924. Untersuchungen sur Genetik der geographischen Variation I. A.E., 101:92–337.

Goodspeed, T. H., and R. E. Clausen. 1928. Interspecific hybridization in Nicotiana. VIII. The *sylvestris-tomentosa-tabacum* hybrid triangle and its bearing on the origin of tabacum. U.C.P.B., 11:245–256.

Gordon, C. 1936. The frequency of heterozygosis in free-living populations of *Drosophila subobscura*. J.G., 33:25–60.

—— H. Spurway, and P. A. R. Street. 1939. An analysis of three wild populations of *Drosophila subobscura*. J.G., 38:37–90.

Gordon, Myron. 1937. The production of spontaneous melanotic neoplasms in fishes by selective matings. II. Neoplasms with macromelano-phores only. III. Neoplasms in day-old fishes. Am. J. Cancer, 30:362-75.

Gordon, Myron, and G. M. Smith. 1938. The production of a melanotic neoplastic disease in fishes by selective matings. IV. Genetics of geographical species hybrids. Am. J. Cancer, 34:543-565.

Gottschewski, G. 1934. Untersuchungen an *Drosophila melanogaster* über die Umstimmbarkeit des Phänotypus und Genotypus durch Temperatureinflüsse. Z.i.A.V., 67:477-528.

Gowen, J. W. 1931. Genetic non-disjunctional forms in Drosophila. A.N., 65:193-213.

Greenleaf, W. H. 1938. Induction of polyploidy in Nicotiana. J. H., 29:451-464.

Gregor, J. W. 1938. Experimental Taxonomy. II. Initial population differentiation in *Plantago maritima L.* of Britain. New Phytologist, 37:15-49.

—— 1939. Experimental Taxonomy. IV. Population differentiation in North American and European sea plantains allied to Plantago maritima L. New Phytologist, 38:293-322.

—— and F. W. Sansome. 1930. Genetics of wild populations. II. *Phleum pratense L. × P. Alpinum L.* J.G., 22:373-387.

Gregory, R. P. 1914. On the genetics of tetraploid plants in *Primula sinensis.* Proc. R. Soc., B, 87:484-492.

Gross, A. O. 1940. The migration of Kent Island herring gulls. Bird Banding, 11:129-155.

Gross, F. 1932. Untersuchungen über die Polyploidy und die Variabilität bei Artemia salina. Naturwissenschaften, 20:962-967.

Gulick, J. T. 1905. Evolution, racial and habitudinal. Carnegie Inst. Washington, Publ., 25:1-269.

Gustafsson, Åke. 1935. The importance of the apomicts for plant geography. Bot. Not., 1935:325-330.

—— 1939. Differential polyploidy within the blackberries. H., 25:33-47.

Guyénot, E., and Duszynska-Wietrzykowska. 1935. Stérilité et virilisme chez des femelles de cobayes issues d'un croisment interspécifique. Revue Suisse Zool., 42: 341-388.

Haase-Bessel, G. 1921. Digitalisstudien II. Z.i.A.V., 27:1-26.

Hackett, L. W. 1937. Malaria in Europe. London.

Hadjinov, M. J. 1937. Sterility in varietal hybrids of Sorghum. Bull. Appl. Bot. Gen. Plant Breeding, II, 7:417-446.

Hagedoorn, A. L., and A. C. Hagedoorn. 1921. The relative value of the processes causing evolution. Martius Nijhoff, The Hague.

Hagerup, O. 1931. Über Polyploidy in Beziehung zu Klima, Ökologie und Phylogenie. H., 16:19-40.

—— 1939. Studies on the significance of polyploidy. III. Deschampsia and Aiva. H., 25:185-192.

Hagerup, O. 1940. Studies on the significance of polyploidy. IV. Oxycoccus. H., 26:399–410.

Håkansson, A. 1929. Chromosomenringe in Pisum und ihre mutmässliche genetische Bedeutung. H., 12:1–10.

—— 1931a. Über Chromosmenverkettung in Pisum. H., 15:17–61.

—— 1931b. Chromosomenverkettung bei Godetia und Clarkia. Ber. Deut. Bot. Ges., 49:228–234.

—— 1933. Die Konjugation der Chromosomen bei einigen Salix-Bastarden. H., 18:199–214.

—— 1934. Chromosomenbindungen in einigen Kreuzungen zwischen halbsterilen Erbsen. H., 19:341–358.

—— 1935. Die Reduktionsteilung in einigen Artbastarden von Pisum. H., 21:215–222.

—— 1940. Die meiosis bei haploiden Pflanzen von Godetia Whitneyi. H., 26:411–429.

Haldane, J. B. S. 1922. Sex-ratio and unisexual sterility in hybrid animals. J.G., 12:101–109.

—— 1924–1932. A mathematical theory of natural and artificial selection. Proc. Cambridge Phil. Soc., 23:19–41, 158–163, 363–372, 607–615, 838–844; 26:220–230; 27:131–142; 28:244–248.

—— 1930. A note on Fisher's theory of the origin of dominance, and on a correlation between dominance and linkage. A.N., 64:87–90.

—— 1932. The causes of evolution. Harper & Bros., New York and London.

—— 1933. The part played by recurrent mutation in evolution. A.N., 67: 5–19.

—— 1935. The rate of spontaneous mutation of a human gene. J. G., 31:317–326.

—— 1937. The effect of variation on fitness. A.N., 71:337–349.

—— 1939. The theory of the evolution of dominance. J.G., 37:365–374.

Hardy, G. H. 1908. Mendelian proportions in a mixed population. S., 28: 49–50.

Harland, S. C. 1932a. The genetics of Gossypium. Bibliogr. Genetica, 9: 107–182.

—— 1932b. The genetics of cotton. V. Reversal of dominance in the interspecific cross G. Barbadense Linn. G. hirsutum Linn. and its bearing on Fisher's theory of dominance. J. G., 25:261–270.

—— 1933. The genetics of cotton. IX. Further experiments on the inheritance of the crinkled dwarf mutant of G. Barbadense L. in interspecific crosses and their bearing on the Fisher's theory of dominance. J.G., 28:315–325.

—— 1935. The genetics of cotton. XII. Homologous genes for anthocyanin pigmentation in new and old world cotton. J. G., 30:465–476.

—— 1936. The genetical conception of the species. Biol. Reviews, 11:83–112.

Harland, S. C., and O. M. Atteck. 1933. Breeding experiments with biological races of *Trichogramma minutum* in the West Indies. Z.i.A.V., 64:54–76.

Harrison, J. W. H. 1920. Genetical studies in the moths of the geometrid genus Oporabia (Oporinia) with a special consideration of melanism in the Lepidoptera. J.G., 9:195–280.

Hartmann, M. 1933. Die methodologischen Grundlagen der Biologie. Felix Meiner, Leipzig.

Hasebroek, K. 1934. Industrie und Grosstadt als Ursache des neuzeitlichen vererblichen Melanismus der Schmetterlinge in England und Deutschland. Zool. Jahrb., alg. zool. Phys. 53:411–460.

Hayes, H. K., and H. E. Brewbaker. 1924. Frequency of mutations for chlorophyll deficient seedlings in maize. J.H., 15:497–502.

Heberer, G. 1924. Die Spermatogenese der Copepoden. I. Die Spermatogenese der Centropagiden nebst Anhang über die Oogenes von *Diaptomus castor*. Z. Wiss. Zool., 123:555–646.

Heikertinger, F. 1933–36. Kritik der Schmetterlingsmimikry I-V. B.Z., 53: 561–590; 54:365–389; 55:461–483; 56:151–166, 463–494.

Heincke, F. 1898. Die Naturgeschichte des Herings. I. Abh. Deut. Seefischerei Vereins, 2:1–178.

Heitz, E. 1933. Die somatische Heteropyknose bei *Drosophila melanogaster* und ihre genetische Bedeutung. Z.Z.m.A., 20:237–287.

—— and H. Bauer. 1933. Beweise für die Chromosomennatur der Kernschleifen in den Knäuelkernen von *Bibio hortulanus*. Z.Z.m.A., 17:67–83.

Helfer, R. G. 1939. Dominance modifiers of Scute in *Drosophila pseudoobscura*. G., 24:278–301.

—— 1941. A comparison of X-ray induced and naturally occurring chromosomal variations in *Drosophila pseudoobscura*. G., 26:1–22.

Helwig, E. R. 1929. Chromosomal variations correlated with geographical distribution in *Circotettix verruculatus* (Orthoptera). J. Morphology, 47:1–36.

Heptner, M. A. 1938. Relation between the mutability of definite genes and their position in the chromosome. B.Z., 7:1121–1138.

Héritier, Ph. L', et G. Teissier. 1934. Une expérience de sélection naturelle. Courbe d'élimination du gène "Bar" dans une population de Drosophiles en équilibre. C. R. Soc. Biol., 117:1049–1051.

—— 1937. Elimination des formes mutantes dans les populations de Drosophile. C. R. Soc. Biol., 124:880–884.

—— 1938. Transmission héréditaire de la sensibilité au gaz carbonique chez la Drosophile. C. R. Acad. Sci., 206:1683–1685.

—— Y. Neefs, et G. Teissier. 1937. Aptérisme des insects et sélection naturelle. C. R. Acad. Sci., 204:907–909.

Hertwig. P. 1936. Artbastarde bei Tieren. Handbuch Vererbungswiss., 21: 1–140.

Hollingshead, L. 1930a. A lethal factor in Crepis effective only in interspecific hybrid. G., 15:114–140.

Hollingshead, L. 1930b. Cytological investigations of hybrids and hybrid derivatives of *Crepis capillaris* and *Crepis tectorum*. Univ. California Publ. Agr. Sci., 6:55–94.

Honing, J. A. 1923. Canna crosses I. Mededeelingen Landbouwhoofeschool Wageningen, 26:1–56.

—— 1928. Canna crosses II. Mededeelingen Landbouwhoofeschool Wageningen, 32:1–14.

Horton, I. H. 1939. A comparison of the salivary gland chromosomes of *Drosophila melanogaster* and *D. simulans*. G., 24:234–243.

Hosino, Y. 1940. Genetical studies on the pattern types of the lady bird beetle, *Harmonia axyridis Pallas*. J.G., 40:215–228.

Hough, W. 1934. Colorado and Virginia strains of codling moth in relation to their ability to enter sprayed and unsprayed apples. J. Agric. Res., 48:533–553.

Hovanitz, W. 1940. Ecological color variation in a butterfly and the problem of "protective coloration." Ecology, 21:371–380.

Howard, H. W. 1938. The fertility of amphidiploids from the cross Raphanus sativus Brassica oberacea. J.G., 36:239–273.

—— 1940. The genetics of Armadillidium vulgare Latr. I. A general survey of the problems. J.G., 40:83–108.

Hubbs, C. L. 1938. Fishes from the caves of Yucatan. Carnegie Inst. Washington, Publ., 491:261–295.

—— 1940. Speciation in fishes. A.N., 74:198–211.

Hughes, R. D. 1939. An analysis of the chromosomes of the two sub-species *Drosophila virilis virilis* and *Drosophila virilis americana*. G., 24:811–834.

Huskins, C. L. 1931. The origin of *Spartina townsendii*. Genetica, 12:531–538.

—— and E. M. Hearne. 1933. Meiosis in asynaptic dwarf oats and wheat. J. R. Micr. Soc., 53:109–117.

—— and S. G. Smith. 1934. A cytological study of the genus *Sorghum Ters*. II. The meiotic chromosomes. J.G., 28:387–395.

Hutchinson, J. B. 1934. The genetics of cotton. X. The inheritance of leaf shape in Asiatic Gossypiums. J.G., 28:437–513.

—— and P. D. Gadkari. 1937. The genetics of lintlessness in asiatic cottons. J.G., 35:161–175.

Huxley, J. S. 1938a. Clines: an auxilliary method in taxonomy. Bijdragen tot de dierkunde, 27:491–520.

—— 1938b. The present standing of the theory of sexual selection. De Beers's Evolution. Oxford.

—— 1940. Towards the new systematics. Huxley's New Systematics. Clarendon Press, Oxford.

Irwin, M. R. 1938. Immuno-genetic studies of species relationships in Columbidae. J.G., 35:351–373.

Irwin, M. R. 1939. A genetic analysis of species differences in Columbidae. G., 24:709–721.

—— and L. J. Cole. 1936a. Immunogenetic studies of species and species hybrids in doves and the separation of species-specific substances in the back-cross. J.E.Z., 73:85–108.

—— 1936b. Immunogenetic studies of species and species hybrids from the cross *Columba livia* and *Streptopelia risoria.* J.E.Z., 73:309–318.

—— 1940. Further studies of the relationships of cellular characters in Columbidae. G., 25:326–336.

—— L. J. Cole, and C. D. Gordon. 1936. Immunogenetic studies of species and species hybrids in pigeons, and the separation of species-specific characters in back-cross generations. J.E.Z., 73:285–308.

—— and R. W. Cumley. 1940. Speciation from the point of view of genetics. A.N., 74:222–231.

Ivanov, M. A. 1938. Experimental production of haploids in *Nicotiana rustica.* Genetica, 20:295–397.

Jenkin, T. J. 1933. Interspecific and intergeneric hybrids in herbage grasses. J.G., 28:205–264.

Jenkins, M. T. 1924. Heritable characters of maize. J.H., 15:467–472.

Jennings, H. S. 1939. *Paramecium bursaria:* mating types and groups, mating behavior, self sterility; their development and inheritance. A.N., 73:414–431.

Johannsen, W. 1909. Elemente der exacten Erblichkeitslehre. Gustav Fischer, Jena.

Jollos, V. 1931. Genetik und Evolutionsproblem. Verh. Deuts. Zool. Ges., 252–295.

—— 1934. Inherited changes produced by heat-treatment in *Drosophila melanogaster.* Genetica, 16:476–494.

—— 1935. Studien zum Evolutionsproblem. B.Z., 55:390–436.

—— 1939a. Further tests of the role of cosmic radiation in the production of mutations in *Drosophila melanogaster.* G., 24:113–130.

—— 1939b. Grundbegriffe der Vererbungslehre. Handb. Vererbungsswissenschaft, 24 (1 D), Borntraeger, Berlin.

Jordan, D. S. 1905. The origin of species through isolation. S., 22:545–562.

Jordan, K. 1905. Der Gegensatz zwischen geographischer und nichtgeographischer Variation. Zeits. wiss. Zool., 83.

Jorgensen, C. A. 1928. The experimental formation of heteroploid plants in the genus Solanum. J.G., 19:133–211.

—— and M. B. Crane. 1927. Formation and morphology of *Solanum chimaeras.* J.G., 18:247–273.

Kaliss, N. 1939. The effect on development of a lethal deficiency in Drosophila melanogaster. G., 24:244–270.

Kammerer, P. 1912. Experiments über Fortpflanzung, Farbe, Augen und Körperreduction bei Proteus anguinus Laur. A.E., 33:349–461.

Karpechenko, G. D. 1927a. The production of polyploid gametes in hybrids. H., 9:349–368.

—— 1927b. Polyploid hybrids of *Raphanus sativus L.* × *Brassica oleracea L.* Bull. Appl. Botany, 17:305–408.

—— 1928. Polyploid hybrids of *Raphanus sativus L.* × *Brassica oleracea L.* Z.i.A.V., 48:1–85.

—— 1935. Theory of remote hybridization. Moscow-Leningrad.

—— 1937. Increasing the crossability of a species by doubling its chromosome number. Bull. Appl. Bot., Gen. Plant Breeding Ser. 2, 7:37–51.

—— and Shchavinskaia. 1929. On sexual incompatibility of tetraploid hybrids *Raphanus Brassica.* Proc. USSR Congr. Genetics, 2:267–276.

Kaston, B. J. 1936. The senses involved in the courtship of some vagabond spiders. Entomologica Americana, 16:97–167.

Katayama, Y. 1936. Chromosome studies in some Alliums. J. Coll. Agr. Tokyo Univ., 13:431–441.

Kato, K. 1936. Experimental studies on the agglutination of mammalian spermatozoa with special reference to its bearing upon fertilization. Mem. Fac. Sci. Agr. Taihoku Univ., 19:1–72.

Katterman, G. 1931. Über die Bildung palyvalenter Chromosomenverbände bei einigen Gramineen. Planta, 12:732–744.

Kaufmann, B. P. 1936. A terminal inversion in *Drosophila ananassae.* P.N.A.S., 22:591–594.

—— 1937. Morphology of the chromosomes of *Drosophila ananassae.* C., Jubilee Volume: 1043–1055.

—— 1939. Distribution of induced breaks along the X-chromosome of *Drosophila melanogaster.* P.N.A.S., 25:571–577.

—— 1940a. Induced changes in chromosomes carrying inverted sections. G., 25:124–125.

—— 1940b. The nature of hybrid sterility—abnormal development in eggs of hybrids between *Drosophila miranda* and *Drosophila pseudoobscura.* J. Morphol., 66:197–213.

—— 1941. The time interval between X-radiation of sperm of Drosophila and chromosome recombination. P.N.A.S., 27:18–24.

—— and M. Demerec. 1937. Frequency of induced breaks in chromosomes of *Drosophila melanogaster.* P.N.A.S., 23:484–488.

Kawaguchi, E. 1928. Zytologische Untersuchungen am Seidenspinner und seine Verwandten. Z.Z.m.A., 7:519–552.

Kerkis, J. 1931. Vergleichende Studien über die Variabilität der Merkmale des Geschlechtsapparats und der äusseren Merkmale bei Eurygaster integriceps Put. Zool. Anz., 93:129–143.

—— 1933. Development of gonads in hybrids between *Drosophila melanogaster* and *Drosophila simulans.* J.E.Z., 66:477–509.

—— 1935. Hybridization of *Drosophila melanogaster* and *Drosophila simulans* in connection with the causes of interspecific hybrid sterility in animals. Bull. Inst. Genetics, Leningrad, 10:83–117.

Kerkis, J. 1936. Chromosome configuration in hybrids between *Drosophila melanogaster* and *Drosophila simulans*. A.N., 70:81–86.

—— 1937. The causes of imperfect conjugation of chromosomes in hybrids of *Drosophila simulans* and *melanogaster*. Bull. Acad. Sci. USSR (Biol.), 1937:459–468.

—— 1938. The frequency of mutations affecting viability. Bull. Acad. Sci. USSR (Biol.), 1938:75–96.

—— 1939. Effect of temperature below 0° upon the process of mutation and some considerations on the causes of spontaneous mutation. C. R. (Doklady) Acad. Sci. URSS, 24:386–388.

Kihara, H. 1919. Über cytologische Studien bei einigen Getreidearten I. Bot. Mag. Tokyo, 32:17–38.

—— 1924. Cytologische und genetische Studien bei wichtigen Getreidearten mit besonderer Rücksicht auf das Verhalten der Chromosomen und die Sterilität in den Bastarden. Mem. Coll. Sci. Kyoto Imp. Univ., 1:1–200.

—— 1935. Genomanalyse bei Triticum und Aegilops VI. C., 6:195–216.

—— 1937. Genomanalyse bei Triticum und Aegilops. VII. Kurze Übersicht über die Ergebnisse der Jahre 1934–1936. Mem. Coll. Agr. Kyoto Univ., 41:1–61.

—— and F. Lilienfeld. 1932. Genomanalyse bei Triticum and Aegilops IV. C., 3:384–456.

—— und J. Nishiyma. 1930. Genomanalyse bei Triticum und Aegilops I. C., 1:263–284.

Kikkawa, H. 1936. Two races of *Drosophila montium*. Jap. J. Genetics, 12:137–142.

—— 1937. The inert chromosomes of *Drosophila ananassae* Doleschall. C., Jubilee Volume:125–128.

—— 1938. Studies on the genetics and cytology of *Drosophila ananassae*. Genetica, 20:458–516.

Kimball, R. F. 1939. Mating types in Euplotes. A.N., 73:451–456.

Kinsey, A. C. 1936. The origin of higher categories in Cynips. Indiana Univ. Publ., Science Series, 4:1–334.

—— 1937a. An evolutionary analysis of insular and continental species. P.N.A.S., 23:5–11.

—— 1937b. Supra-specific variation in nature and its classification. A.N., 71:206–222.

Kirikov, S. V. 1934. Sur la distribution géographique du hamster noir et ses relations avec la form normale de *Cricetus cricetus*. Zool. Zhurnal (Moscow), 13:361–368.

Klingstedt, H. 1933. Chromosomenstudien an Neuropteren. I. Ein Fall von heteromorphen Chromosomenpaaren als Beispiel vom Mendeln der Chromosomen. Med. Soc. Fauna Flora Fennica, 10:3–11.

—— 1937. A taxonomic survey of the genus *Cyrnus Steph.* including the description of a new species, with some remarks on the principles of taxonomy. Acta Soc. Fauna Flora Fennica, 60:573–598.

Klingstedt, H. 1938. Failure of anaphase separation in species hybrids. Nature, 141:606.

—— 1939. Taxonomic and cytological studies on grasshopper hybrids. I. Morphology and spermatogenesis of *Chorthippus bicolor Charp.* × *Ch. biguttulus L.* J.G., 37:389–420.

Knuth, P., and J. R. Ainsworth Davis. 1906–9. Handbook of flower pollination. Clarendon Press, Oxford, 3 volumes.

Koller, P. Ch. 1932. The relation of fertility factors to crossing over in the *Drosophila obscura* hybrids. Z.i.A.V., 60:137–151.

—— 1936a. Structural hybridity in *Drosophila pseudoobscura*. J.G., 32: 79–102.

—— 1936b. Cytological studies on the reproductive organs. Chromosome behavior in the male grey squirrel (Sciurus carolinensis leucopus). Proc. R. Soc. Edinburgh., 56:196–209.

—— 1937. The genetical and mechanical properties of sex chromosomes. III. Man. Proc. R. Soc. Edinburgh, 57:194–214.

—— 1938. Asynapsis in Pisum sativum. J.G., 36:275–306.

—— 1939a. Genetics of natural populations. III. Gene arrangements in populations of *Drosophila pseudoobscura* from contiguous localities. G., 24:22–33.

—— 1939b. A new race of *Drosophila miranda*. J.G., 38:477–492.

Kondakowa, A. A. 1935. Einfluss des Jods auf das Auftreten letaler mutationen im III. Chromosom von *Drosophila melanogaster*. B.Zh., 4: 721–726.

Kosiupa, D. E. 1936. The effect of sublimate on the occurrence of lethal mutations in *Drosophila melanogaster*. Bull. Biol. Med. Exp. URSS, 2:87–89.

Kossikov, K. V., and H. J. Muller. 1935. Invalidation of the genetic evidence for branched chromonemas in the case of pale translocation in Drosophila. J.H., 26:305–317.

Kosswig, C. 1929a. Über die veränderte Wirkung von Farbgenen des Platypoecilus in der Gattungskreuzung mit Xiphophorus. Z.i.A.V., 50: 63–73.

—— 1929b. Zur Frage der Geschwulstbildung bei Gattungsbastarden der Zahnkarpfen Xiphophorus und Platypoecilus. Z.i.A.V., 52:114–120.

—— 1937. Über die veränderte Wirkung von Farbgenen in fremden Genotypen. Biol. Generalis, 13:276–293.

—— and L. Kosswig. 1940. Die Variabilität bei Asellus aquaticus, unter besonderer Berücksichtigung der Variabilität in isolierten unter- und oberirdischen Populationen. Rev. Fac. Sci. Univ. Istanbul, B, 5:1–55.

Kostoff, D. 1936. Polyploid hybrids. *Nicotiana rustica var. texana L.* × *Nicotiana glauca Grah.* Bull. Appl. Bot., Ser. 2, 9:153–162.

Kostoff, D. 1938a. Polyploid plants produced by colchicine and acenaphthene. Current Science, 7:108–110.

—— 1938b. Studies on polyploid plants. XXI. Cytogenetic behavior of the allopolyploid hybrids Nicotiana glauca Grah. × Nicotiana Langsdorfii Weinm. and their evolutionary significance. JG., 37:129–209.

Kozhevnikov, B. Th. 1933. Partial non-homology of the sex chromosomes in Drosophila melanogaster and Drosophila simulans. B.Zh., 3:585–601.

—— 1936. Experimentally produced karyotypical isolation. B.Zh., 5: 727–752.

Kramer, G., and R. Mertenş. 1938. Rassenbildung bei west-istrianischen Inseleidechsen in Abhängigkeit von Isolierungsalter und Arealgrösse. Arch. Naturg., NF, 7:189–234.

Krishnaswamy, N. 1939. Cytological studies in a haploid plant of Triticum vulgare. H., 25:77–86.

Kühl, O. 1937. Genanalyse bei Antirrhinum-Artbastarden. Z.i.A.V., 74: 125–160.

Kühn. 1932. Entwicklungsphysiologische Wirkung einiger Gene von Ephestia kuhniella. Naturwissenschaften, 20:947–977.

Laibach, F. 1925. Das Taubwerden von Bastardsamen und die Künstliche Aufzucht früh absterbender Bastardembryonen. Zeits. Botanik, 17:417–459.

Lamm, R. 1936. Cytological studies on inbred rye. H., 22:217–240.

Lammerts, W. E. 1931. Interspecific hybridization in Nicotiana XII. The amphidiploid rustica-paniculata hybrid; the origin and cytogenetic behavior. G., 16:191–211.

—— 1934a. Derivative types obtained by back-crossing Nicotiana rustica-paniculata to N. paniculata. J.G., 29:355–366.

—— 1934b. On the nature of chromosome association in Nicotiana tabacum haploid. C., 6:38–50.

Lamprecht, H. 1939. Translocation, Gespaltung und Mutation bei Pisum. H., 25:431–458.

Lancefield, D. E. 1929. A genetic study of two races or physiological species in Drosophila obscura. Z.i.A.V., 52:287–317.

Landauer, W. 1938. Notes on cross-beak in fowl. J.G., 37:51–68.

Lattin, G., de. 1939. Untersuchungen an Isopodenaugen. Zool. Jahrb. Anat. Ont., 65:417–468.

Law, L. W. 1938. The effects of chemicals on the lethal mutation rate in Drosophila melanogaster. P.N.A.S., 24:546–550.

Lawrow, P. A. 1935. Einfluss erhöhter Temperatur auf den Mutationsprocess von Drosophila melanogaster. B.Zh., 4:983–992.

Lehmann, E., and J. Schwemmle. 1927. Genetische Untersuchungen in der Gattung Epilobium. Bibl. Bot., 95.

Leiner, M. 1934. Die drei europäische Stichlinge (Gasterosteus aculeatus L., Gasterosteus pungitius L. and Gasterosteus spinachia L.) und ihre Kreuzungsprodukte. Zeits. Morph. Ökol. Tiere, 28:107–154.

Lesley, M. M., and J. W. Lesley. 1930. The mode of origin and chromo-some behavior in pollen mother cells of a tetraploid seedling tomato. J.G., 22:419–425.

Levan, A. 1935a. Cytological studies in Allium VI. The chromosome mor-phology of some diploid species of Allium. H. 20:289–330.

—— 1935b. Die Zytologie von *Allium cepa* × *fistulosum*. H., 21:195–214.

—— 1938. The effect of colchicine on root mitosis in Allium. H., 24:471–486.

—— 1939. Tetraploidy and octoploidy induced by colchicine in diploid Petunia. H., 25:109–131.

—— 1940a. The effect of acenaphthene and colchicine on mitosis of Al-lium and Colchicum. H., 26:262–276.

—— 1940b. The cytology of Allium amplectens and the occurrence in nature of its asynapsis. H., 26:353–394.

—— and S. L. Emsweller. 1938. Structural hybridity in Notoscordum fragrans. J.H., 29:291–294.

Lewis, I. M. 1934. Bacterial variation with special reference to behaviour of some mutable strains of colon bacteria in synthetic media. J. Bac-teriol., 28:619.

Lilienfeld, F., and H. Kihara. 1934. Genomanalyse bei Triticum and Aegi-lops. C., 6:87–122.

Liljefors, A. 1936. Zytologische Studien über den F_1 Bastard *Triticum turgidum* × *Secale cereale*. H., 21:240–262.

Lillie, F. R. 1921. Studies of fertilization. VIII. On the measure of speci-ficity in fertilization between two associated species of the sea-urchin genus Strongilocentrotus. B.B., 40:1–22.

Ljungdahl, H. 1924. Über die Herkunft der in der Meiosis konjugierenden Chromosomen bei Papaver-Hybriden. Svensk. Bot. Tidsk., 18:279–291.

Lobashov, M. E. 1935a. Über die Natur der Einwirkung der chemischen Agentien auf den Mutationsprocess bei *Drosophila melanogaster*. Ge-netica, 19:200–241.

—— 1935b. Über die Wirkung der Asfiktion auf den Mutationsprozess bei *Drosophila melanogaster*. Bull. Soc. Natur. Leningrad, 63:371–378.

—— and F. Smirnov. 1934. On the nature of the action of chemical agents on the mutational process in *Drosophila melanogaster*. II. The effect of ammonia on the occurrence of lethal transgenations. C.R. Acad. Sci. URSS, 3:174–176.

Lotsy, J. P. 1911. Hybride entre espèces d'Antirrhinum. C.R. IV Confér. Internat. Génétique: 416–428.

—— 1916. Evolution by means of hybridization. M. Nijhoff, The Hague.

—— 1931. On the species of the taxonomist in its relation to evolution. Genetica, 13:1–16.

Lüers, H. 1935. Die Beeinflussung der Vitalität durch multiple Allele, untersucht an vestigial Allelen von *Drosophila melanogaster*. A.E., 133: 88–117.

Lutkow, A. N. 1930. Interspecific hybrids of *Pisum humile Boiss* × *Pisum sativum L.* Proc. USSR Congr. Genetics, 2:353–367.

—— (Lutkov) 1938. Tetraploidy in flax caused by the action of high temperature on the zygote. C.R. (Doklady) Acad. Sci. URSS, 19:87–90.

Lutz, F. E. 1911. Experiments with *Drosophila ampelophila* concerning evolution. Carnegie Inst. Washington, Publ. 143:1–35.

Lynch, C. J. 1919. An analysis of certain cases of intraspecific sterility. G., 4:501–533.

McAtee, W. L. 1932. Effectiveness in nature of the so-called protective adaptations in the animal kingdom, chiefly as illustrated by the food habits of Nearctic birds. Smithsonian Misc. Coll., 85:1–201.

McClintock, B. 1931. A cytological demonstration of the location of an interchange between the non-homologous chromosomes of *Zea mays*. P.N.A.S., 16:791–796.

—— 1932. Cytological observations in Zea on the intimate association of non-homologous parts of chromosomes in the mid-prophase of meiosis and its relation to diakinesis configurations. P.VI.C.G., 2:126–128.

—— 1933. The association of non-homologous parts of chromosomes in the mid-prophase of meiosis in *Zea mays*. Z.Z.m.A., 19:191–237.

—— 1934. The relation of a particular chromosomal element to the development of the nucleoli in *Zea mays*. Z.Z.m.A., 21:294–328.

—— 1938. The production of homozygous deficient tissues with mutant characteristics by means of the aberrant mitotic behavior of ring-shaped chromosomes. G., 23:315–376.

—— 1939. The behavior in successive nuclear divisions of a chromosome broken at meiosis. P.N.A.S., 25:405–416.

McClung, C. E. 1917. The multiple chromosomes of Hesperotettix and Mermiria. J. Morphol., 29:519–605.

McCray, F. A. 1933. Embryo development in Nicotiana species hybrids. G., 18:95–110.

MacKnight, R. H. 1939. The sex-determining mechanism of *Drosophila miranda*. G., 24:180–201.

Magrzhikovskaja, K. V. 1938. The effect of CuSO₄ on the mutation process in *Drosophila melanogaster*. B.Zh., 7:635–642.

Mainland, G. B. 1941. Studies in Drosophila speciation. III. The *Drosophila macrospina* group. G., 26:160–161.

Mangelsdorf, P. C. 1926. The genetics and morphology of some endosperm characters in maize. Connecticut Agr. Exp. Sta., Bull. 279:513–614.

—— and D. F. Jones. 1926. The expression of Mendelian factors in the gametophyte of maize. G., 11:423–455.

—— and R. G. Reeves. 1939. The origin of Indian corn and its relatives. Texas Agr. Exp. Sta. Bull., 574:1–315.

Mann-Lesley, M., and H. B. Frost. 1927. Mendelian inheritance of chromosome shape in Mathiola. G., 12:449–460.

Manton, I. 1932. Introduction to the general cytology of Cruciferae. Ann. Bot., 46:509–556.

—— 1934. The problem of *Biscutella laevigata* L. Z.i.A.V., 67:41–57.

—— 1937. The problem of *Biscutella laevigata* L. Ann. Bot., N.S., 1: 439–462.

Marshall, W. W., and H. J. Muller. 1917. The effect of long-continued heterozygosis on a variable character in Drosophila. J.E.Z., 22:457–470.

Mather, K. 1935. The behavior of meiotic chromosomes after X-radiation. H., 19:302–322.

—— 1935. Chromosome behavior in a triploid wheat hybrid. Z.Z.m.A., 23:117–138.

—— and Th. Dobzhansky. 1939. Morphological differences between the "races" of *Drosophila pseudoobscura*. A.N., 73:5–25.

—— and S. B. North. 1940. Umbrous: A case of dominance modification in mice. J.G., 40:229–241.

—— and L. H. A. Stone. 1933. The effect of X-radiation upon somatic chromosomes. J.G., 28:1–24.

Mayr, E. 1932. Birds collected during the Whitney South Sea expedition. Amer. Museum Novitates, 20:1–22; 21:1–23.

—— 1940. Speciation phenomena in birds. A.N., 74:249–278.

Meise, W. 1928. Die Verbreitung der Aaskrähe (Formenkreis Corvus corone L.). J. Ornithologie, 76:1–203.

—— 1936. Zur Systematik und Verbreitungsgeschichte der Haus- und Weidensperlinge, Passer domesticus (L.) und hispaniolensis (T.). J. Ornithologie, 84:631–672.

Meister, N., and N. A. Tjumjakoff. 1928. Rye-wheat hybrids from reciprocal crosses. J.G., 20:233–245.

Metz, C. W. 1914. Chromosome studies in Diptera I. J.E.Z., 17:45–56.

—— 1937. Small deficiencies and the problem of genetic units in the giant chromosomes. G., 22:543–556.

—— 1938. Observations on evolutionary changes in the chromosomes of Sciara (Diptera). Cooperation in Research, Carnegie Inst. Washington, Publ. 501:275–294.

—— and R. D. Boche. 1939. Observations on the mechanism of induced chromosome rearrangements in Sciara. P.N.A.S., 25:280–284.

—— and E. G. Lawrence. 1938. Preliminary observations on Sciara hybrids. J.H., 29:179–186.

Meurman, O. 1928. Cytological studies in the genus Ribes L. H., 11:289–356.

—— 1929. *Prunus laurocerasus* L., a species showing high polyploidy. J.G., 21:85–94.

Michaelis, P. 1933. Entwicklungsgeschichtlich-genetische Untersuchungen an Epilobium II. Z.i.A.V., 65:1–71, 353–411.

Michaelis, P. 1938. Über die Konstanz des Plasmons. Z.i.A.V., 74:435–459.

Miller, A. H. 1940. A hybrid between *Zonotrichia coronata* and *Zonotrichia leucophrys*. Condor, 42:45–48.

Miller, D. D. 1939. Structure and variation of the chromosomes in *Drosophila algonquin*. G., 24:699–708.

Moenkhaus, W. J. 1910. Cross fertilization among fishes. Proc. Indiana Acad. Sci., 353–393.

Mohr, O. L. 1939. Lethal genes in higher animals and man. Relaz. IV Congr. Internat. Patologia Comp., 1:247–263.

Moore, J. A. 1939. Temperature tolerance and rates of development in the eggs of Amphibia. Ecology, 20:459–478.

—— 1940. Adaptive differences in the egg membranes of frogs. A.N., 74:89–93.

Morgan, L. V. 1939. A spontaneous somatic exchange between non-homologous chromosomes in *Drosophila melanogaster*. G., 24:747–752.

Morgan, T. H. 1911. The origin of five mutations in eye color in Drosophila and their modes of inheritance. S., 33:534–537.

—— 1913. Factors and unit characters in Mendelian heredity. A.N., 47: 5–16.

—— 1918. Concerning the mutation theory. Sci. Monthly, 25:385–405.

Muller, H. J. 1925. Why polyploidy is rarer in animals than in plants. A.N., 59:346–353.

—— 1928a. The problem of genic modification. V.K.V., 1:234–260.

—— 1928b. The measurement of gene mutation rate in Drosophila, its high variability, and its dependence upon temperature. G., 13:279–357.

—— 1932. Further studies on the nature and causes of gene mutations. P.VI.C.G., 1:213–255.

—— 1935. A viable two-gene deficiency. J.H., 26:469–478.

—— 1936. On the variability of mixed races. A.N., 70:409–442.

—— 1939. Reversibility in evolution considered from the standpoint of genetics. Biol. Reviews, 14:261–280.

—— 1940a. Bearing of the "Drosophila" work on systematics. Huxley's New Systematics, pp. 185–268.

—— 1940b. An analysis of the process of structural change in chromosomes of Drosophila. J.G., 40:1–66.

—— A. A. Prokofyeva-Belgovskaja, and K. V. Kossikov. 1936. Unequal crossing-over in the bar mutant as a result of duplication of a minute chromosome section. C.R. Acad. Sci. URSS, 1(10):87–88.

—— and F. Settles. 1927. The non-functioning of the genes in spermatozoa. Z.i.A.V., 43:285–312.

Müntzing, A. 1930. Outlines to a genetic monograph of the genus Galeopsis. H., 13:185–341.

—— 1932. Cyto-genetic investigations on synthetic *Galeopsis Tetrahit*. H., 16:105–154.

Müntzing, A. 1933. Quadrivalent formation and aneuploidy in *Dactylis glomerata*. Bot. Notiser, 198–205.

—— 1934. Chromosome fragmentation in a Crepis hybrid. H., 19:284–302.

—— 1935a. Cyto-genetic studies on hybrids between two Phleum species. H., 20:103–136.

—— 1935b. Chromosome behavior in some Nicotiana hybrids. H., 20:251–272.

—— 1936. The evolutionary significance of autopolyploidy. H., 21:263–378.

—— 1937a. The effects of chromosomal variation in Dactylis. H., 23:113–235.

—— 1937b. Multiple alleles and polymeric factors in Galeopsis. H., 23:371–400.

—— 1938. Sterility and chromosome pairing in intraspecific Galeopsis hybrids. H., 24:117–188.

—— 1939. Chromosomenaberrationen bei Pflanzen und ihre genetische Wirkung. Z.i.A.V., 76:323–350.

—— 1940. Further studies on apomixis and sexuality in Poa. H., 26:115–190.

—— and R. Prakken. 1940. The mode of chromosome pairing in Phleum twins with 63 chromosomes and its cytological consequences. H., 26:464–501.

—— G. Tometorp, and K. Mundt-Petersen. 1937. Tetraploid barley produced by heat treatment. H., 22:401–406.

Muretov, G. D. 1939. Physiological mutations and dynamics of the genic composition of *Drosophila melanogaster* populations. C.R. (Doklady) Acad. Sci. URSS, 24:471–474.

Murie, A. 1933. The ecological relationship of two subspecies of Peromyscus in the Glacier Park region, Montana. Occ. Papers Mus. Zool., Univ. Michigan, 270:1–17.

Murphy, R. C. 1939. Man-o-war. Nat. History (New York), 44:133–143.

Naumenko, V. A. 1936. Lethal mutations of *Drosophila melanogaster* induced by potassium permanganate. Bull. Biol. Med. Exp. USSR, 1:204–206.

Nawashin, M. S. 1929. Über die Veränderung von Zahl und Form der Chromosomen infolge der Hybridization. Z.Z.m.A., 6:195–233.

—— 1932. The dislocation hypothesis of evolution of chromosome numbers. Z.i.A.V., 63:224–231.

—— 1934. Chromosome alterations caused by hybridization and their bearing upon certain genetic problems. C., 5:169–203.

—— and H. Gerassimova. 1937. Nature and causes of mutations. I. On the nature and importance of chromosomal mutations taking place in resting plant embryos due to their aging. B.Zh., 4:593–634.

Nawashin, S. 1912. Sur le dimorphisme nucléaire des cellules somatiques de *Galtonia candicans*. Bull. Acad. Imp. Sci. Petersbourg, VI série, 4: 373–385.

—— 1927. Zellkerndimorphismus bei *Galtonia candicans Des.* und einigen verwandten Monokotylen. Ber. Deut. Bot. Ges., 45:415–428.

Nebel, B. R., and M. L. Ruttle. 1938. The cytological and genetical significance of colchicine. J.H., 29:3–9.

Newman, H. H. 1914. Modes of inheritance in teleost hybrids. J.E.Z., 16: 447–499.

—— 1915. Development and heredity in heterogenic teleost hybrids. J.E.Z., 18:511–576.

Newton, W. C. F., and C. Pellew. 1929. Primula kewensis and its derivatives. J.G., 20:405–467.

Nice, M. M. 1937. Studies in the life history of the song sparrow. I. Trans. Linnaean Soc. New York, 4:1–247.

Nichols, Ch. 1941. Spontaneous chromosome aberrations in Allium, G., 26:89–100.

Nicholson, A. J. 1933. The balance of animal populations. J. Animal Ecology, Suppl. II:132–178.

—— and V. A. Bailey. 1935. The balance of animal populations. Proc. Zool. Soc. London, 1935:551–598.

Nikoro, Z., S. N. Gussev, E. Pavlov, and I. Griasnov. 1935. The regularities of sex isolation in some stocks of *Drosophila melanogaster*. B.Zh., 4: 569–585.

—— (Nikoro), and S. N. Gussev. 1938. Experimental analysis of the action of the automatic genetic processes. B.Zh., 7:197–216.

Niethammer, G. 1937. Ergebnisse von Markierungsversuchen an Wildkaninchen. Zeits. Morph. Ökol., 33:297–312.

Nilsson, F. 1934. Studies in fertility and inbreeding in some herbage grasses. H., 19:1–162.

—— 1935. Amphidiploidy in the hybrid *Festuca arundinacea* × *gigantea*. H., 20:181–198.

Nishiyama, J. 1934. The genetics and cytology of certain cereals. VI. Chromosome behavior and its bearing on inheritance in triploid Avena hybrids. Mem. Coll. Agr. Kyoto, 32:1–157.

Noble, G. K. 1934. Experiments with the courtship of lizards. Natural History, 34:1–15.

Nordenskiöld, H. 1937. Intra- and interspecific hybrids of *Phleum pratense* and *Ph. alpinum*. H., 23:304–316.

Olenov, J., and I. Kharmac. 1938. Dynamics of the gene composition in wild *Drosophila melanogaster* populations. C.R. (Doklady) Acad. Sci. URSS, 19:409–412.

—— K. Galkovskaya, and G. Muretov. 1939. Factors responsible for the genic composition of wild *Drosophila melanogaster* populations. C.R. (Doklady) Acad. Sci. URSS, 24:466–470.

Oliver, C. P. 1932. An analysis of the effect of varying the duration of X-ray treatment upon the frequency of mutation. Z.i.A.V., 61:447–488.

—— 1940. A reversion to wild-type associated with crossing over in *Drosophila melanogaster*. P.N.A.S., 26:452–454.

—— and E. W. Van Atta. 1932. Genetic and cytological correlation of chromosome aberrations of Drosophila. P.VI.C.G., 2:145–147.

Ormancey. 1849. Recherches sur l'étui penial considéré comme limite de l'espèce dans les Coleoptères. Ann. Sci. Nat., Zool., ser. 3, 12.

Osborn, H. F. 1927. The origin of species. V. Speciation and Mutation. A.N., 61:5–42.

Östergren, G. 1940. Cytology of Agropyron junceum, *A. repens* and their spontaneous hybrid. H., 26:305–316.

Painter, T. S. 1928. A comparison of the chromosomes of the rat and mouse with reference to the question of chromosome homology in mammals. G., 13:180–189.

—— 1934. A new method for the study of chromosome aberrations and the plotting of chromosome maps in *Drosophila melanogaster*. G., 19: 175–188.

—— and H. J. Muller. 1929. The parallel cytology and genetics of induced translocations and deletions in Drosophila. J.H., 20:287–298.

—— and W. Stone. 1935. Chromosome fusion and speciation in Drosophila. G., 20:327–341.

Pariser, K. 1927. Die Zytologie und Morphologie der triploiden Intersexe des rückgekreuzten Bastards von *Saturnia pavonia L.* und *Saturnia pyri Schiff.* Z.Z.m.A., 5:415–447.

Pätau, K. 1935. Chromosomenmorphologie bei *Drosophila melanogaster* und *Drosophila simulans* und ihre genetische Bedeutung. Naturwiss., 23: 537–543.

—— 1938. Die mathematische Analyse der Evolutionsvorgänge. Z.i.A.V., 76:220–228.

Patterson, J. T., and J. F. Crow. 1940. Hybridization in the mulleri group of Drosophila. Univ. Texas Publ., 4032:251–256.

Patterson, J. T., and H. J. Muller. 1930. Are "progressive" mutations produced by X-rays? G., 15:495–578.

Patterson, J. T., W. S. Stone, and A. B. Griffen. 1940. Evolution of the virilis group in Drosophila. Univ. Texas Publ., 4032:218–250.

Pearson, K. 1904. On a generalized theory of alternative inheritance, with special reference to Mendel's laws. Philos. Trans. R. Soc. A., 203: 53–86.

Pellew, C., and E. R. Sansome. 1932. Genetical and cytological studies on the relations between Asiatic and European varieties of *Pisum sativum*. J.G., 25:25–54.

Peto, F. H. 1933. The cytology of certain intergeneric hybrids between Festuca and Lolium. J.G., 28:113–156.

Philip, U. 1938. Mating systems in wild populations of *Dermestes vulpinus* and *Mus musculus*. J.G., 36:197–211.

Philiptchenko, Jur. 1934. Genetics of soft wheats. Ogiz, Moscow-Leningrad.

Phillips, J. C. 1915. Experimental studies of hybridization among ducks and pheasants. J.E.Z., 18:69–143.

—— 1921. A further report on species crosses in birds. G., 6: 366–383.

Philp, J., and C. L. Huskins. 1931. The cytology of *Matthiola incana R. Br.* especially in . . . the inheritance of double flowers. J.G., 24:359–404.

Piaget, J. 1929. Les races lacustres de la *Limnaea stagnalis L.* Bull. Biol. France Belgique, 63:424–455.

Pictet, A. 1936. La zoogéographie expérimentale dans ses rapports avec la génétique. Mem. Musée Hist. Natur. Belgique, Série 2, 3:233–282.

Pinney, E. 1918. . . . The relation of the behavior of the chromatin to development and heredity in teleost hybrids. J. Morphol., 31:225–291.

—— 1922. The initial block to normal development in cross-fertilized eggs. J. Morphol., 36:401–419.

Pipkin, B. S. 1940. Segregation and crossing over in a 2, 3 translocation in *Drosophila melanogaster*. Univ. Texas Publ., 4032:73–125.

Plough, H. H. and C. F. Holthausen. 1937. A case of high mutation frequency without environmental change. A.N., 71:185–187.

Plough, H. H., and P. T. Ives. 1935. Induction of mutations by high temperature in Drosophila. G., 20:42–69.

Plough, H. H., P. T. Ives, and G. P. Child. 1939. Frequenza di mutazioni autosomiche letali in Drosophila e composizione genetica di popolazioni selvatiche. Sci. Genetica, 1:247–254.

Plunkett, C. R. 1932. Temperature as a tool of research in phenogenetics: methods and results. P.VI.C.G., 2:158–160.

Poll, H. 1910. Über Vogelmischlinge. Ber. V. Internat. Ornithol. Kongr., 399–468.

—— 1920. Pfaumischlinge (Mischlingsstudien VII). Arch. mikr. Anat. Festschrift Hertwig :365–458.

Ponomarev, V. P. 1937–1938. The effect of lead nitrate on mutation in *Drosophila melanogaster*. B.Zh., 7:619–634.

Poole, C. 1931. The interspecific hybrid, *Crepis rubra* × *C. foetida*, and some of its derivatives. I. Univ. Calif. Publ. Agric., 6:169–200.

—— 1932. The interspecific hybrid, *Crepis rubra* × *C. foetida*, and some of its derivatives. II. Univ. Calif. Publ. Agric., 6:231–255.

Poulson, D. F. 1937. Chromosomal deficiencies and the embryonic development of *Drosophila melanogaster*. P.N.A.S., 23:133–137.

—— 1940. The effects of certain X-chromosome deficiencies on the embryonic development of *Drosophila melanogaster*. J.E.Z., 83:271–325.

Prabhu, S. S. 1939. Sterility mutations in *Drosophila melanogaster*. J.G., 38:177–191.

Pratt, H. S. 1935. A manual of the common invertebrate animals exclusive of insects. Blakiston's, Philadelphia.

Promptoff, A. 1930. Die geographische Variabilität des Buchfinkenschlags (Fringilla coelebs L.). B. Z., 50:478–503.

Quayle, H. J. 1938. The development of resistance in certain scale insects to hydrocyanic acid. Hilgardia, 11:183–225.

Rajewsky, B. N., and N. W. Timofeeff-Ressovsky. 1939. Hühenstrahlung und die Mutationsrate von Drosophila melanogaster. Z.i.A.V., 77:488–500.

Rancken, C. 1934. Zytologische Untersuchungen an einigen wirtschaftlich wertvollen Wiesengräsern. Acta Agralia Fennica, 29:1–92.

Randolph, L. F. 1932. Some effects of high temperature on polyploidy and other variations in maize. P.N.A.S., 18:222–229.

Rapoport, J. A. 1936. Quadruple-Bar in Drosophila melanogaster. Bull. Biol. Med. Exper., 11:242–244.

Reinig, W. F. 1938. Elimination und Selektion. Gustav Fischer, Jena.

—— 1939. Die genetisch-chorologischen Grundlagen der gerichteten geographischen Variabilität. Z.i.A.V., 76:260–308.

Renner, O. 1929. Artbastarde bei Pflanzen. Borntraeger, Berlin.

—— 1934. Die pflanzlichen Plastiden als selbständige Elemente der genetischen Konstitution. Ber. Mat. Phys. Klasse Sachsischen Akad. Wiss., 86:241–266.

—— 1936. Zur Kenntnis der nichtmendelnden Buntheit der Laubblätter. Flora, 30:218–290.

Rensch, B. 1929. Das Prinzip geographischer Rassenkreise und das Problem der Artbildung, Borntraeger, Berlin.

—— 1933. Zoologische Systematik und Artbildungsproblem. Verh. Deut. Zool. Ges., 1933:19–83.

—— 1936. Studien über klimatische Parallelität der Merkmalsausprägung bei Vogeln und Saugern. Arch. Naturgesch., N.F., 5:317–363.

—— 1937. Untersuchungen über Rassenbildung und Erblichkeit von Rassenmerkmalen bei sizilischen Landschnecken. Z.i.A.V., 72:564–588.

—— 1938. Bestehen die Regeln klimatischer Parallelität bei der Merkmalsausprägung von homöothermen Tieren zu Recht? Arch. Naturgesch., 7:364–389.

—— 1939a. Klimatische Auslese von Grössenvarianten. Arch. Naturgesch., 8:89–129.

—— 1939b. Typen der Artbildung. Biol. Reviews, 14:180–222.

Rhoades, M. M. 1936. The effect of varying gene dosage on aleurone colour in maize. J.G., 33:347–354.

—— 1938. Effect of the Dt gene on the mutability of the a_1 allele in maize. G., 23:377–397.

—— 1940. Studies of a telocentric chromosome in maize with reference to the stability of its centromere. G., 25:483–513.

Ribbands, C. R. 1937. The consequences of structural hybridity at meiosis in Lilium X testaceum. J.G., 35:1–24.

Richardson, M. M. 1935. Meiosis in Crepis II. Failure of pairing in *Crepis capillaris* (*L*) *Wallr.* J.G., 31:119–143.

—— 1936. Structural hybridity in *Lilium martagon album* × *L. hansonii.* J.G., 32:411–450.

Richhardia, R. H. 1937. Cytological investigation of Raphanus sativus, *Brassica oleracea,* and their F_1 and F_2 hybrids. J.G., 34:19–44.

Riley, H. P. 1939. Introgressive hybridization in a natural population of Tradescantia. G., 24:753–769.

Robertson, W. R. B. 1915. Chromosome studies. III. Inequalities and deficiencies in homologous chromosomes; their bearing upon synapsis and the loss of unit characters. J. Morphol., 26:109–141.

Robson, G. C., and O. W. Richards. 1936. The variations of animals in nature. Longmans Green, London.

Rokizky, P. F. 1930. Über das Hervorrufen erblicher Veränderungen bei Drosophila durch Temperatureinwirkung. B.Z., 50:554–566.

Romaschoff, D. D. 1931. On the conditions of equilibrium in populations. B.Zh., 7:442–454.

Rosenberg, O. 1909. Cytologische und morphologische Studien an *Drosera longifolia* × *rotundifolia.* K. Svensk. Vet. Handl., 43:1–64.

—— 1930. Apogamie und Parthenogenesis bei Pflanzen. Borntraeger, Berlin.

Russell, E. S. 1937. Fish migrations. Biol. Reviews, 12:320–337.

Rybin, V. A. 1927. Polyploid hybrids of *Nicotiana tabacum L.* × *Nicotiana rustica L.* Bull. Appl. Botany, 17:191–240.

—— 1929. Über einen allotetraploiden Bastard von *Nicotiana tabacum* × *Nicotiana sylvestris.* Ber. Deut. Bot. Ges., 37:385–394.

Sacharow, W. W. 1935. Iod als chemischer Faktor, der auf den Mutationsprozess von *Drosophila melanogaster* wirkt. B.Zh., 4:107–112.

—— 1936. Iod als chemischer Faktor, der auf den Mutationsprozess von *Drosophila melanogaster* wirkt. Genetica, 18:193–216.

Salisbury, E. J. 1940. Ecological aspects of plant taxonomy. Huxley's New Systematics. Clarendon Press, Oxford.

Salt, G. 1937. The egg parasite of *Sialis lutaria:* a study of the influence of the host upon a dimorphic parasite. Parasitology, 29:539–553.

Saltykovsky, A. I., and V. S. Fedorov. 1936. Chlorophyll abnormalities in white mustard (*Synapis alba*). Bull. Appl. Bot., Ser. 2, 9:287–305.

Samjatina, N. D., and O. T. Popowa. 1934. Der Einfluss von Iod auf die Entstehung von Mutationen bei *Drosophila melanogaster.* B.Zh., 3: 679–693.

Sansome, E. R. 1931. Chromosome associations in Pisum. J.G., 25:35–54.

—— 1938. A cytological study of an F_1 between *Pisum sativum* and *P. humile,* and some types from the cross. J.G., 36:469–499.

Sapehin, A. A. 1928. Hylogenetic investigations of the vulgare group of Triticum. Bull. Appl. Bot., 19:127–166.

Sapehin, L. A. 1928. Hylogenetics of durum wheat. Bull. Appl. Bot., 19: 167–224.

Satina, S., and A. F. Blakeslee. 1935. Fertilization in the incompatible cross *Datura stramonium* ✕ *D. metel*. Bull. Torrey Bot. Club, 62:301–312.

Saveliev, V. 1928. On the manifold effect of the gene vestigial in *Drosophila melanogaster*. Travaux Soc. Natur. Leningrad, 63:65–88.

Sax, K. 1922. Sterility in wheat hybrids. II. Chromosome behavior in partially sterile hybrids. G., 7:513–552.

—— 1935. The cytological analysis of species hybrids. Bot. Review, 1: 100–117.

—— 1938. Chromosome aberrations induced by X-rays. G., 23:494–516.

—— 1940. An analysis of X-ray induced chromosomal aberrations in Tradescantia. G., 25:41–68.

—— and Edgar Anderson. 1933. Segmental interchange in chromosomes of Tradescantia. G., 18:53–94.

—— and H. J. Sax. 1924. Chromosomes in genus cross. G., 9:454–464.

Scheuring, L. 1929–30. Die Wanderungen der Fische. Ergebnisse Biol., 5: 405–691; 6:4–304.

Schindewolf, O. H. 1936. Paläontologie, Entwicklungslehre und Genetik. Borntraeger, Berlin.

Schmidt, J. 1917. Statistical investigations with *Zoarces viviparus*. J.G., 7:105.

—— 1923. Racial investigations. V. Experimental investigations with *Zoarces viviparus* L. C.R. Travaux Lab. Carlsberg, 14, 9:1–14.

Schnakenbeck, W. 1931. Zum Rassenproblem bei den Fischen. Zeit. Morph. Ökol. Tiere, 21:409–566.

Schrader, F. 1926. Notes on the English and American races of the greenhouse white fly (Trialeurodes vaporariorum). Ann. Appl. Biol., 13: 189–196.

—— 1935. Notes on the mitotic behavior of long chromosomes. C., 6: 422–430.

—— and S. Hughes-Schrader. 1931. Haploidy in Metazoa. Quart. Rev. Biol., 6:411–438.

Schultz, J. 1926. Radiation and the study of mutations in animals. Biol. Effects of Radiation, 2:1209–1261.

—— and Th. Dobzhansky. 1933. Triploid hybrids between *Drosophila melanogaster* and *Drosophila simulans*. J.E.Z., 65:73–82.

Schwab, J. J. 1940. A study of the effects of a random group of genes on shape of spermatheca in *Drosophila melanogaster*. G., 25:157–177.

Sears, E. R. 1939. Cytogenetic studies with polyploid species of wheat. I. Chromosomal aberrations in the progeny of a haploid *Triticum vulgare*. G., 24:509–523.

—— 1940. Monofactorially conditioned inviability of an intergeneric hybrid in the Triticinae. G., 25:134.

Seiler, J. 1925. Zytologische Vererbungsstudien an Schmetterlingen I. J. Klaus Arch. Vererb. Sozialanthrop., Rassenhygiene, 1:63–117.

—— 1927. Ergebnisse aus der Kreuzung parthenogenetischer und zweigeschlechtlichen Schmetterlinge. B.Z., 47:426–446.

—— 1937. Ergebnisse aus der Kreuzung parthenogenetischer und zweigeschlechtlicher Schmetterlinge. V. Revue Suisse Zool., 44:283–307.

Semenov-Tian-Shansky, A. 1910. Die taxonomische Grenzen der Art und ihrer Unterabteilungen. Berlin.

Serebrovsky, A. S. 1929. A general scheme for the origin of mutations. A.N., 63:374–378.

—— 1935. Hybridization of animals. Biomedgiz, Moscow-Leningrad.

Sexton, E. W., and A. R. Clark. 1936. Heterozygotes in a wild population of Gammarus chevreuxi Sexton. J. Marine Biol. Assoc., 21:319–356.

Shapiro, N. J. 1938. The mutation process as an adaptive character of a species. Zool. Zhurnal (Moscow), 17:592–601.

—— and K. V. Volkova. 1938. Studies on the natural process of mutation. Rate of the mutation process in males and females in different stocks of *Drosophila melanogaster*. B.Zh., 7:571–580.

Silow, R. A. 1939a. The genetics of leaf shape in diploid cottons and the theory of gene interaction. J.G., 38:229–276.

—— 1939b. The genetics and taxonomic distribution of some specific lint quantity genes in asiatic cottons. J.G., 38:277–298.

Simpson, G.G. 1937. Supra-specific variation in nature and its classification. A.N., 71:236–267.

Singleton, W. R. 1932. Cytogenetic behavior of fertile tetraploid hybrids of *Nicotiana rustica* and *Nicotiana paniculata*. G., 17:510–544.

Sitko, P. 1938. The dependence of the mutational process on chromosome reconstruction in translocations. Mem. Genetics Acad. Sci. Ukrainian SSR., 2:31–49.

Sjögren, T. 1931. Die juvenile amaurotische Idiotie. H., 14:197–425.

Skovsted, A. 1929. Cytological investigations of the genus Aesculus L. H., 12:64–70.

—— 1935. Cytological studies on cotton. III. A hybrid between *Gossypium davidsonii Kell.* and *G. sturtii F. Muell.* J.G., 30:397–405.

Slizynski, B. M. 1938. Salivary chromosome studies of lethals in *Drosophila melanogaster*. G., 23:283–290.

Smith, H. H. 1939. The induction of polyploidy in Nicotiana species and species hybrids. J.H., 30:291–306.

Smith, H. S. 1939. Insect populations in relation to biological control. Ecol. Monographs, 9:311–320.

—— 1941. The segregation of insect populations into races, and its significance in applied entomology. J. Econ. Entom., 34 (in press).

Smith, L. 1936. Cytogenetic studies in *Triticum monococcum L.* and *T. aegilopoides Bal.* Univ. Missouri Agric. Exp. Sta., Res. Bull., 248:1–38.

Smith, S. G. 1935. Chromosome fragmentation produced by crossing over in *Trillium erectum* L. J.G., 30:227–233.

Sonneborn, T. M. 1939. Paramecium aurelia: mating types and groups; lethal interactions; determination and inheritance. A.N., 73:390–413.

Sorokin, H. 1927. Cytological and morphological investigations on gynandromorphic and normal forms of *Ranunculus acris* L. G., 12:59–83.

Southern, H. N. 1939. The status and problem of the bridled guillemot. Proc. Zool. Soc. London (A), 109:31.

Spencer, W. P. 1932. The vermilion mutant of Drosophila hydei breeding in nature. A.N., 66:474–479.

—— 1938. Multiple alleles at the bobbed locus in populations of *Drosophila hydei*. G., 23:170.

—— 1940a. Subspecies, hybrids and speciation in *Drosophila hydei* and *Drosophila virilis*. A.N., 74:157–179.

—— 1940b. Levels of divergence in Drosophila speciation. A.N., 74:299–311.

Spett, G. 1931. Gibt es eine partielle sexuelle Isolation unter den Mutationen und der Grundform von *Drosophila melanogaster* Meig. Z.i.A.V., 60:63–83.

Spooner, G. M. 1932. An experiment on breeding wild pairs of Gammarus chevreuxi at a high temperature with an account of two new recessive types of red eye. J. Marine Biol. Assoc., 18:337–354.

Stadler, L. J. 1929. Chromosome number and the mutation rate in Avena and Triticum. P.N.A.S., 15:876–881.

—— 1932. On the genetic nature of induced mutations in plants. P.VI. C.G., 1:274–294.

—— 1933. On the genetic nature of induced mutations in plants. II. A. haplo-viable deficiency in maize. Missouri Agr. Exp. Sta. Res. Bull., 204:1–29.

—— and G. F. Sprague. 1936. Genetic effects of ultra-violet radiation in maize. II. Filtered radiations. P.N.A.S., 22:579–583.

Stakman, E. C., W. L. Popham, and R. C. Cassell. 1940. Observations on stem rust epidemiology in Mexico. Amer. J. Bot., 27:90–99.

Standfuss, M. 1896. Handbuch der paläarktischen Grossschmetterlinge für Forscher und Sammler. G. Fischer, Jena.

Stebbins, G. L., Jr. 1938. Cytogenetic studies in Paeonia. II. The cytology of the diploid species and hybrids. G., 23:83–110.

—— 1939. Structural hybridity in *Paeonia californica* and *P. Brownii*. J.G., 38:1–36.

—— 1940. The significance of polyploidy in plant evolution. A.N., 74:54–66.

Stegmann, B. 1931. Die Vögel des dauro-mandschurischen Übergangsgebietes. J. Ornithol., 79:137–236.

Stern, C. 1929. Untersuchungen über Aberrationen des Y-Chromosoms von *Drosophila melanogaster*. Z.i.A.V., 51:253–353.

Stern, C. 1936. Interspecific sterility. A.N., 70:123–142.

Stone, L. H. A. 1933. The effect of X-radiation on the meiotic and mitotic divisions of certain plants. Ann. Bot., 47:815–825.

Stone, W. S., and A. B. Griffen. 1940. Changing the structure of the genome in *Drosophila melanogaster*. Univ. Texas Publ. 4032:208–217.

Storer, T. J., and P. W. Gregory. 1934. Color aberrations in the pocket gopher and their probable genetic explanation. J. Mammalogy, 15:300–312.

Strasburger, E. H. 1936. Über Störungen der Eientwicklung bei Kreuzungen von *Epilachna chrysomelina F.* mit *Epilachna capensis Thumb*. Z.i.A.V., 71:538–545.

Stresemann, E. 1926. Mutationsstudien. J. Ornithol., 74:377–385.

—— 1936. The formenkreis theory. The Auk, 53:150–158.

Stubbe, H. 1930–32. Untersuchungen über experimentelle Auslösung von Mutationen bei *Antirrhinum majus*. Z.i.A.V., 56:1–38; 60:474–513.

—— 1933. Labile Gene. Bibliogr. Genetica, 10:299–356.

—— 1935. Das Merkmal acorrugata, eine willkürlich auslösbare, dominante und labile Genmutation von *Antirrhinum majus*. Nachr. Ges. Wiss. Göttingen, Biol., N.F., 2:57–88.

—— 1936. Die Erhöhung der Genmutationsrate in alternden Gonen von Antirrhinum majus L. B.Z., 56:562–567.

—— 1937. Spontane und strahleninduzierte Mutabilität. George Tieme, Leipzig.

—— 1938. Genmutation. Handbuch Vererbungsw., 2 (Lief. 23), Borntraeger, Berlin.

—— 1940. Neue Forschungen zur experimentellen Erzeugung von Mutationen. B.Z., 60:113–129.

Sturtevant, A. H. 1915a. A sex-linked character in *Drosophila repleta*. A.N., 49:189–192.

—— 1915b. Experiments on sex recognition and the problem of sexual selection in Drosophila. J. Animal Behavior, 5:351–366.

—— 1917. Genetic factors affecting the strength of linkage in Drosophila. P.N.A.S., 3:555–558.

—— 1918. An analysis of the effects of selection. Carnegie Inst. Wash., Publ., 264:1–68.

—— 1920–21. Genetic studies on *Drosophila simulans*. G., 5:488–500; 6:179–207.

—— 1921. The North American species of Drosophila. Carnegie Inst. Wash., Publ. 301:1–150.

—— 1923. Inheritance of direction of coiling in Limnaea. S., 58:269–270.

—— 1925. The effect of unequal crossing over at the Bar locus of Drosophila. G., 10:117–147.

—— 1926. A crossover reducer in *Drosophila melanogaster* due to inversion of a section of the third chromosome. B.Z., 46:697–702.

Sturtevant, A. H. 1929a. The genetics of *Drosophila simulans*. Carnegie Inst. Wash., Publ. 399:1–62.

—— 1929b. The claret mutant type of *Drosophila simulans;* a study of chromosome elimination and of cell lineage. Zeit. wiss. Zool., 135:323–355.

—— 1931. Known and probable inverted sections of the autosomes of *Drosophila melanogaster*. Carnegie Inst. Wash., Publ. 42:1–27.

—— 1937a. Autosomal lethals in wild populations of *Drosophila pseudoobscura*. B.B., 73:542–551.

—— 1937b. An effect of the Y-chromosome on the sex-ratio of interracial hybrids of *Drosophila pseudoobscura*. P.N.A.S., 23:360–362.

—— 1937c. Essays on evolution. I. On the effects of selection on the mutation rate. Quart. Rev. Biol., 12:464–467.

—— 1938. Essays on evolution. III. On the origin of interspecific sterility. Quart. Rev. Biol., 13:333–335.

—— 1939. High mutation frequency induced by hybridization. P.N.A.S., 7:308–310.

—— 1940. Genetic data on *Drosophila affinis*, with a discussion of the relationships in the subgenus Sophophora. G., 25:337–353.

—— and G. W. Beadle. 1936. The relations of inversions in the X-chromosome of *Drosophila melanogaster* to crossing over and disjunction. G., 21:554–604.

—— and G. W. Beadle. 1939. An introduction to genetics. Saunders, Philadelphia.

—— and Th. Dobzhansky. 1936. Geographical distribution and cytology of "sex ratio" in *Drosophila pseudoobscura*. G., 21:473–490.

—— and K. Mather. 1938. The interrelations of inversions, heterosis and recombination. A.N., 72:447–452.

—— and C. R. Plunkett. 1926. Sequence of corresponding third chromosome genes in *Drosophila melanogaster* and *Drosophila simulans*. B.B., 50:56–60.

—— and C. C. Tan. 1937. The comparative genetics of *Drosophila pseudoobscura* and *D. melanogaster*. J.G., Vol. 34.

Sukatschew, W. 1928. Einige experimentelle Untersuchungen über den Kampf ums Dasein zwischen Biotypen derselben Art. Z.i.A.V., 47:54–74.

Sumner, F. B. 1923. Results of experiments in hybridizing subspecies of Peromyscus. J.E.Z., 38:245–292.

—— 1924a. The stability of subspecific characters under changed conditions of environment. A.N., 58:481–505.

—— 1924b. Hairless mice. J.H., 15:475–481.

—— 1929. The analysis of a concrete case of intergradation between two subspecies. P.N.A.S., 15:110–120, 481–493.

—— 1930. Genetic and distributional studies of three subspecies of Peromyscus. J.G., 23:275–376.

Sumner, F. B. 1932. Genetic, distributional, and evolutionary studies of the subspecies of deer mice (Peromyscus). Bibliogr. Genetica, 9:1–116.

—— 1935. Evidence for the protective value of changeable coloration in fishes. A.N., 69:245–266.

—— and R. R. Huestis. 1925. Studies of coat-color and foot pigmentation in subspecific hybrids of *Peromyscus eremicus*. B.B., 48: 37–55.

—— and M. C. Sargent. 1940. Some observations on the physiology of warm spring fishes. Ecology, 21:45–54.

Suomalainen, E. 1940a. Polyploidy in parthenogenetic Curculionidae. H., 26:51–64.

—— 1940b. Beiträge zur Zytologie der Parthenogenetischen Insekten. Ann. Acad. Sci. Fennicae, A, 54:1–143.

Sutton, E. 1940. Terminal deficiencies in the X-chromosome of *Drosophila melanogaster*. G., 25:628–635.

Sutton, W. S. 1903. The chromosomes in heredity. B.B., 4:231–251.

Sveshnikova, I. N. 1936. Translocations in hybrids as an indicator of "karyotype evolution." B.Zh., 5:303–326.

—— and J. Belekhova. 1936. Translocations in an interspecific hybrid. Bull. Appl. Bot., Ser. 2, 9:63–70.

Swanson, C. R. 1940. The distribution of inversions in Tradescantia. G., 25:438–465.

Tan, C. C. 1935. Salivary gland chromosomes in the two races of *Drosophila pseudoobscura*. G., 20:392–402.

—— and J. C. Li. 1934. Inheritance of the elytral color patterns of the lady-bird beetle, *Harmonia axyridis Pallas*. A.N., 68:252–265.

Tarnavsky, N. D. 1939. On the role of nucleic acid in the production of directed mutations. C.R. Ukrainian Acad. Sci., Biology, 1:47–49.

Tedin, O. 1925. Vererbung, Variation und Systematik in der Gattung Camelina. H., 6:275–386.

Thompson, W. P. 1925. The correlation of characters in hybrids of *Triticum durum* and *Triticum vulgare*. G., 10:285–304.

—— 1931. Cytology and genetics of crosses between fourteen- and seven-chromosome species of wheat. G., 16:309–324.

—— and M. G. Thompson. 1937. Reciprocal chromosome translocations without semi-sterility. C., Jubilee Volume :336–342.

Thorpe, W. H. 1930. Biological races in insects and allied groups. Biol. Reviews, 5:177–212.

—— 1940. Ecology and the future of systematics. Huxley's New Systematics, pp. 341–364.

Timofeeff-Ressovsky, H. 1935. Divergens, eine Mutation von *Epilachna chrysomelina F.* Z.i.A.V., 68:443–453.

—— and N. W. Timofeeff-Ressovsky. 1927. Genetische Analyse einer freilebenden *Drosophila melanogaster* Population. A.E., 109:70–109.

Timofeeff-Ressovsky, N. W. 1929. Rückgenovariationen und die Genovariabilität in verschiedenen Richtungen. I. Somatische Genovariationen der Gene W, w^e, und w bei *Drosophila melanogaster* unter dem Einfluss der Röntgenbestrahlung. A.E., 115:620–634.

Timofeeff-Ressovsky, N. W. 1931. Reverse genovariations, and gene mutations in different directions. II. The production of reverse genovariations in *Drosophila melanogaster* by X-ray treatment. J.H., 22:67–70.

—— 1932. Verschiedenheit der "normalen" Allele der white-Series aus zwei geographisch getrennten Populationen vom *Drosophila melanogaster*. BZ., 52:468–476

—— 1933a. Rückgenmutationen und die Genmutabilität in verschiedenen Richtungen. III. Röntgenmutationen in entgegengesetzten Richtungen am forked-Locus von *Drosophila melanogaster*. Z.i.A.V., 64:173–175.

—— 1933b. Rückgenmutationen und die Genmutabilität in verschiedenen Richtungen. IV. Röntgenmutationen in verschiedenen Richtungen am white-Locus von *Drosophila melanogaster*. Z.i.A.V., 65:278–292.

—— 1933c. Rückgenmutationen und die Genmutabilität in verschienden en Richtungen. V. Gibt es ein wiederholtes Auftreten identischer Allele innerhalb der white-Allelenreihe von *Drosophila melanogaster*? Z.i.A.V., 66:165–179.

—— 1933d. Über die relative Vitalität von *Drosophila melanogaster* Meigen und *Drosophila funebris Fabricius* unter berschiedenen Zuchtbedingungen, in Zusammenhang mit den Verbreitungsarealen dieser Arten. Arch. Naturgesch., N.F., 2:285–290.

—— 1934a. The experimental production of mutations. Biol. Reviews, 9:411–457.

—— 1934b. Über den Einfluss des genotypischen Milieus und der Ausenbedingungen auf die Realisation des Genotyps. Nachr. Ges. Wiss. Göttingen, Biologie, N.F., 1:53–106.

——1934c. Über die Vitalität einiger Genmutationen und ihrer Kombinationen bei *Drosophila funebris* und ihre Abhängigkeit vom "genotypischen" und vom äusseren Mileau. Z.i.A.V., 66:319–344.

—— 1934d. Auslösung von Vitalitätsmutationen durch Röntgenbestrahlung bei *Drosophila melanogaster*. Strahlentherapie, 51:658–663.

—— 1935a. Über geographische Temperaturrassen bei *Drosophila funebris F*. Arch. Naturgesch., N.F., 4:245–257.

—— 1935b. Auslösung von Vitalitätsmutationen durch Röntgenbestrahlung bei *Drosophila melanogaster*. Nach. Ges. Wiss. Göttingen, Biologie, N.F., 1:163–180.

—— 1935c. Über die Wirkung der Temperatur auf den Mutationsprozess bei *Drosophila melanogaster*. I. Versuche innerhalb normaler Temperaturgrenzen. Z.i.A.V., 70:125–129.

—— 1937. Experimentelle Mutationsforschung in der Vererbungslehre. Theodor Steinkopff, Dresden and Leipzig.

—— 1939a. Genetik und Evolution. Z.i.A.V., 76:158–218.

—— 1939b. Sulla questione dell' isolamento territoriale entro popolazioni specifiche. Scientia Genetica, 1:76–85.

Timofeeff-Ressovsky, N. W. 1939c. Le mécanisme des mutations et la structure du gène. Actual. Sci. Industr., No. 812. Hermann, Paris.

—— 1939d. Genetik und Evolution. Z.i.A.V., 76:158–218.

—— 1940a. Mutations and geographical variation. Huxley's New Systematics, pp. 73–136.

—— 1940b. Zur Analyse des Polymorphismus bei *Adalia bipunctata L.* B.Z., 60:130–137.

—— and H. A. Timofeeff-Ressovsky. 1934. Polare Schwankungen in der phänotypischen Manifestierung einiger Genmutationen bei Drosophila. Z.i.A.V., 67:246–254.

—— K. G. Zimmer, and M. Delbrück. 1935. Über die Natur der Genmutation und der Genstruktur. Nachr. Ges. Wiss. Göttingen, Biologie, N.F. 1:189–245.

Tischler, G. 1934. Die Bedeutung der Polyploide für die Verbreitung der Angiospermen. Bot. Jahrb., 67:1.

Tometorp, G. 1939. Cytological studies on haploid Hordeum distichum. H., 25:241–254.

Toyama, K. 1912. On certain characteristics of the silk-worm which are apparently non-Mendelian. B.Z., 32:593–607.

Tschetwerikoff, S. S. 1926. On certain features of the evolutionary process from the viewpoint of modern genetics. J. Exp. Biol. (Russian), 2:3–54.

—— 1937. Über die genetische Beschaffenheit wilder Population. V.K.V., 2:1499–1500.

Turesson, G. 1922. The genotypical response of the plant species to the habitat. H., 3:211–350.

—— 1925. The plant species in relation to habitat and climate. H., 3: 147–236.

—— 1926. Studien über *Festuca ovina L.* H., 8:161–206.

—— 1929. Ecotypical selection in Siberian *Dactylis glomerata.* H., 12: 335–351.

—— 1930. The selective effect of climate upon the plant species. H., 14: 99–152.

—— 1931. The geographical distribution of the alpine ecotypes of some Eurasiatic plants. H., 15:329–346.

Turrill, W. B. 1940. Experimental and synthetic plant taxonomy. Huxley's New Systematics, Clarendon Press, Oxford.

Upcott, M. 1936. The parents and progeny of *Aesculus carnea.* J.G., 33: 135–149.

—— 1937a. The external mechanics of the chromosomes. VI. The behavior of the centromere at meiosis. Proc. R. Soc. London, 124: 336–361.

—— 1937b. The genetic structure of Tulipa. II. Structural hybridity. J.G., 34:339–398.

—— 1939. The nature of tetraploidy in Primula kewensis. J.G., 39:79–100.

426 LITERATURE

Vandel, A. 1928. La parthénogenèse géographique. Bull. Biol. France Belgique, 62:164–281.

—— 1934. La parthénogenèse géographique. Bull. Biol. France Belgique, 68:419–463.

—— 1938a. Chromosome number, polyploidy, and sex in the animal kingdom. Proc. Zool. Soc. London, 107:519–541.

—— 1938b. Contribution à la génétique des isopodes du genre Trichoniscus. I. Bull. Biol. France Belgique, 72:121–146.

Vavilov, N. I. 1922. The law of homologous series in variation. J.G., 12: 47–89.

—— 1928. Geographische Genzentren unserer Kulturpflanzen. V.K.V., 1:342–369.

Vries, H. de. 1901. Die Mutationstheorie. Veit, Leipzig.

Waagen, W. 1869. Die Formenreihe des Ammonites subradiatus. Benecke geognostisch-paläontologische Beiträge, 2:179–257.

Wahlund, S. 1928. Zusammensetzung von Populationen und Korrelationserscheinungen vom Standpunkt der Vererbungslehre aus betrachtet. H., 11:65–106.

Wallace, J. M. 1932. Physiologic specialization as a factor in the epiphytology of *Puccinia graminis tritici*. Phytopathology, 22:105–142.

Warmke, H. E., and A. F. Blakeslee. 1940. The establishment of a 4N dioecious race in Melandrium. Amer. J. Bot., 27:751–762.

Watkins, A. E. 1930. The wheat species: a critique. J.G., 23:173–263.

—— 1932. Hybrid sterility and incompatibility. J.G., 25:125–162.

Webber, J. M. 1930. Interspecific hybridization in Nicotiana XI. The cytology of a sesquidiploid hybrid between *tabacum* and *sylvestris*. U.C.P.B., 11:319–354.

Welch, D'Alte A. 1938. Distribution and variation of *Achatinella mustellina Michels* in the Waianae Mountains, Oahu. Bull. Bishop Museum, 152: 1–164.

Westergaard, M. 1940. Studies on cytology and sex determination in polyploid forms of *Melandrium album*. Dansk. Bot. Arkiv, 10, No. 5: 1–131.

Wettstein, V. von. 1924. Morphologie und Physiologie des Formwechsels der Moose auf genetischer Grundlage. Z.i.A.V., 33:1–236.

—— 1928. Morphologie und Physiologie des Formwechsels der Moose auf genetischer Grundlage. II. Bibliot. Genetica, 10:1–216.

—— 1937a. Experimentelle Untersuchungen zum Artbildungsproblem. I. Zellgrössenregulation und Fertilwerden einer polyploiden Bryum-Sippe. Z.i.A.V., 74:34–53.

—— 1937b. Die genetische und entwicklungsphysiologische Bedeutung des Cytoplasmas. Z.i.A.V., 73:349–366.

Weyer, F. 1935. Die Rassenfrage bei *Culex pipiens* in Deutschland. Zeit. Parasitenkunde, 8:104–115.

White, B., E. S. Robinson, and L. A. Barnes. 1938. The biology of Pneumococcus. The Commonwealth Fund, New York.

White, M. J. D. 1940a. The origin and evolution of multiple sex-chromosome mechanisms. J.G., 40:303–336.

—— 1940b. A translocation in a wild population of grasshoppers. J.H., 31:137–140.

—— 1940c. Evidence of polyploidy in the hermaphrodite groups of animals. Nature, 146:132.

Wichler, G. 1913. Untersuchungen über den Bastard Dianthus armeria × Dianthus deltoides nebst Bemerkungen über einige andere Art Kreuzungen der Gattung Dianthus. Z.i.A.V., 10:177–232.

Wiebe, G. A. 1934. Complementary factors in barley giving a lethal progeny. J.H., 25:273–274.

Wiegand, K. M. 1935. A taxonomist's experience with hybrids in the wild. S., 81:161–166.

Winge, O. 1917. The chromosomes, their number and general importance. C.R. Trav. Lab. Carlsberg, 13:131–275.

Winkler, H. 1916. Über die experimentelle Erzeugung von Pflanzen mit abweichenden Chromosomenzahlen. Zeit. Bot., 8:417–531.

Woolsey, C. I. 1915. Linkage of chromosomes correlated with reduction in numbers among the species of a genus, also within a species of the Locustidae. B.B., 28:163–187.

Wright, S. 1921. Systems of mating. G., 6:111–178.

—— 1925. The factors of the albino series of guinea-pigs and their effects on black and yellow pigmentation. G., 10:223–260.

—— 1929. Fisher's theory of dominance. A.M., 63:247–279.

—— 1930. The genetical theory of natural selection. J.H., 21:349–356.

—— 1931a. Evolution in Mendelian populations. G., 16:97–159.

—— 1931b. Statistical theory of evolution. Amer. Stat. J. Suppl.: 201–208.

—— 1932. The rôles of mutation, inbreeding, crossbreeding, and selection in evolution. P.VI.C.G., 1:356–366.

—— 1934. Physiological and evolutionary theories of dominance. A.N., 68:24–53.

—— 1935. Evolution in populations in approximate equilibrium. J.G., 30:257–266.

—— 1937. The distribution of gene frequencies in populations. P.N.A.S., 23:307–320.

—— 1938a. The distribution of gene frequencies under irreversible mutation. P.N.A.S., 24:253–259.

—— 1938b. Size of population and breeding structure in relation to evolution. S., 87:430–431.

—— 1939. The distribution of self-sterility alleles in populations. G., 24:538–552.

Wright, S. 1940a. The statistical consequences of Mendelian heredity in relation to speciation. Huxley's New Systematics, pp. 161–183.

—— 1940b. Breeding structure of populations in relation to speciation. A.N., 74:232–248.

Yamamoto, Y. 1938. Karyogenetische Untersuchungen bei der Gattung Rumex. VI. Mem. Coll. Agr. Kyoto Univ., 43:1–59.

Yarnell, S. H. 1931. Genetic and cytological studies on Fragaria. G., 16: 422–454.

Zimmermann, K. 1931. Studien über individuelle und geographische Variabilität paläarktischer Polistes und verwandter Vespiden. Zeit. Morph. Ökol. Tiere, 22:173–230.

—— 1933. Über Mutationen in wilden Populationen. Mitt. Zool. Museum Berlin, 19:439–452.

—— 1935. Zur Rassenanalyse der mitteleuropäischen Feldmäuse. Arch. Naturgesch., 4:258–273.

—— 1936. Die geographische Rassen von *Epilachna chrysomelina F.* und ihre Beziehungen zu *Epilachna capensis Thunb.* Z.i.A.V., 71:527–537.

Zuitin, A. I. 1937. Influence of temperature contrasts on the frequency of lethal mutations in *Drosophila melanogaster.* C.R. (Doklady) Acad. Sci. URSS, 15:351–354.

—— 1938a. The influence of the change of the thermal regime upon the frequency of occurrence of lethal mutations in *Drosophila melanogaster.* C.R. (Doklady) Acad. Sci. URSS, 21:53–55.

—— 1938b. The combined effect of change of the thermal regime and the subsequent temperature contrast upon the frequency of lethal mutations in *Drosophila melanogaster.* C.R. (Doklady) Acad. Sci. URSS, 21:56–58.

INDEX

INDEX